Catalogue 2003

www.phaidon.com

Contents

General Non-Fiction

General
Non-Fiction
History/
Photography
NEW TITLE

Art

Photography

Collector's
Editions

Film

Architecture

250 × 189 mm
9⁷⁄₈ × 7³⁄₈ inches
320 pp
c.300 b&w illus.

Hardback
0 7148 4308 3

£ **24.95** UK
$ **39.95** US
€ **39.95** EUR
$ **59.95** CAN
$ **69.95** AUS

Related exhibitions
One-man show to open
at the Hôtel du Sully in
Paris in summer 2003 to
tour internationally
until 2005

Marketing information
Major advertising
programme; international
author campaign

Point of Sale
20-copy display tower
available

Published September

Red-Color News Soldier

Photographs and text by Li Zhensheng, with an introduction by Jonathan Spence

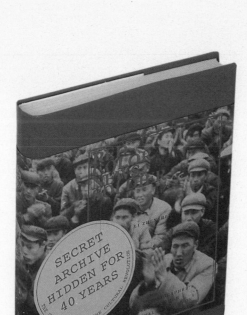

- **Only known existing photographic documentation of the Chinese Cultural Revolution (1966–76)**
- **Controversial visual record of an infamous, misunderstood period of modern history that has been largely hidden from the public eye, both within China and abroad**
- **Exceptional story of one photojournalist, Li Zhensheng (b.1940), who took and concealed for decades, at great personal risk, thousands of pictures**
- **Written narrative by the photographer himself, who was granted unusual access, providing both a historical and personal context**
- **Introduction by Jonathan Spence, Yale professor and pre-eminent scholar of Chinese history**

Li Zhensheng was born in Dalian, China, in 1940. After studying film, he joined *The Heilongjiang Daily* as a photojournalist in 1963 and documented the Chinese Cultural Revolution in its entirety. His work has appeared in major magazines worldwide including *Time* and *The New York Times Magazine*
Jonathan Spence is Sterling Professor of History at Yale University. Considered one of the foremost experts on modern China, Spence is the author of a distinguished body of work, including the seminal book, *The Search for Modern China* (1990)

Design

Fashion &
Contemporary Culture

Decorative Arts

Music &
Performing Arts

Video

Index

III.

At the end of September 1966, I went to Beijing to cover the "big networking" of the Red Guards and Chairman Mao's fifth appearance before them in Tiananmen Square. Mao would review the Red Guards eight times between August and November of that year, receiving over eleven million altogether, and this was the biggest gathering yet, with well over a million and a half of the faithful pouring into the capital, the "center of world revolution," from all over the country to catch a glimpse of the Great Helmsman and Commander-in-Chief.

I accompanied the rebel groups from the Harbin Military Engineering Institute. The whole trip — transportation, lodging, meals — was arranged by state authorities and it was all free. A special train took us directly from Harbin to Beijing. Once there, the students slept in middle schools on makeshift beds made out of tables. Journalists from the *Heilongjiang Daily*, including myself, stayed at a small hotel near the front gate of Tiananmen Square.

After National Day on 1 October, Red Guards and rebels filled the square day and night, waiting for Mao. They knew he would review them sometime soon, but didn't know exactly when, this information was always kept secret until the last moment. In the meantime, zealous guards made passionate speeches promoting Mao Zedong Thought, sang revolutionary songs, and tirelessly danced the *Loyalty Dance*.

Finally, on the evening of 17 October, the loudspeakers announced that Mao would make his appearance the following day. Hearing the news, a surge of excitement swept through the crowd and everyone stayed up all night celebrating. I was excited, too,

Li (center) in Beijing with
colleagues from the *Heilongjiang
Daily*. Beijing, 15 October 1966

Harbin, 1 October 1966

A diary-style narrative
by Li illustrated with
personal pictures and
archival documents,
and printed on news-
paper-type paper
appears in between
the sections of his
photographs of the
Cultural Revolution.
The exact date and
location of the images
appear in red along
the bottom of
each spread

Harbin, 27 April 1967

General
Non-Fiction
Biography/History/
Photography
NEW TITLE

Art

Photography

Collector's
Editions

Film

Architecture

290 × 250 mm
11³⁄₈ × 9⁷⁄₈ inches
304 pp
c.210 duotone,
80 col illus.

Hardback
0 7148 4362 8

£ **24.95** UK
$ **39.95** US
€ **39.95** EUR
$ **59.95** CAN
$ **69.95** AUS

Marketing information
Extensive media and
serialization campaigns
commemorating 40th
anniversary of Kennedy's
assassination

Point of Sale
20-copy display tower
available

Published October

John Fitzgerald Kennedy

A Life in Pictures

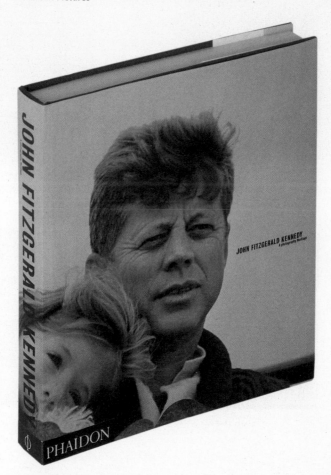

- A celebration in photographs of the life of John F. Kennedy (1917–63), the 35th president of the United States
- Published to commemorate the 40th anniversary of his assassination in Dallas on 22 November 1963
- A collection of the best photographs, many previously unpublished, together with campaign memorabilia and personal notes that tell the behind-the-scenes story of the youngest man to be elected president
- Illustrates the glamour and success of his life, from childhood and student days to congress, fatherhood and the presidency, revealing the tragedy of his untimely death
- Offers a unique insight into the family man, as well as the world leader who held firm when the country trembled on the brink of nuclear war and whose economic programmes launched America on its longest sustained expansion since World War I
- Includes a biography, famous quotes, handwritten documents and correspondence

Design

Fashion &
Contemporary Culture

Decorative Arts

Music &
Performing Arts

Video

Index

Spreads showing,
from top, childhood
photographs,
1960 Presidential
campaign and family
photographs off the
coast of Hyannis
port 1963.

General Non-Fiction
History/ Photography

Art

Photography

Collector's Editions

Film

Architecture

Large format
250 × 250 mm
10 × 10 inches
1120 pp
1,072 col and duotone photos

Hardback
0 7148 3848 9

£ **39.95** UK
$ **59.95** US
€ **65.00** EUR
$ **89.95** CAN
$ **98.00** AUS

Mini format
125 × 125 mm
4⁷⁄₈ × 4⁷⁄₈ inches
1224 pp
c.1,090 col and
duotone photos

Hardback
0 7148 4279 6

£ **9.95** UK
$ **14.95** US
€ **14.95** EUR
$ **24.95** CAN
$ **29.95** AUS

Awards

Winner of a Merit Award
from the New York
Art Director's Club,
1999

Illustrated Book
of the year,
British Book Awards,
1999

Winner of a Special Award
for photojournalism
from France Info,
2000

CENTURY

One Hundred Years of Human Progress, Regression, Suffering and Hope
Conceived and edited by Bruce Bernard

- An extraordinary, award-winning history of the last century in photographs, by acclaimed picture editor Bruce Bernard
- An educational, nostalgic, intimate and monumental insight into our recent history. *Century* covers politics and war, art and invention, culture and social history
- Arranged in chronological order, the photographs depict the people and events, both famous and unknown, that have shaped our history, with extended historical background information on every scene depicted
- Available in the original format and in a pocket-sized version updated to include the attacks on the World Trade Center

Bruce Bernard (1929–2000) was Picture Editor of *The Sunday Times Magazine* and in 1980 he produced *Photodiscovery* – a highly respected account of the revolution in attitudes to photography. Bernard was Visual Arts Editor of the *Saturday Independent Magazine* for its first four years. He curated the exhibition 'All Human Life' at London's Barbican Centre in 1996, and was the curator of a private collection of photographs. *Century* is the culmination of his extensive knowledge and the experience he gained during 30 years of looking at pictures.
Terence McNamee, who acted as historical advisor and wrote the historical background for *Century*, studied politics and international relations at the University of British Columbia, Vancouver, and at McGill University, Montreal

Design

Fashion &
Contemporary
Culture

Decorative Arts

Music &
Performing Arts

Video

Index

'Picture editors sometimes possess a startlingly accurate 'photographic memory' and an intuitive divining-rod which leads them through vast archives to the images they need. Bruce Bernard is one of these. I don't know anyone else with either the chutzpah or the qualifications to attempt a book like this. A great showman and a serious chronicler, he retains one's attention and faith right the way through. *Century* is extraordinary. A wonderbook.' Mark Haworth-Booth, *Spectator*

'The heavyweight champ of photo books.' Bob Minzesheimer, *USA Today*

'This is a great book. As photographic history, its sweep and grandeur are incomparable. The culmination of the career of our most revered picture editor, Bruce Bernard has produced the monument to photo-journalism he has long had in mind. Certainly every prime minister and sixth-former should have a copy and refer to it every day.'

John McEwen, *Literary Review*

'A complex and suggestive book. It's a triumph, maybe a masterpiece.'

Tim Hilton, *Independent on Sunday*

'A veritable road map of the 20th century's seminal events.'

Rynn Williams, *American Photo*

'Bruce Bernard has unrivalled knowledge and discernment in the field of photography, as well as a firm grasp of the history and culture of the 20th century. Nobody could have done this job better than he and his publishers. This enormous, beautifully produced volume is very good value. The book as a whole gives an impression of an extraordinary century that feels both true and natural.' Alexander Chancellor, *The Oldie*

General
Non-Fiction
History/
Photography

Art

Photography

Collector's
Editions

Film

Architecture

290 × 250 mm
11³⁄₈ × 9⁷⁄₈ inches
512 pp
c.500 b&w, 100 col photos

Hardback
0 7148 4270 2

£ **39.95** UK
$ **59.95** US
€ **65.00** EUR
$ **89.95** CAN
$ **120.00** AUS

Freedom

A Photographic History of the African American Struggle
Text by Manning Marable and Leith Mullings, picture-editing by Sophie Spencer-Wood

- An outstanding visual record of the African American struggle for civil rights
- The first photography book on this subject to extend beyond the 'movement' period of 1954–68, beginning in the 19th century and continuing to the present
- Unprecedented array of photographs from famous images to pictures never published before
- Authors are eminent historians who provide thoughtful scholarship and unparalleled authority
- Highly controversial subject matter that is extremely relevant today

Manning Marable is a prominent voice on the history of race in America. He is the Founding Director of the Institute for Research in African American Studies at Columbia University in New York City, and is the author of more than fifteen books on the subject, including the highly acclaimed *Black Leadership*
Leith Mullings is Presidential Professor of Anthropology at the Graduate Center of the City University of New York and the author of many books on African American communities. She co-edited with Marable an anthology of African American texts, *Let Nobody Turn Us Around*
Sophie Spencer-Wood, photo-editor at Phaidon Press, worked with Bernard Bruce on *Century* and is the photo-editor of *Gandhi*, Phaidon

'A masterpiece of historiography, a fine example for how historians may use photography to its full potential: an art with great documentary meaningfullness.' *(Tages-Anzeiger*, Zurich)

Design

Fashion & Contemporary Culture

Decorative Arts

Music & Performing Arts

Video

Index

250 × 250 mm
9⅞ × 9⅞ inches
320 pp
294 duotone photos

Hardback
0 7148 4103 X

£ **24.95** UK
$ **39.95** US
€ **39.95** EUR
$ **59.95** CAN
$ **69.95** AUS

Gandhi

A Photo Biography
Peter Rühe

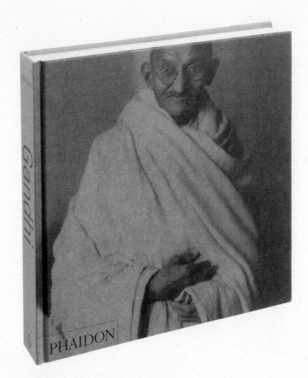

- **Documents Mahatma Gandhi's life (1869–1948) through a fascinating collection of nearly 300 photographs, many never seen before**
- **An amazing record of the life of one of the most inspiring figures of the 20th century**
- **Images range from his early life in India through his law studies in London to his work in South Africa and his return to lead the struggle for Indian independence**
- **Shows the sweep of world politics and the struggles of the poor in the life of a man whose philosophy of peaceful resistance elevated him to the status of a saint**

Peter Rühe lives in Berlin and Mumbai, India. He is a specialist in the conservation of visual material of Mahatma Gandhi. He is the founder of Gandhiserve, a registered charity which aims to teach others about Gandhi's life and work. In 1992 he was recognized by the Gujarati Writer's Association in Rajkot, India for his support of Gandhi

'A magnificent, luminous collection.' *(Los Angeles Times)*

**General
Non-Fiction** History

Art

Photography

Collector's
Editions

Film

Architecture

210 × 148 mm
8¹⁴ × 5⁷⁸ inches
224 pp
156 col, 29 b&w illus.
plus maps, charts
and genealogies

Paperback
0 7148 2652 9

£ **9.95** UK
$ **14.95** US
€ **16.95** EUR
$ **24.95** CAN
$ **27.95** AUS

The Story of England

Christopher Hibbert

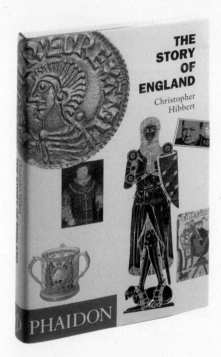

- The perfect concise introduction to England's past for readers of all ages
- Clear fast-moving narrative written by a master storyteller
- Covers the whole sweep of English history from the Stone Age to the present
- Vivid character sketches, telling details and well-chosen anecdotes bring people and places to life
- Profusely illustrated in colour
- Well supplied with maps, genealogies, fold-out chronological charts and a comprehensive index

Christopher Hibbert is a well-known and highly successful popular historian and biographer

'The best short introduction to English history we have seen.' (*Good Book Guide*)

Design

Fashion & Contemporary Culture

Decorative Arts

Music & Performing Arts

Video

Index

Christopher Hibbert is 'perhaps the most gifted popular historian we have.'

Times Educational Supplement

General
Non-Fiction
Creativity/Self-Development
Art
Photography
Collector's Editions
Film
Architecture

178 × 120 mm
7 × 4¾ inches
128 pp
c.40 col and b&w illus.

Paperback
0 7148 4337 7

£ **4.95** UK
$ **7.95** US
€ **7.95** EUR
$ **11.95** CAN
$ **12.95** AUS

It's Not How Good You Are, It's How Good You Want To Be

The world's best-selling book
Paul Arden

- A concise guide to making the most of yourself by ad-man Paul Arden
- A pocket bible for the talented and timid to make the unthinkable thinkable and the impossible possible
- Offers insights into the value of being fired and why it's often better to be wrong than to be right
- An uplifting and humorous little book that gives original and logical answers to everyday questions

Paul Arden spent a stormy eighteen years in advertising and then found his *Alma Mater* in Saatchi & Saatchi in 1977, where he worked for fifteen years. During his tenure as Executive Creative Director he was responsible for some of Britain's most successful advertising campaigns – including British Airways, Silk Cut, Intercity and Fuji – and famous slogans, such as 'The Car in front is a Toyota' and 'The Independent – It is. Are you?' Paul Arden now runs Arden Sutherland-Dodd, a London-based film production company.

'Please forgive my enthusiasm for quoting Paul Arden extensively, but his wisdom has recently insired me … This magnificent little manifesto is for true creative types to read, savor and carry in their pocket. It should remind us that nothing is impossible.' (*PAPER*)
'Talented but timid? This noted ad-man is here to tell you that ambition, not just mere ability, is the key to success…' (*i-D*)

Design

Fashion & Contemporary Culture

Decorative Arts

Music & Performing Arts

Video

Index

245 × 210 mm
9⅝ × 8¼ inches
1,064 pp
295 col, 390 b&w illus.

Hardback
0 7148 3449 1

£ **24.95** UK
$ **39.95** US
€ **39.95** EUR
$ **59.95** CAN
$ **65.00** AUS

Awards

Winner of a Silver Medal from the Art Director's Club, 2001

Awarded a Certificate of Typographic Excellence by the Type Director's Club, 2001

The Art of Looking Sideways

Alan Fletcher

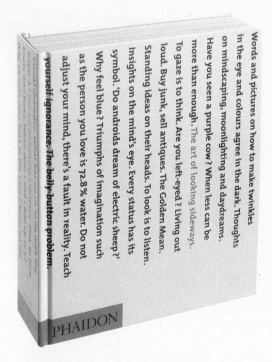

- A primer in visual intelligence that explores the workings of the eye, the hand, the brain and the imagination
- An exhaustible mine of anecdotes, quotations, curious facts, useless information, oddities, serious science, jokes and memories
- 'Essential reading for anyone with imagination, a pair of eyes and a sense of humour' – Peter Mayle
- 'Nobody should enter the real world until they have read and been stimulated by Alan Fletcher's amazing Baedeker of practical and erudite information' – Terence Conran
- 'You can forget Stephen Hawking and all that astrophysics malarkey. Alan Fletcher is much nearer to having a complete theory of everything. Funny, clever, entertaining and beautiful' – Stephen Bayley

Alan Fletcher belongs to that elite international group of designers who have transcended conventional boundaries of their craft. He is a founder member of the design group Pentagram and has tackled every facet of design with a unique style and purpose. He is consultant Art Director to Phaidon Press

**General
Non-Fiction** Popular Science

Art

Photography

Collector's
Editions

Film

Architecture

242 × 300 mm
9¹⁄₂ × 11³⁄₄ inches
400 pp
c.290 col, 60 b&w illus.

Hardback
0 7148 4280 X

£ **29.95** UK
$ **49.95** US
€ **49.95** EUR
$ **75.00** CAN
$ **89.95** AUS

Award

New York Public
Library's Books
for the Teenage List

Heaven & Earth

Unseen by the naked eye
With an introduction by David Malin and text by Katherine Roucoux

- An awe-inspiring voyage of discovery through the infinite world of science
- Reveals amazing phenomena unseen by the naked eye
- Explores the complexity and beauty of nature in ascending order of size and distance, from the smallest particles on the earth's surface to gigantic galaxies thousands of light years away
- Educational and inspirational

David Malin is a well-known astronomer and a leader in astronomical photography. He was formerly Photographic Scientist at the Anglo-Australian Observatory in New South Wales and is currently Adjunct Professor of Scientific Photography at the Royal Melbourne Institute of Technology. Recent winner of the prestigious Lennart Nilsson prize, Malin's pioneering photographs of space have revolutionized our knowledge and understanding of the universe. Widely published, Malin has written numerous scientific papers and books. He has also lectured on science, astronomy and photography at institutions worldwide
Katherine Roucoux is a freelance science writer. She has a PhD in Quaternary Palaeoecology from the University of Cambridge and an MSc in Science Communication from Imperial College of Science, Technology and Medicine, London. Her recent projects include research and presenting work for the BBC Science Radio Unit.

Design

Fashion &
Contemporary
Culture

Decorative Arts

Music &
Performing Arts

Video

Index

'Visually, the book is a work of art but the subject is scientifically fascinating … An exceptional book celebrating the beauty and detail of our world.' *Focus*

'endlessly intriguing … a unique exploration of the boundless relationship between science and art.' *Creative Review*

'Heaven & Earth sends us back with renewed vision to the heaven and earth in which we live, more able, as the poet William Blake wrote:"To see the world in a grain of sand / And a heaven in a wild flower / Hold infinity in the palm of your hand / And eternity in an hour". *Times Educational Supplement*

'A breathtaking ride in the universe of the visible and invisible.' *Libération*

Art

General
Non-Fiction

Art
Contemporary &
Modern
NEW TITLE

Photography

Collector's
Editions

Film

Architecture

250 × 290 mm
9⅞ × 11⅜ inches
400 pp
c.550 col, 130 b&w illus.

Hardback with slipcase
0 7148 4087 4

£ **150.00** UK
$ **250.00** US
€ **250.00** EUR
$ **375.00** CAN
$ **450.00** AUS

Published November

Andy Warhol Catalogue Raisonné Volume 2

Paintings and Sculptures 1964–1965
Edited by Georg Frei and Neil Printz, executive editor Sally King-Nero

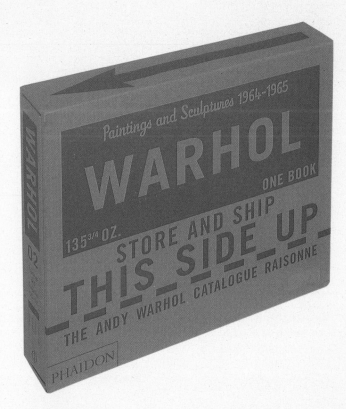

- **Second volume of this highly praised definitive reference to Warhol's voluminous artistic production**
- **Warhol (1928–87) is one of the most famous and popular artists of the 20th century**
- **Documents the pivotal period known as 'The Factory Years'**
- **Includes well-known series such as Thirteen Most Wanted Men, the box sculptures, Marilyn, Jackie and Flowers**
- **Incorporates rare photographs of works and people inside The Factory, and archival photographs of gallery and museum installations**

Georg Frei has been a curator, art critic and editor affiliated with Thomas Ammann Fine Art AG in Zurich since 1988
Neil Printz is an art historian with a focus on 20th-century American art. He is currently Editor of the Isamu Noguchi Catalogue Raisonné for the Isamu Noguchi Foundation in New York and is Professor of Art History at Caldwell College in Caldwell, New Jersey
Sally King-Nero has been Curator of Drawings and Photographs at the Andy Warhol Foundation for the Visual Arts in New York since 1993

Design

Fashion &
Contemporary
Culture

Decorative Arts

Music &
Performing Arts

Video

Index

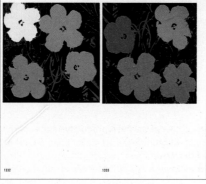

Volumes are organized
according to series
and catalogue
number: works are
reproduced in colour,
in numerical order,
followed by entry
texts. For each work,
the text lists
dimensions, date,
present owner,
inscriptions,
provenance,
exhibitions, literature
and relevant notes.
Supplementary figure
illustrations run in
black columns
alongside the
entry texts

General
Non-Fiction

Art
Contemporary &
Modern
NEW TITLE

Photography

Collector's
Editions

Film

Architecture

220 × 160 mm
8³⁄₄ × 6¹⁄₄ inches
240 pp
c.400 duotone illus.

Hardback
0 7148 4322 9

£ **24.95** UK
$ **39.95** US
€ **39.95** EUR
$ **59.95** CAN
$ **69.95** AUS

Published October

A Year in the Life of Andy Warhol

Photographs by David McCabe, with text by David Dalton

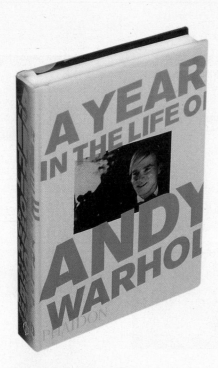

- Photographic diary of 1964–5, one of the most productive and eventful years in Warhol's life
- A significant majority of these photographs have never been published before and are presented together for the first time
- Unique photographic documentation of Warhol, his world and the New York art scene of the mid-1960s
- Many original quotes from celebrities and Warhol's friends, based on interviews conducted by Dalton

David McCabe is a New York-based photographer who was asked by Andy Warhol in late 1964 to document his life for a year. His work has been published in various magazines and newspapers including *Life*, *Harper's Bazaar*, *Mademoiselle* and *The Times*
David Dalton was one of Warhol's first assistants and a founding editor of *Rolling Stone*

Design

Fashion &
Contemporary
Culture

Decorative Arts

Music &
Performing Arts

Video

Index

Above: Warhol poses with Edie Sedgwick wearing a Betsey Johnson's silver lamé jumpsuit on the roof of
David McCabe's studio in midtown Manhattan, spring 1965.

Opposite: Betsey Johnson's first line of clothing fashion shoot for *Mademoiselle* magazine. From top:
Warhol, Chuck Wein, Gerard Malanga, Edie Sedgwick, spring 1965.

112

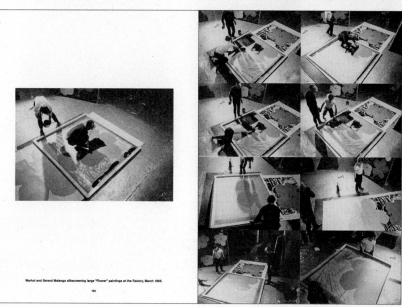

Warhol and Gerard Malanga silkscreening large "Flower" paintings at the Factory, March 1965.

152

Photographs are
grouped by theme or
event, and are
presented in
chronological order.
Texts and captions
give context and
background
information

General
Non-Fiction

Art
Contemporary
Artists
NEW TITLE

Photography

Collector's
Editions

Film

Architecture

290 × 250 mm
11³⁄₈ × 9⁷⁄₈ inches
160 pp
c.120 col, 30 b&w illus.

Paperback
0 7148 4300 8

£ **24.95** UK
$ **39.95** US
€ **39.95** EUR
$ **59.95** CAN
$ **69.95** AUS

Related exhibitions
Major retrospective
at Victoria & Albert
Museum, London,
opening in 2004

Published September

Lucy Orta

*Survey by Roberto Pinto, Interview by Nicholas Bourriaud, Focus by Maia Damianovic, Artist's Choice
text by Eduardo Galeano, Writings by Lucy Orta, featuring an interview with Paul Virilio*

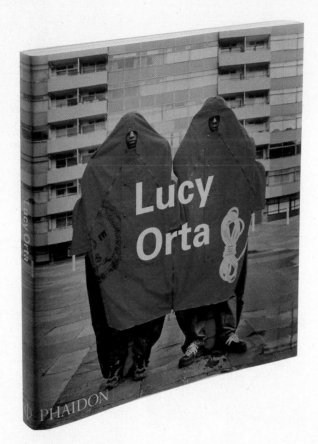

- **Paris-based British artist Lucy Orta (b.1966) bridges the boundaries of the visual arts by merging fashion, social engagement, poetry and performance**
- **This is the only monograph on her work**
- **Orta's work encourages active participation from diverse members of the community**
- **This volume will have a broad audience; subjects covered include art, fashion, politics and poetry**

Roberto Pinto is a Milan-based art critic and curator
Nicholas Bourriaud is a French curator and theorist and Director of the Palais de Tokyo in Paris
Maia Damianovic is a writer and curator based in Austria
Eduardo Galeano is a Uruguayan journalist and historian. During the 1970s he was forced to flee
to Spain following the military coups in Uruguay and Argentina
Paul Virilio is a French theorist

Design

Fashion & Contemporary Culture

Decorative Arts

Music & Performing Arts

Video

Index

Survey   Lucy Orta   Roberto Pinto

Introduction

Focus   Maia Damianovic   The Human Element: *70 x 7 The Meal*

spreads from Lucy Orta showing (from top) Refuge Wear City Interventions, graphitti, 1993–6 and 70 x 7 The Meal, act III, Innsbruck 2000, Installation for 63 guests, Kunstraum Innsbruck Connector Mobile Village + M.I.U. 2001. Reconditioned military Red Cross ambulance, military trailer, Connector Mobile Village I 260 x 860 x 260 cm Installation, Westfälisches Landes-museum für Kunst und Kulturgeschichte, Munster

General
Non-Fiction

Art
Contemporary
Artists
REVISED AND
EXPANDED EDITION

Photography

Collector's
Editions

Film

Architecture

290 × 250 mm
11³⁄₈ × 9⁷⁄₈ inches
260 pp
c.250 col, 40 b&w illus.

Paperback
0 7148 4298 2

£ **24.95** UK
$ **39.95** US
€ **39.95** EUR
$ **59.95** CAN
$ **69.95** AUS

Related exhibitions
Major retrospective
at Tate Modern, London,
opening in 2004

Published August

Luc Tuymans

Survey by Ulrich Loock, Interview by Juan Vicente Aliaga, Focus by Nancy Spector, Artist's Choice text by Andrei Platonov, Writings by Luc Tuymans, Update by Hans Rudolf Reust

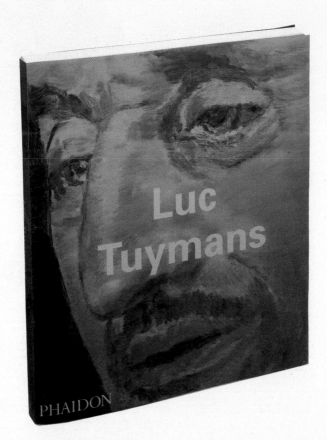

- Luc Tuymans (b.1958) is a Belgian artist who emerged in the late 1980s and whose work fuses the traditions of old master Flemish and Spanish genre painting with a late 20th-century sensibility
- Only monograph that spans his entire career to date
- Nearly all of Tuymans' paintings are reproduced, most in full-page format
- Tuymans' works represent domestic scenes or commonplace objects while other paintings have directly political source material
- This revised edition has been expanded by 100 pages to include most of the artist's recent work

Ulrich Loock is Director of the Kunstmuseum Luzern
Juan Vicente Aliaga is Lecturer at the Faculty of Fine Arts, Valencia, and is a curator, editor and art critic
Nancy Spector is Curator of Contemporary Art at the Solomon R. Guggenheim Museum, New York
Andrei Platonov was a Russian novelist and poet
Hans Rudolf Reust is Director of Art at the Hochschule der Künste in Bern

Design

Fashion & Contemporary Culture

Decorative Arts

Music & Performing Arts

Video

Index

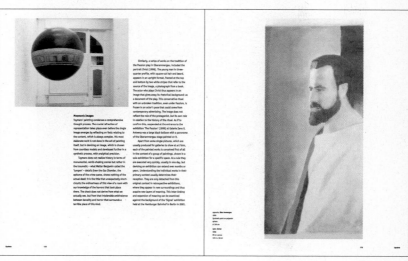

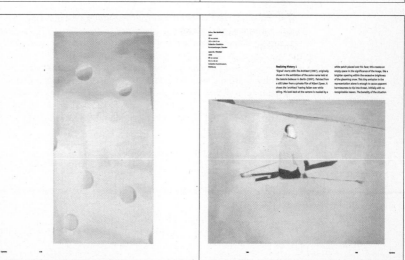

spreads from Luc Tuymans showing (from top, left to right), Paul Cézanne, Still Life, c.1900, oil on canvas; Still-life, 2002, oil on canvas; Ober Ammergau, 1999, synthetic paint on polyester sphere; Christ, 1998, oil on canvas; Der Architekt, 1997, oil on canvas, Collection Staatliche Kunstsammlungen, Dresden; Himmler, 1998, oil on canvas, Collection Kunstmuseum, Wolfsburg

General
Non-Fiction

Art
Impressionist &
19th Century
NEW IN PAPERBACK

Photography

Collector's
Editions

Film

Architecture

290 × 250 mm
11³⁄₈ × 9⁷⁄₈ inches
512 pp
620 col, 7 b&w illus.

Paperback
0 7148 4359 8

£ 24.95 UK
$ 45.00 US
€ 45.00 EUR
$ 69.95 CAN
$ 89.95 AUS

Hardback
0 7148 3776 8

£ 45.00 UK
$ 69.95 US
€ 75.00 EUR
$ 99.95 CAN
$ 125.00 AUS

**Paperback published
September**

Victorian Painting

Lionel Lambourne

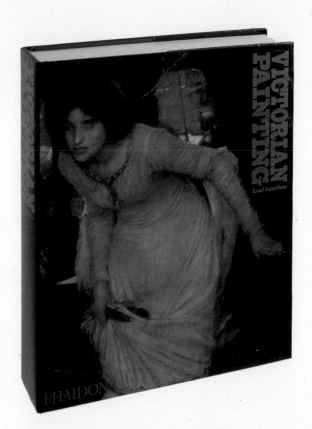

- Comprehensive, scholarly and highly entertaining survey of one of the richest and most popular periods in art history
- Presents a rich panorama of a fertile and exuberant period, embracing work created in the UK, the US, Canada, Australia, New Zealand and South Africa
- A vivid overview of an age of unparalleled energy and creativity
- Full of illuminating anecdotes and with over 600 colour illustrations
- A valuable reference work, containing a wealth of fine work by lesser-known artists

Lionel Lambourne, OBE, was Head of Paintings at the Victoria & Albert Museum in London from 1986 to 1993

'Authoritative and carefully researched … an extraordinarily vivid account of a fascinating time of change and reform.' (*Guardian*)

Design

Fashion &
Contemporary
Culture

Decorative Arts

Music &
Performing Arts

Video

Index

Jacket image:
John William
Waterhouse, *The Lady of
Shalott* (detail), 1894
Spreads from Victorian
Painting showing (from
top, left to right) works
by James Tissot, James
Whistler, Dante Gabriel
Rossetti, Edward Burne-
Jones, Frederic
Leighton, George Catlin,
John James Audubon,
Albert Bierstadt and
Frederic Remington

General
Non-Fiction

Art
Impressionist &
19th Century
NEW IN PAPERBACK

Photography

Collector's
Editions

Film

Architecture

Lawrence Alma-Tadema

Rosemary J Barrow

290 × 250 mm
11³⁄₈ × 9⁷⁄₈ inches
208 pp
147 col, 49 b&w illus.

Paperback
0 7148 4358 X

£ **19.95** UK
$ **29.95** US
€ **29.95** EUR
$ **49.95** CAN
$ **59.95** AUS

Hardback
0 7148 3918 3

£ **35.00** UK
$ **49.95** US
€ **59.95** EUR
$ **75.00** CAN
$ **99.95** AUS

**Paperback published
September**

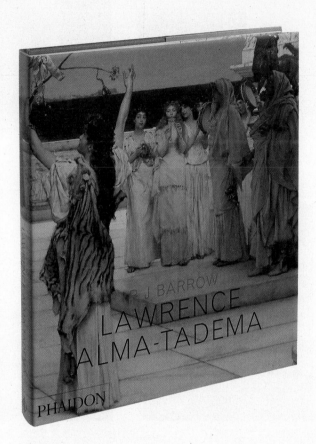

- Sir Lawrence Alma-Tadema (1836–1912) was one of the finest and most distinctive of the Victorian painters
- An absorbing and often amusing portrait of an artist famous for his depictions of the luxury and decadence of the Roman Empire
- Fresh and intriguing new insights into his personality and intentions provide a challenging reassessment of a major artist
- Reveals that Alma-Tadema, a knowledgeable student of antiquity, repeatedly used literary and archaeological allusions in his paintings to subvert their apparently innocent meaning

Rosemary J Barrow is Lecturer in the School of Humanities, King's College, London, and has lectured and published widely on Alma-Tadema

Design

Fashion & Contemporary Culture

Decorative Arts

Music & Performing Arts

Video

Index

. Jacket image:
A Dedication to Bacchus, 1889, Hamburger Kunsthalle, Hamburg Spreads from Lawrence Alma-Tadema showing (from top, left to right) *A Sculptor's Model*, 1877, private collection; Venus Esquilina, 1st century BC, Conservatori Museum, Rome; Edward Poynter, *Diadumene*, 1884, Royal Albert Memorial Museum, Exeter; *The Roses of Heliogabalus*, 1888, and *Resting*, 1882, private collections; *Coign of Vantage*, 1895, J Paul Getty Museum, Malibu

Hardback
290 × 250 mm
11³⁄₈ × 9⁷⁄₈ inches
512 pp
500 col illus.

0 7148 2984 6

£ **29.95** UK
$ **45.00** US
€ **49.95** EUR
$ **69.95** CAN
$ **79.95** AUS

Paperback mini format
163 × 123 mm
6³⁄₈ × 4⁷⁄₈ inches
516 pp
500 col illus.

0 7148 3625 7

£ **6.95** UK
$ **9.95** US
€ **11.95** EUR
$ **14.95** CAN
$ **16.95** AUS

Point of sale
Book tower and
counterpack available

Award

Illustrated Book of the Year,
British Book Awards, 1994

The Art Book

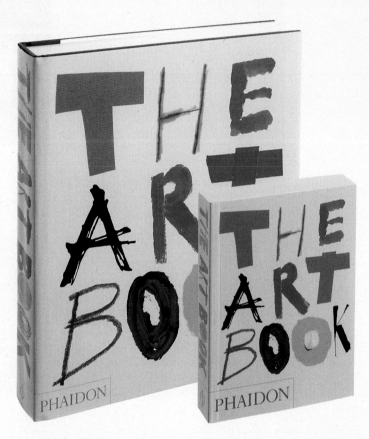

- An A to Z guide to 500 great painters and sculptors from medieval to modern times
- Debunks art-historical classifications by juxtaposing brilliant examples of all periods, schools, visions and techniques
- Glossaries of artistic movements and technical terms make this a valuable work of reference
- A celebrated landmark in the art book world, published in more than twenty languages
- The compact mini edition presents the whole package in an easily portable format

'An anthology crackling with visual energy.' *(The Times)*
'Big, fun, well-designed guide to 500 favorite painters and sculptors.' *(Wall Street Journal)*
'Beautifully designed. Thoroughly cross-referenced, the book presents a fresh perspective and is fantastic value.' *(Good Book Guide)*

Design

Fashion &
Contemporary
Culture

Decorative Arts

Music &
Performing Arts

Video

Index

An essential, original and educational survey. Breaks the mould of art books. They may never be the same again.'

The Times

General Non-Fiction

Art

Photography

Collector's Editions

Film

Architecture

Box dimensions
174×135 mm
6⁶₈×5²₈ inches

Postcard box (50 cards)
0 7148 3770 9
Greeting card box (25 cards)
(Blue) 0 7148 3764 4
Greeting card box (25 cards)
(Green) 0 7148 3765 2
Greeting card box (25 cards)
(Red) 0 7148 3766 0
Greeting card box (25 cards)
(Yellow) 0 7148 3767 9

Each box
incl. VAT £ **12.95** UK
$ **16.95** US
€ **19.95** EUR
$ **24.95** CAN
$ **29.95** AUS

The Art Box Cards

- Five specially designed card boxes with sliding tray, containing images from the best-selling *Art Book*
- Postcard box contains 50 postcards, each a different image
- The four greeting card boxes (blue, green, red and yellow) each contain 25 greeting cards, each a different image, with envelopes
- Fun, informative and beautifully presented, the *Art Box* card collections offer stationery with an artistic flair – and educational value
- On the front of each card is an image from *The Art Book*, while on the back of each card the accompanying text from the book gives information both about the work of art and its creator
- Each greeting card is blank inside, leaving space for personal messages

Design

Fashion &
Contemporary
Culture

Decorative Arts

Music &
Performing Arts

Video

Index

185 × 123 mm
8³⁄₄ × 6¹⁄₄ inches
528 pp
481 col, 20 duotone,
16 b&w illus.

Hardback
0 7148 3959 0

£ **19.95** UK
$ **29.95** US
€ **35.00** EUR
$ **45.00** CAN
$ **55.00** AUS

500 Self-Portraits

Introduction by Julian Bell

· **A compelling collection of self-portraits from throughout recorded history**
· **Organized chronologically, from ancient Egypt to the late 20th century**
· **Includes works by many of the world's greatest painters and sculptors**
· **Each image is both a work of art and a study in psychology and self-perception – viewed together, they create a gallery of powerful and evocative reflections**

Julian Bell, grandson of the artist Vanessa Bell, is a painter and writer, and author of *Bonnard* (1994) in Phaidon's Colour Library series

'A rich and sweeping historical survey … Perhaps no other book has ever packaged such a colourful range of self-depictions as this one. Almost any artist who might come to mind is here.' *(San Francisco Chronicle)*

General
Non-Fiction

Art

Photography

Collector's
Editions

Film

Architecture

156 × 136 mm
6¼ × 5½ inches
256 pp
123 col, 3 b&w illus.

Hardback
0 7148 3939 6

£ **12.95** UK
$ **19.95** US
€ **22.95** EUR
$ **29.95** CAN
$ **35.00** AUS

Annunciation

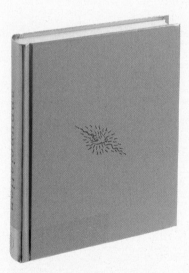

- A collection of over 100 masterpieces depicting scenes of the Annunciation
- Demonstrates how the event has been depicted by artists from the middle ages to the present day
- Offers a sequence of compelling images, each presented on a single page with a caption opposite
- Fascinating as art history, the chronological sequence reveals changing styles and interpretations over the centuries

'Executed with rare intelligence.' (Neil MacGregor, Director of the British Museum, London, *World of Interiors*)

Design

Fashion &
Contemporary
Culture

Decorative Arts

Music &
Performing Arts

Video

Index

156 × 136 mm
6¹₄ × 5¹₂ inches
256 pp
106 col, 1 b&w illus.

Hardback
0 7148 3940 X

£ **12.95** UK
$ **19.95** US
€ **22.95** EUR
$ **29.95** CAN
$ **35.00** AUS

Last Supper

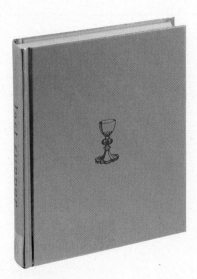

- A collection of over 100 images of one of the most intensely dramatic episodes in the Gospels, the Last Supper
- A chronological sequence of masterpieces that depict the last supper Christ held with his disciples
- It is also the scene in which Christ foretells his betrayal
- The subject presents the supreme artistic challenge of portraying complex interactions among many different characters
- This selection of masterpieces shows how the scene has been interpreted over the centuries by the greatest artists, from Duccio to Andy Warhol, providing an endless source of meditation

General
Non-Fiction

Art

Photography

Collector's
Editions

Film

Architecture

156 × 136 mm
6¼ × 5½ inches
256 pp
119 col, 5 b&w illus.

Hardback
0 7148 3941 8

£ **12.95** UK
$ **19.95** US
€ **22.95** EUR
$ **29.95** CAN
$ **35.00** AUS

Crucifixion

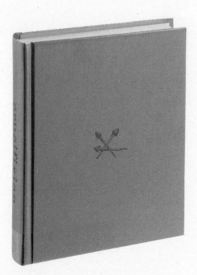

- A sequence of over 120 masterpieces that depict the pivotal scene and supreme image of Christianity
- Works arranged in chronological order from a fresco by Giotto to a Robert Mapplethorpe photograph
- Demonstrates how artists of every age have responded to the starkness and horror of the scene
- *Crucifixion*, with images spanning over 1,500 years, reflects the range of responses that great artists can bring to the same event
- Includes illuminated manuscripts, ivories, frescos, oil paintings, etchings, sculpture, watercolour and photography

Design

Fashion &
Contemporary
Culture

Decorative Arts

Music &
Performing Arts

Video

Index

156 × 136 mm
6¼ × 5½ inches
256 pp
100 col, 6 b&w illus.

Hardback
0 7148 3942 6

£ **12.95** UK
$ **19.95** US
€ **22.95** EUR
$ **29.95** CAN
$ **35.00** AUS

Descent

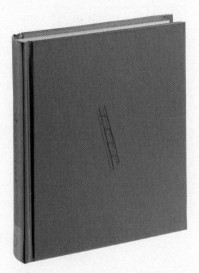

- The Descent from the Cross, or Deposition, is the last act in the human drama of Christ's mission on earth, depicted in over 100 ways by the masters of western art
- Contains images of this psychologically complex scene, as despair is portrayed but hope is suggested, unknown to the participants
- The rich selection of images in this book concludes the series and presents the viewer with a source of profound meditation on the human and divine drama of the Christian story, seen through the medium of great art
- Includes works by Duccio, Donatello, Hans Memling, Michelangelo, Rembrandt, Eric Gill and Barnett Newman

General
Non-Fiction

Art

Photography

Collector's
Editions

Film

Architecture

290 × 250 mm
11³⁄₈ × 9⁷⁄₈ inches
512 pp
500 col illus.

Hardback
0 7148 3845 4

£ **29.95** UK
$ **45.00** US
€ **49.95** EUR
$ **69.95** CAN
$ **79.95** AUS

Mini format
163 × 123 mm
6³⁄₈ × 4⁷⁄₈ inches
520 pp
446 col, 54 b&w illus.

Paperback
0 7148 4119 6

£ **6.95** UK
$ **9.95** US
€ **11.95** EUR
$ **14.95** CAN
$ **16.95** AUS

Point of Sale
Book tower, counterpack
and poster available

The American Art Book

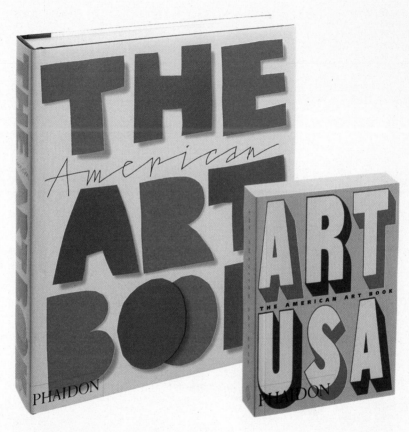

- Accessible authoritative survey of American art
- An unparalleled overview of the most influential American artists from Colonial times to the present
- Presents 500 artists and their works, from Puritan portraits to the Hudson River School and the American Impressionists, to the videos and digital works of today's Conceptual artists
- Easy to use A to Z format departs from the usual emphasis on genres and time periods
- Includes a glossary of artistic terms and movements, and a directory of public collections across the United States and around the world with important holdings in American art
- Compact mini format presents all the same material in a handy format

'Well-produced and broad in its selection, … a highly comprehensive and thought-provoking publication.' *(Good Book Guide)*

Design

Fashion &
Contemporary
Culture

Decorative Arts

Music &
Performing Arts

Video

Index

'Embracing everything from Folk Art to Pop Art, this is a lavish glimpse not only into American Art, but into the history of a century as well.' *The Times*

General
Non-Fiction

Art

Photography

Collector's
Editions

Film

Architecture

The 20th Century Art Book

290 × 250 mm
11³⁄₈ × 9⁷⁄₈ inches
512 pp
500 col illus.

Hardback
0 7148 3542 0

£ **29.95** UK
$ **45.00** US
€ **49.95** EUR
$ **69.95** CAN
$ **79.95** AUS

Mini format
163 × 123 mm
6³⁄₈ × 4⁷⁄₈ inches
520 pp
500 col illus.

Paperback
0 7148 3850 0

£ **6.95** UK
$ **9.95** US
€ **11.95** EUR
$ **14.95** CAN
$ **16.95** AUS

- An A to Z guide to the art of an extraordinary century
- Complements the highly successful *The Art Book* in offering a new and original way of bringing art alive
- Showcases 500 artists in alphabetical order, placing early stars like Monet, Picasso and Dalí alongside the most innovative contemporary artists
- Documents the myriad of new media utilized by artists – from oil and collage to sculpture and readymades to installation and video
- Each artist is represented by a full-page colour plate and a biographical text that both explains the image and introduces its creator
- Easy to use: cross-references make connections between artists, while a glossary defines terms and artistic movements, and an international directory of museums and galleries helps readers to encounter the art face to face
- The mini edition has all of the visual impact and educational value of the original in a lightweight, portable format

'This superbly illustrated, alphabetically arranged celebration of 500 modern artists is a model of its kind.' (*The Times*)
'Demystifies the art of this century ... it chronicles every artist you could ever need to know about in an easy to use A-Z format.' (*Elle Decoration*)

Design

Fashion & Contemporary Culture

Decorative Arts

Music & Performing Arts

Video

Index

The 20th Century Art Box Cards

Box dimensions
174 × 135 mm
6⁶⁸ × 5³⁸ inches

Postcard box (50 cards)
0 7148 3947 7

**Greeting card box (25 cards)
(Selection one)**
0 7148 3943 4

**Greeting card box (25 cards)
(Selection two)**
0 7148 3945 0

Each box
incl. VAT £ **12.95** UK
$ **16.95** US
€ **19.95** EUR
$ **24.95** CAN
$ **29.95** AUS

- Three specially designed card boxes with sliding tray, containing images from the best-selling *20th Century Art Book*
- A wide selection of imagery that covers the entire spectrum of 20th-century art from J W Waterhouse to Nan Goldin
- Each card features an image from the book and its accompanying text giving information about the work and its creator
- Postcard box contains 50 postcards, each a different image
- Greeting card box (selection one) contains 25 greeting cards, each a different image, blank for personal messages, with envelopes
- Greeting card box (selection two) contains a further 25 greeting cards, each a different image, blank for personal messages, with envelopes

General
Non-Fiction

Art
Themes &
Movements

Photography

Collector's
Editions

Film

Architecture

Themes and Movements

'Phaidon's Themes and Movements series seeks to provide the late twentieth-century art history books of the future, and these two recent additions to the series are no exception.' *Art Monthly*

- Ground-breaking series that situates the work of individual artists in the context of modern art
- Source books and a unique point of reference for uninitiated readers and scholars to understand the prevailing art tendencies of our times
- Features an introductory essay charting the genealogy of the theme or movement
- c.250 plates presenting the most significant works of art, including rarely published installation shots and preliminary drawings
- An anthology of documents, including artists' statements, interviews, manifestos, project notes; reviews and articles by key critics; parallel texts from other cultural, philosophical and literary sources
- Biographies of all the artists and authors
- Comprehensive bibliography

Design

Fashion & Contemporary Culture

Decorative Arts

Music & Performing Arts

Video

Index

290 × 250 mm
11³⁄₈ × 9⁷⁄₈ inches
304 pp
175 col, 82 b&w illus.

Hardback
0 7148 3529 3

£ **45.00** UK
$ **75.00** US
€ **75.00** EUR
$ **115.00** CAN
$ **140.00** AUS

Art and Feminism

Edited by Helena Reckitt, with a survey by Peggy Phelan

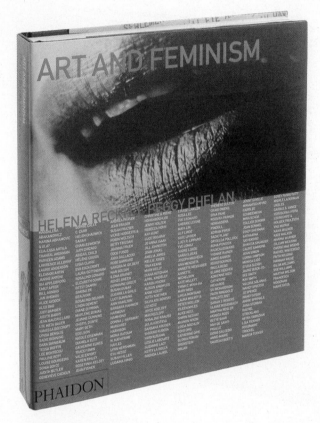

- Feminism redefined the terms of late 20th-century art, exposing assumptions about gender, politicizing the link between private and public, and stressing the specificity of art marked by gender, race, age and class
- Researched and selected by editor and curator Helena Reckitt, this is the first major volume to present the rich diversity of art informed by feminism from the 1960s to the present
- Introduced with a comprehensive survey essay by Peggy Phelan, one of the foremost feminist theorists of contemporary art and performance

Helena Reckitt is Curator at Atlanta Contemporary Art Center, Georgia. A former commissioning editor at Routledge and Head of Talks at the Institute of Contemporary Arts, London, she has a longstanding critical research interest in feminist art and theory
Peggy Phelan is the author of landmark studies such as *Unmarked: The Politics of Performance* (1993) and *Mourning Sex: Performing Public Memories* (1997). She is the Ann O'Day Maples Chair in the Arts at Stanford University and a Visiting Professor at Harvard University

'Art and Feminism is a handsome, meaty volume which provides an excellent overview of the influence of feminist theory and politics on four decades of art by women artists ... The sheer heft of lavishly produced images will be indispensable to scholars, critics and artists.' (Cherry Smyth, *Art Monthly*)

General
Non-Fiction

Art
Themes &
Movements

Photography

Collector's
Editions

Film

Architecture

290 × 250 mm
11³⁄₈ × 9⁷⁄₈ inches
304 pp

Hardback
0 7148 4286 9

£ **45.00** UK
$ **75.00** US
€ **75.00** EUR
$ **115.00** CAN
$ **140.00** AUS

Art and Photography

Edited by David Campany

- The photographic image is central to contemporary art, yet only in the last few decades have museums and the art establishment recognized its importance and status. This volume is the first major survey of photography's place in recent art history
- The work of major artists of the last four decades is presented across an extended 208 pages of colour and duotone images
- As an artform, photography has inspired reflections by some of the most significant theoretical writers of the late 20th century, including Roland Barthes, Jean Baudrillard and artists Victor Burgin and Jeff Wall, whose texts are reprinted in the Documents section
- Essential reading for students, professionals and general readers interested in contemporary art, photography and media
- A book to keep returning to, for its images as much as its value as a reference book

David Campany is Senior Lecturer in the History and Theory of Photography at Surrey Institute of Art and Design, Farnham, England. His essays have been published in *Rewriting Conceptual Art* (1999) and *Postcards on Photography; Photorealism and the Reproduction* (1998)

Design

Fashion & Contemporary Culture

Decorative Arts

Music & Performing Arts

Video

Index

290 × 250 mm
11³⁄₈ × 9⁷⁄₈ inches
304 pp
129 col, 218 b&w illus.

Hardback
0 7148 3413 0

£ 45.00 UK
$ 75.00 US
€ 75.00 EUR
$ 115.00 CAN
$ 140.00 AUS

Arte Povera

Edited by Carolyn Christov-Bakargiev

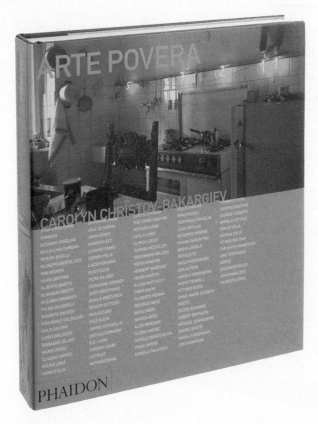

- In 1967 critic Germano Celant defined the work of 13 young Italian artists as Arte Povera ('poor art'). It became Italy's most famous modern art movement
- Arte Povera explored the relation between art and life, made manifest through natural materials and simple human artefacts, and experienced through the body
- Its artists – Anselmo, Boetti, Calzolari, Fabro, Kounellis, Mario Merz, Marisa Merz, Paolini, Pascali, Penone, Pistoletto, Prini and Zorio – remain internationally renowned and exhibited in major museums worldwide
- Edited and with a survey essay by critic and curator Carolyn Christov-Bakargiev, one of the world's leading authorities on Arte Povera
- The definitive overview and anthology of the artworks and writings associated with this influential art movement

Carolyn Christov-Bakargiev is an internationally recognized scholar of late 20th century Italian art. Chief Curator at the Castello di Rivoli, Turin, she was formerly Senior Curator at P.S.1 Contemporary Art Center, New York (1999–2001)

General
Non-Fiction

Art
Themes &
Movements

Photography

Collector's
Editions

Film

Architecture

290 × 250 mm
11³⁄₈ × 9⁷⁄₈ inches
304 pp
265 col and b&w illus.

Hardback
0 7148 3502 1

£ **45.00** UK
$ **75.00** US
€ **75.00** EUR
$ **115.00** CAN
$ **140.00** AUS

The Artist's Body

Edited by Tracey Warr, with a survey by Amelia Jones

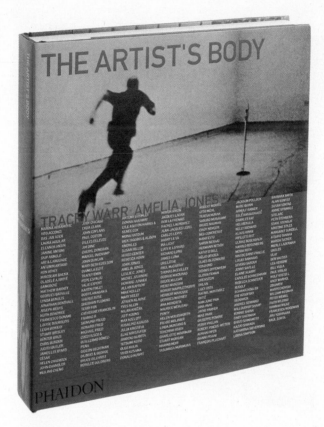

- From the 1950s to the present artists have increasingly used their bodies as the subject and the actual material of the artwork, giving rise to new forms of expression such as Body art, Happenings, performance and live art
- In over 250 images this volume brings together for the first time the largely uncharted history of these often extreme and controversial artworks
- Amelia Jones, an authority on Body art and performance, surveys and discusses how these works uniquely inform us about the social and cultural upheavals of the last five decades

Tracey Warr is a curator specializing in site-specific and performance art projects. She has worked with a range of international artists including Stelarc, Marina Abramovic, Guillermo Gomez Pena, Coco Fusco, Jimmie Durham, Helen Chadwick, Cornelia Parker and James Turrell **Amelia Jones** is Professor of Art History at the University of California, Riverside. Her books include *Postmodernism and the Engendering of Marcel Duchamp* (1987), and *Body Art/Performing the Subject* (1998)

'*The Artist's Body* is a fabulous book and you should go out and buy it immediately … Richly illustrated with great graphics and a comprehensive collection of texts by key writers on the subject … a must-have for anyone interested in contemporary art.' (*Exhibit A*)

290 × 250 mm
11³⁄₈ × 9⁷⁄₈ inches
304 pp
c.296 col and b&w illus.

Hardback
0 7148 3930 2

£ 45.00 UK
$ 75.00 US
€ 75.00 EUR
$ 115.00 CAN
$ 140.00 AUS

Conceptual Art

Edited by Peter Osborne

- In the 1960s a revolution took place as a whole generation of artists experimented with the idea of art as … an idea
- They challenged traditional notions of the art object through new, unprecedented uses of language, actions, processes and forms derived from mass media
- Becoming known as Conceptual art, their work has exerted a major influence on all subsequent art practice, providing an indispensable key to understanding art today
- As a philosopher of art, Peter Osborne provides one of the most rigorous, authoritative surveys available of a movement which made a major contribution not only to art but to the history of thought, with an influence far beyond America and Europe

Peter Osborne is Professor of Modern European Philosophy and Tutor on the Graduate Programme in Aesthetics and Art Theory at Middlesex University, London. He is the author of *The Politics of Time: Modernity and the Avant-Garde* (1995) and *Philosophy in Cultural Theory* (2000)

General
Non-Fiction

Art
Themes &
Movements

Photography

Collector's
Editions

Film

Architecture

290 × 250 mm
11³⁄₈ × 9⁷⁄₈ inches
304 pp
206 col, 95 b&w illus.

Hardback
0 7148 3514 5

£ **45.00** UK
$ **75.00** US
€ **75.00** EUR
$ **115.00** CAN
$ **140.00** AUS

Land and Environmental Art

Edited by Jeffrey Kastner, with a survey by Brian Wallis

- Our idea of landscape was radically transformed in the 1960s when artists such as Michael Heizer, Nancy Holt, Robert Smithson, Walter de Maria and Richard Long stopped merely representing the land and made their mark directly in the environment
- This book not only fully documents the breathtaking earthworks and structures of early Land art but comprehensively surveys artists who work with the natural environment up to the present day
- Earthworks, environments, performances and actions are illustrated with stunning colour photographs, sketches and project notes

Jeffrey Kastner is a New York-based writer on art and culture and Senior Editor of *Cabinet* magazine. A former senior editor of *ARTnews*, he has contributed to international art magazines and journals including *Artforum*, *Flash Art*, *Art Monthly* and *frieze*
Brian Wallis is Chief Curator and Director of Exhibitions at the International Center of Photography, New York. As well as curating, he has taught critical theory at Yale University and was a former senior editor of Art in America. Books on contemporary culture he has edited include *Art After Modernism* (1986)

290 × 250 mm
11³⁄₈ × 9⁷⁄₈ inches
304 pp
296 col and b&w illus.

Hardback
0 7148 3460 2

£ **45.00** UK
$ **75.00** US
€ **75.00** EUR
$ **115.00** CAN
$ **140.00** AUS

Minimalism

Edited by James Meyer

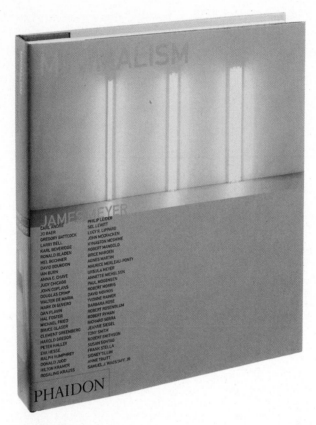

- Originating in the United States in the 1960s, Minimalism is one of the key movements in late 20th-century art
- The term Minimalism was coined to describe the work of a group of artists who developed a new kind of whole or serial geometric abstraction, which has had an enormous influence on subsequent artists, architects, composers and designers
- Critic and art historian James Meyer examines Minimalism from inception to its broader cultural influence
- Beautifully illustrated, this is the most comprehensive sourcebook available on this fundamental moment in 20th-century art history

James Meyer is Associate Professor of Art History at Emory University, Atlanta, Georgia. An internationally recognized authority on the Minimal artists, he is also the author of *Minimalism: Art and Polemics in the Sixties* (2001)

'Readers will learn as much about the subject as one book can be expected to deliver.' (Barry Schwabsky, *Bookforum*)

General
Non-Fiction

Art
Contemporary
Artists

Photography

Collector's
Editions

Film

Architecture

Contemporary Artists

'The boldest, best-executed and most far-reaching publishing project devoted to contemporary art. These books will revolutionize the way contemporary art is presented and written about.' *Artforum*

'The combination of intelligent analysis, personal insight, useful facts and plentiful pictures is a superb format; invaluable for specialists but also interesting for casual readers, it makes these books a must for the library of anyone who cares about contemporary art.' *Time Out*

'A unique series of informative monographs on individual artists.'
The Sunday Times

'Gives the reader the impression of a personal encounter with the artists. Apart from the writing which is lucid and illuminating, it is undoubtedly the wealth of lavish illustrations which makes looking at these books a satisfying entertainment.' *The Art Book*

- **The most comprehensive source books currently available on important contemporary artists**
- **Each title features approximately 120 colour illustrations documenting the artist's career to date**
- **The books provide multiple perspectives on the artists' work through three new texts: a Survey text, which gives an overview of the artist's whole career; an interview with the artist; and a Focus concentrating on a single work of art**
- **In the Artist's Choice the artist selects a text from literature, philosophy or science which has influenced him or her**
- **A selection of the artist's writings complete the book, along with a fully illustrated chronology**

Design

Fashion & Contemporary Culture

Decorative Arts

Music & Performing Arts

Video

Index

290 × 250 mm
11³⁄₈ × 9⁷⁄₈ inches
160 pp
c.120 col, 30 b&w illus.

Paperback
0 7148 4002 5

£ **24.95** UK
$ **39.95** US
€ **39.95** EUR
$ **59.95** CAN
$ **69.95** AUS

Vito Acconci

Survey by Frazer Ward, Interview by Mark C Taylor, Focus by Jennifer Bloomer, Artist's choice text by Alain Robbe-Grillet, Writings by Vito Acconci

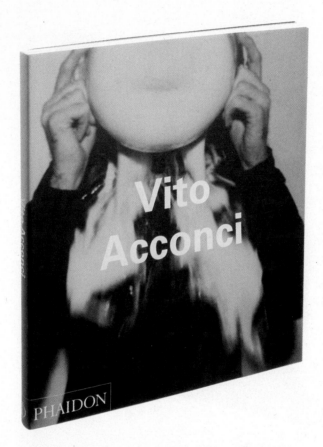

- American artist Vito Acconci (b.1940) is a pioneer of performance and video art
- Associated with Conceptual art and Body art in the late 1960s, he is perhaps best known for his notorious Seedbed (1972), when he masturbated beneath a ramp on the gallery floor, his fantasies about the unseen visitors amplified into the gallery above
- Since 1974 he no longer places his own body within his artworks but has continued exploring social themes with sculpture, installation and experimental architecture

Frazer Ward is Assistant Professor of Art History at the Maryland Institute, College of Art, Baltimore
Mark C Taylor is Professor of Humanities at Williams College, Massachusetts
Jennifer Bloomer is a Principal of jennifer bloomer/robert segrest architecture in Athens, Georgia
Alain Robbe-Grillet is a novelist and leader of the nouveau roman group

General
Non-Fiction

Art
Contemporary
Artists

Photography

Collector's
Editions

Film

Architecture

290 × 250 mm
11³⁄₈ × 9⁷⁄₈ inches
160 pp
c.120 col, 30 b&w illus.

Paperback
0 7148 3989 2

£ **24.95** UK
$ **39.95** US
€ **39.95** EUR
$ **59.95** CAN
$ **69.95** AUS

Doug Aitken

Survey by Daniel Birnbaum, Interview Amanda Sharp, Focus by Jörg Heiser, Artist's choice text by Jorge Luis Borges, Writings by Doug Aitken

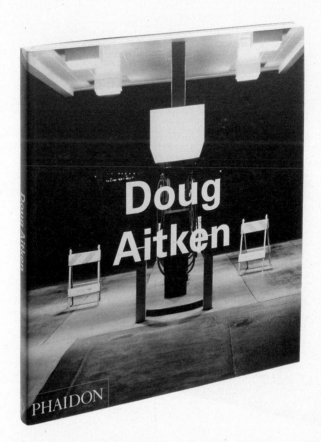

- American video and installation artist Doug Aitken (b.1968) exploded onto the international art scene with his multi-screen work electric earth at the Venice and Whitney Biennales in 1999
- Focusing on the bizarre nocturnal experiences of a young man exploring the edges of Los Angeles, electric earth's dream-like sequences rearrange the linear flow of narrative into a series of unforgettable, disjointed photographic tableaux
- Aitken's work creates unexpected yet beautiful imagery which encircles the viewer and creates a suspended, hyper-real portrait of contemporary life

Daniel Birnbaum is the Director of Portikus and the Städelschule Art Academy, Frankfurt
Amanda Sharp is the publisher and co-founder of *frieze*, the contemporary art and culture magazine
Jörg Heiser is an art historian and critic based at Humboldt University, Berlin
Jorge Luis Borges (1899–1986) was one of Argentina's most acclaimed writers of poetry, essays and fiction

Design

Fashion &
Contemporary
Culture

Decorative Arts

Music &
Performing Arts

Video

Index

290 × 250 mm
11³⁄₈ × 9⁷⁄₈ inches
160 pp
c.120 col, 30 b&w illus.

Paperback
0 7148 3658 3

£ **24.95** UK
$ **39.95** US
€ **39.95** EUR
$ **59.95** CAN
$ **69.95** AUS

Christian Boltanski

*Survey by Didier Semin, Interview by Tamar Garb, Focus by Donald Kuspit, Artist's choice text
by Georges Perec, Writings by Christian Boltanski*

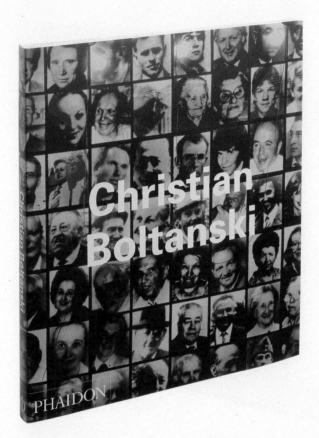

- Christian Boltanski (b.1945), one of the most important French contemporary artists, evades
  definition; his work has ranged from the creation of an 'ironic museum of the self' to snapshots
  of an unspecified family
- Boltanski gathers old photos, clothes and personal objects, which are presented as archival
  artefacts tracing individual lives, and dramatizes them through his deployment of darkness
  and light
- His art has been presented in museums worldwide and hovers between the extermination
  camp depot and the memorial shrine

Didier Semin is Curator for the contemporary art collection at the Centre Georges Pompidou
Tamar Garb is a critic and historian of 19th- and 20th-century visual culture and a reader in
history of art at University College, London
Donald Kuspit is Professor of Art History and Philosophy at the State University of New York
at Stony Brook, and at Cornell University, Ithaca, New York. He is also Editor of *Art Criticism*
Georges Perec (1936-82) was a Paris-born master of language who experimented with every
conceivable genre of writing, from crosswords to recipes to novels and memoirs

General
Non-Fiction

Art
Contemporary
Artists

Photography

Collector's
Editions

Film

Architecture

290×250 mm
11³⁄₈ × 9⁷⁄₈ inches
160 pp
c.120 col, 30 b&w illus.

Paperback
0 7148 4122 6

£ **24.95** UK
$ **39.95**   US
€ **39.95** EUR
$ **59.95** CAN
$ **69.95** AUS

Louise Bourgeois

Survey by Robert Storr, Interview by Paulo Herkenhoff (with Thyrza Goodeve), Focus by Allan Schwartzman, Artist's choice text by Françoise Sagan, Writings by Louise Bourgeois

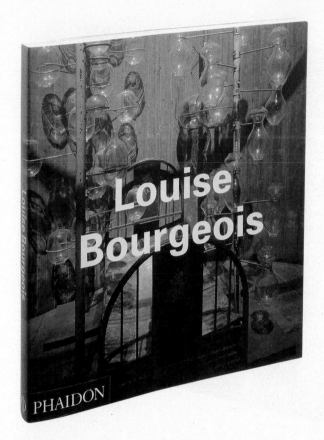

- Born in Paris, Louise Bourgeois (b.1911) is an exceptional figure in the contemporary art world
- Her career spans some 70 years and touches upon such key movements as Surrealism, Abstract Expressionism and feminism; after a lifetime of little artistic recognition, Bourgeois now enjoys cult status
- An extraordinarily influential sculptor, she has worked, often experimentally, with a huge variety of materials
- She is equally admired for her intimate drawings and her highly personal writings
- Themes such as the Other, the feminine and the masculine, and the body – as well as her own specific biography – spin a tangled and intense life-long body of work of unusual profundity
- Because Bourgeois is a notoriously reclusive artist, the interview alone is of great appeal to her followers

Paulo Herkenhoff is a curator at The Museum of Modern Art, New York
Robert Storr is Professor of Modern Art at the Institute of Fine Arts, New York University
Allan Schwartzman is an art critic and founding curator of the New Museum of Contemporary Art, New York
Françoise Sagan is a French novelist and essayist

290 × 250 mm
11³⁄₈ × 9⁷⁄₈ inches
160 pp
c.120 col, 30 b&w illus.

Paperback
0 7148 4075 0

£ **24.95** UK
$ **39.95** US
€ **39.95** EUR
$ **59.95** CAN
$ **69.95** AUS

Cai Guo-Qiang

Survey by Dana Friis-Hansen, Interview by Octavio Zaya, Focus by Takashi Serizawa,
Artist's choice texts by Qiao Liang and Wang Xianhui, Writings by Cai Guo-Qiang

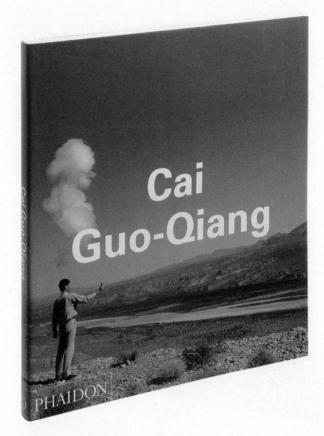

- Cai Guo-Qiang (b.1960) is one of the most important Chinese artists to have emerged internationally in the 1990s
- Best known for his spectacular gunpowder projects, Cai has explored a diversity of media and art forms, including works such as an extension of the Great Wall of China made from fire, designed to be seen from outer space by extraterrestrial beings; feng shui rearrangements of public and private spaces; participatory projects with kites, jacuzzis and mini golf courses; and sculptures constructed from melted-down cars or abandoned boats
- Cai's projects are strongly influenced by their location and the works are frequently altered or developed as they are exhibited at new sites

Dana Friis-Hansen is Chief Curator of the Austin Museum of Art, Texas
Octavio Zaya is a New York-based critic and curator
Takashi Serizawa is Director of P3 art and environment in Tokyo
Qiao Liang and **Wang Xianhui** are senior Chinese Air Force officers

General
Non-Fiction

Art
Contemporary
Artists

Photography

Collector's
Editions

Film

Architecture

Revised and
expanded edition
Mini format
134 × 156 mm
6¹⁄₄ × 5¹⁄₂ inches
212 pp
c.200 col, c.40 b&w illus.

Paperback
0 7148 4306 7

£ 12.95 UK
$ 19.95 US
€ 22.95 EUR
$ 29.95 CAN
$ 39.95 AUS

Maurizio Cattelan

Survey by Francesco Bonami, Update by Massimiliano Gioni, Interview by Nancy Spector,
Focus by Barbara Vanderlinden, Artist's choice texts by Philip Roth and Marc Etkind (ed.),
Writings by Maurizio Cattelan

- Maurizio Cattelan (b.1960) is among the best-known Italian artists to have emerged
  internationally in the 1990s
- Cattelan's work mocks art history (his giant, Disneyland-style 'Pablo Picasso' welcomed
  visitors at New York's Museum of Modern Art, 1998), monumentality (his granite plaque
  commemorating all the England football team losses, London, 1999), and nationalism
  (his rug based on the Bel Paese cheese wrapper map of Italy was placed to be trampled
  by visitors at a major show of new Italian art, 1994)
- His work has been shown at the Venice Biennale since 1993 and in major venues worldwide
- New mini edition conceived by the artist, is updated to include over 50 additional pages
  documenting the artist's work to date

Francesco Bonami is Senior Curator at the Museum of Contemporary Art ,Chicago
Massimiliano Gioni is an art critic and curator based in Milan and New York
Nancy Spector is Curator of Contemporary Art at the Solomon R.Guggenheim Museum, New York
Barbara Vanderlinden is an independent curator and Director of Roomade in Brussels
Philip Roth is an award-winning American novelist

Design

Fashion &
Contemporary
Culture

Decorative Arts

Music &
Performing Arts

Video

Index

'This book is a truly superb production. It should be enjoyed by everyone interested in contemporary art or just puzzled by the seeming obscurities of Postmodernism.'

World of Interiors

General Non-Fiction

Art Contemporary Artists

Photography

Collector's Editions

Film

Architecture

Revised and expanded edition
290 × 250 mm
11³⁄₈ × 9⁷⁄₈ inches
212 pp
c.180 col, 40 b&w illus.

Paperback
0 7148 3949 3

£ 24.95 UK
$ 39.95 US
€ 39.95 EUR
$ 59.95 CAN
$ 69.95 AUS

Richard Deacon

Survey by Jon Thompson, Update by Penelope Curtis, Interview by Pier Luigi Tazzi,
Focus by Peter Schjeldahl, Artist's choice text by Mary Douglas, Writings by Richard Deacon

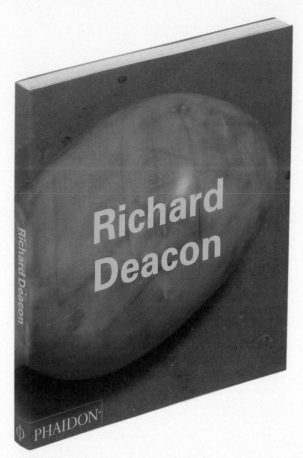

- Awarded the Turner Prize in 1987, Richard Deacon (b.1949) has occupied the foreground of British sculpture since the early 1980s
- His virtuoso constructions in wood, metal and plastic range in scale from the domestic to the monumental; they loop and curve across space like three-dimensional drawings, or hover on the floor like great drops of liquid
- New edition is updated to include over 50 additional pages documenting the artist's work since 1995, including a major retrospective at the Tate Gallery, Liverpool, in 1999

Jon Thompson is an artist, teacher, writer and curator. He is currently Research Professor at Middlesex University
Pier Luigi Tazzi is an Italian art critic and curator
Peter Schjeldahl is the art critic of *The New Yorker* magazine
Mary Douglas is a British social anthropologist
Penelope Curtis is Curator at the Henry Moore Institute in Leeds

'This impressive volume catalogues the many works of this notable 20th-century artist, providing an authoritative and highly illustrated study of his projects.' *(Architectural Interior)*

Design

Fashion & Contemporary Culture

Decorative Arts

Music & Performing Arts

Video

Index

290 × 250 mm
11³⁄₈ × 9⁷⁄₈ inches
160 pp
c.120 col, 30 b&w illus.

Paperback
0 7148 3659 1

£ **24.95** UK
$ **39.95** US
€ **39.95** EUR
$ **59.95** CAN
$ **69.95** AUS

Mark Dion

*Survey by Lisa Graziose Corrin, Interview by Miwon Kwon, Focus by Norman Bryson,
Artist's choice text by John Berger, Writings by Mark Dion*

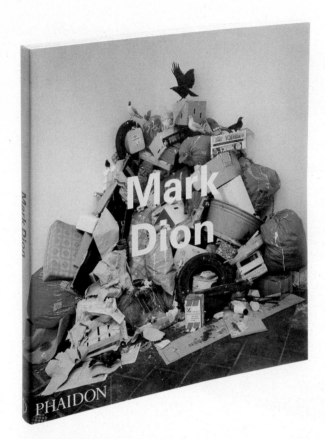

- Mark Dion (b.1961) is an American artist who metamorphoses into an explorer, biochemist, detective and archaeologist
- In his installations since the 1980s, Dion has constructed the laboratories and museum caches of the great historical naturalists – following in their footsteps in his own adventurous, eco-inspired journeys to the tropics
- His research and magical collections are presented in installational still lifes that combine taxidermic animals and lab equipment with artefacts, like walk-through Wunderkammers and life-sized cabinets of curiosity

Lisa Graziose Corrin is a Curator at The Contemporary, Baltimore
Miwon Kwon is Assistant Professor of Contemporary Art History at UCLA
Norman Bryson is a British-born art historian and Professor of Art History at Harvard University, Cambridge, Massachusetts
John Berger is a British novelist, essayist and art critic

'An exquisite and absorbing exploration of Dion's practice ... richly rewarding.' *(Stills)*

General Non-Fiction

Art Contemporary Artists

Photography

Collector's Editions

Film

Architecture

290 × 250 mm
11³⁄₈ × 9⁷⁄₈ inches
160 pp
c.120 col, 30 b&w illus.

Paperback
0 7148 3796 2

£ **24.95** UK
$ **39.95** US
€ **39.95** EUR
$ **59.95** CAN
$ **69.95** AUS

Stan Douglas

Survey by Scott Watson, Interview by Diana Thater, Focus by Carol J Clover, Artist's choice text by Gilles Deleuze, Writings by Stan Douglas

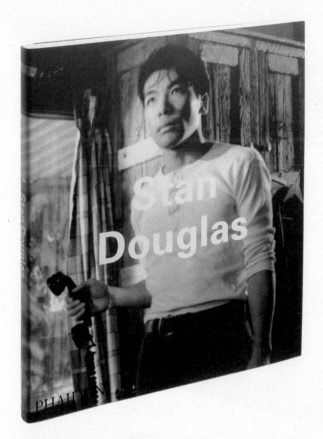

- Canadian artist Stan Douglas (b.1960) combines traditional cinematic techniques with new technologies to produce remarkable video installations
- These visually complex works look at the history of television, video and film, and can result in dramatic contemporary portraits
- From his early brief dramas for television, to his spectacular large-screen installation *Der Sandmann* exploring childhood trauma, Douglas's work is layered with the artist's observations on social alienation and psychic states
- Featured in two Documentas and nominated for the Hugo Boss/Guggenheim prize in 1997, Douglas has emerged as an international figure

Scott Watson is a curator and critic based in Vancouver
Diana Thater is a Los Angeles-based artist who works in video installation
Carol J Clover is Professor of Rhetoric (Film) and Scandinavian (Medieval Studies) at the University of California, Berkeley
Gilles Deleuze is of France's most influential late 20th-century philosophers

290 × 250 mm
11³⁄₈ × 9⁷⁄₈ inches
160 pp
c.120 col, 30 b&w illus.

Paperback
0 7148 3823 3

£ **24.95** UK
$ **39.95** US
€ **39.95** EUR
$ **59.95** CAN
$ **69.95** AUS

Marlene Dumas

*Survey by Dominic van den Boogerd, Interview by Barbara Bloom, Focus by Mariuccia Casadio,
Artist's choice texts by Oscar Wilde and Jean Genet, Writings by Marlene Dumas*

- Marlene Dumas (b.1953), born in South Africa and based in Amsterdam, is one of the Netherlands' most internationally admired artists
- A highly skilled 'painter's painter', she comments through her work on the state of painting today and asks the question: What does it mean to be a woman working within the predominantly male genre of expressionist art?
- Dumas has exhibited since the late 1970s; solo exhibitions have included the Museum für Moderne Kunst, Frankfurt (1998) and the Tate Gallery, London (1996); in 1995 she represented the Netherlands at the 46th Venice Biennale

Dominic van den Boogerd is currently Director of de Ateliers, international artists' institute in Amsterdam
Barbara Bloom is a New York-based artist
Mariuccia Casadio is a freelance writer on contemporary art, fashion and design
Jean Genet (1910–86) was a French writer
Oscar Wilde (1854–1900) was an English author and playwright

General Non-Fiction

Art Contemporary Artists

Photography

Collector's Editions

Film

Architecture

290 × 250 mm
11³⁄₈ × 9⁷⁄₈ inches
160 pp
c.120 col, 30 b&w illus.

Paperback
0 7148 3348 7

£ **24.95** UK
$ **39.95** US
€ **39.95** EUR
$ **59.95** CAN
$ **69.95** AUS

Jimmie Durham

Survey by Laura Mulvey, Interview by Dirk Snauwaert, Focus by Mark Alice Durant, Artist's choice text by Italo Calvino, Writings by Jimmie Durham

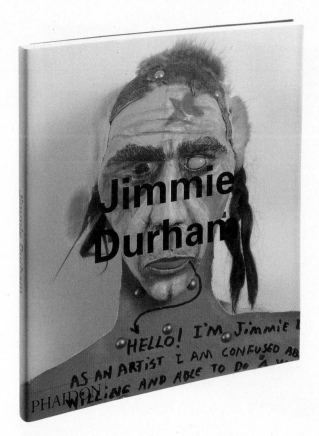

- Jimmie Durham (b.1940) is an internationally acclaimed artist, writer and poet of Cherokee descent
- Durham collages discarded objects and fragments of organic matter, transforming them with dazzling colour into startling, anthropomorphic sculptures and installations
- His ersatz ethnographic displays deliver ironic assaults on the colonizing procedures of Western culture
- An activist in the American Indian movement during the 1970s, he has also published poetry, fiction and critical theory

Laura Mulvey is Postgraduate Studies Co-ordinator at the British Film Institute
Dirk Snauwaert is an art historian based in Belgium
Mark Alice Durant is a Los Angeles-based artist and author
Italo Calvino was an Italian author

'Revelatory about his life experience as a writer and artist.' *(Artforum)*

290 × 250 mm
11³⁄₈ × 9⁷⁄₈ inches
160 pp
c.120 col, 30 b&w illus.

Paperback
0 7148 4036 X

£ **24.95** UK
$ **39.95** US
€ **39.95** EUR
$ **59.95** CAN
$ **69.95** AUS

Olafur Eliasson

Survey by Madeleine Grynsztejn, Interview by Daniel Birnbaum, Focus by Michael Speaks,
Artist's choice text by Henri Bergson, Writings by Olafur Eliasson

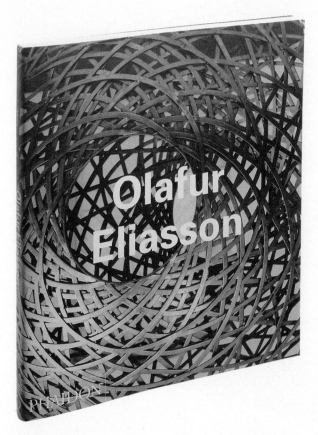

- Young sculptor, photographer and installation artist, Olafur Eliasson (b.1967) creates works
  that explore the relationships between human beings, nature and technology
- Based in Berlin, the artist rebuilds in the gallery fragments of the environment: icebergs
  at the Musée d'Art Moderne de la Ville de Paris, a wind tunnel at the Louisiana Museum in
  Humlebaek, Denmark
- For Eliasson, immaterial sensations such as temperature, smell, taste, air and magnetic waves
  become sculptural elements when presented in an art context
- Nominated in 2002 for the prestigious Hugo Boss prize, Eliasson has become a favourite in
  recent Biennales of contemporary art
- Olafur Eliasson's writings include essays on topics such as the weather and colour, as well as an
  open letter entitled 'Dear Everybody,' addressed to the viewers moving through his artwork

Madeleine Grynsztejn is Senior Curator of Painting and Sculpture at the San Francisco Museum
of Modern Art
Daniel Birnbaum is Director of Portikus and the Städelschule Art Academy, Frankfurt
Michael Speaks is Director of the Metropolitan Research and Design Postgraduate Program
at the Southern Institute of Architecture, Los Angeles
Henri Bergson (1859–1941) was a French philosopher

290 × 250 mm
11³⁄₈ × 9⁷⁄₈ inches
160 pp
c.120 col, 30 b&w illus.

Paperback
0 7148 3986 8

£ **24.95** UK
$ **39.95** US
€ **39.95** EUR
$ **59.95** CAN
$ **69.95** AUS

Tom Friedman

Survey by Bruce Hainley, Interview by Dennis Cooper, Focus by Adrian Searle, Artist's choice texts by Robert Walser and Timothy Leary, Writings by Tom Friedman

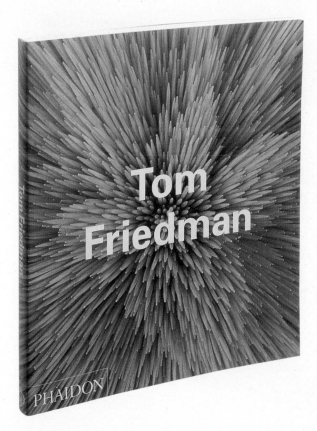

- Tom Friedman (b.1965) is an unusual young American sculptor who produces quirky yet beautiful sculptures out of household objects – pencils, plastic cups, laundry detergent, paper straws
- Featured in *cream* and in a one-person presentation at The Museum of Modern Art, New York, Friedman has quickly gained an impressive following of some of the most attentive and influential contemporary art-watchers in the United States
- This is art which raises questions about the making and seeing of art, about the pleasures of small transformations producing sudden beauty
- Friedman's first major American museum show toured 2000–2

Bruce Hainley teaches in the graduate fine arts programme at Art Center College of Design, Pasadena
Dennis Cooper is a Los Angeles-based novelist, poet, curator and art critic
Adrian Searle is a London-based curator and art critic for the *Guardian*
Robert Walser (1878–1956) was a Swiss-born writer
Timothy Leary (1920–96) was an American psychologist

Revised and expanded edition
290 × 250 mm
11³⁄₈ × 9⁷⁄₈ inches
212 pp
c.180 col, 40 b&w illus.

Paperback
0 7148 3952 3

£ **24.95** UK
$ **39.95** US
€ **39.95** EUR
$ **59.95** CAN
$ **69.95** AUS

Antony Gormley

Survey by John Hutchinson, Update by W J T Mitchell, Interview by E H Gombrich, Focus by Lela B Njatin, Artist's choice text by St Augustine, Writings by Antony Gormley

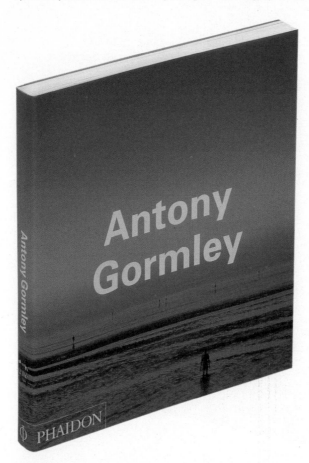

· **Recipient of the 1994 Turner Prize, Antony Gormley (b.1950) is an internationally acclaimed British artist who has revitalized the human figure in sculpture**
· **Often cast from his own body, his lead and iron figures are sites for the exploration of states of being; his public sculptures raise key issues about the relation between art, society and the environment**
· **The new edition of this monograph has been updated with over 50 additional pages documenting the artist's work since 1995, including ambitious site-specific projects and monuments such as The Angel of the North (1998) and Quantum Cloud (2000)**

John Hutchinson is the Director of the Douglas Hyde Gallery in Dublin
E H Gombrich was one of the world's most celebrated art historians
Lela B Njatin is an author and an advisor to the Scientific Research Centre of the Slovenian Academy for Sciences and Arts
W J T Mitchell is Professor of English and Art History at the University of Chicago
St. Augustine (396–430) was a bishop, born in Tagaste, Algeria

General
Non-Fiction

Art
Contemporary
Artists

Photography

Collector's
Editions

Film

Architecture

290 × 250 mm
11³⁄₈ × 9⁷⁄₈ inches
160 pp
c.120 col, 30 b&w illus.

Paperback
0 7148 3964 7

£ **24.95** UK
$ **39.95** US
€ **39.95** EUR
$ **59.95** CAN
$ **69.95** AUS

Dan Graham

Survey by Birgit Pelzer, Interview by Mark Francis, Focus by Beatriz Colomina, Artist's choice text by Philip K Dick, Writings by Dan Graham

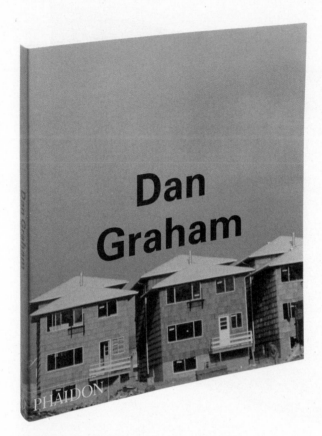

- Dan Graham (b.1942) is among the most influential of the Conceptual artists who emerged in America during the mid-1960s
- A pioneer in performance and video art in the 1970s, Graham later turned his attention to architectural projects designed for social interaction in public spaces, among them The Children's Pavilion (1989) conceived with Jeff Wall
- His writings range from early Conceptual art pieces inserted in mass-market magazines to texts about his fellow artists
- During the 1990s Graham has been offered major public commissions throughout North America and Europe

Birgit Pelzer is Professor of Modern Aesthetics and Philosphy at the École Supérieure des Arts Plastiques Saint-Luc und ERG in Brussels
Mark Francis is a curator and writer
Beatriz Colomina is Associate Professor in the School of Architecture at Princeton University, New Jersey
Philip K Dick (1928-82) was a science fiction writer

290 × 250 mm
11³/₈ × 9⁷/₈ inches
160 pp
c.120 col, 30 b&w illus.

Paperback
0 7148 3550 1

£ **24.95** UK
$ **39.95** US
€ **39.95** EUR
$ **59.95** CAN
$ **69.95** AUS

Paul Graham

Survey by Andrew Wilson, Interview by Gillian Wearing, Focus by Carol Squiers, Artist's choice texts by Kazuo Ishiguro and Haruki Murakami, Writings by Paul Graham

· Paul Graham's (b.1956) jewel-like colours and unsettling compositions reveal how social relations and political trauma are inscribed in the everyday
· This book brings together for the first time all of Graham's successive series, from his journey along the A1 road in Britain to intimate studies of Japan
· Graham's work has been seen at venues around the world, including The Museum of Modern Art, New York, and the Tate Gallery, London

Gillian Wearing is a London-based artist
Andrew Wilson is an art historian based in London
Carol Squiers is a writer, editor and curator based in New York
Kazuo Ishiguro is a London-based, Japanese novelist who came to Britain in 1960

General Non-Fiction

Art Contemporary Artists

Photography

Collector's Editions

Film

Architecture

290 × 250 mm
11³⁄₈ × 9⁷⁄₈ inches
160 pp
c.120 col, 30 b&w illus.

Paperback
0 7148 3660 5

£ **24.95** UK
$ **39.95** US
€ **39.95** EUR
$ **59.95** CAN
$ **69.95** AUS

Mona Hatoum

Survey by Guy Brett, Interview by Michael Archer, Focus by Catherine de Zegher, Artist's choice texts by Piero Manzoni and Edward Saïd, Writings by Mona Hatoum

- Born in Lebanon, Mona Hatoum (b.1952) was exiled to London in the 1970s, where she was nominated for the prestigious Turner Prize in 1995
- Through performance, video, sculpture and installation, she immerses her audiences in emotional states – as they journey through all the orifices of the artist's body or watch her 'drowning' in mud in a glass box
- Often exquisitely beautiful, Hatoum's works are nonetheless powerful evocations of statelessness, denial and otherness

Guy Brett is a writer and curator based in London
Michael Archer is an art critic and teaches art history at Chelsea and Goldsmiths' Colleges in London
Catherine de Zegher is a Belgian curator
Piero Manzoni (1933-63) was a Milan-based sculptor and performance artist
Edward Saïd is Professor of Comparative Literature at Columbia University, New York

'This valuable retrospective demonstrates the sense of alienation her work intends to create, and reinforces her artistic statements with essays from cultural commentators, including brilliant fellow-Palestinian Edward Saïd.' *(The Big Issue)*

Design

Fashion &
Contemporary
Culture

Decorative Arts

Music &
Performing Arts

Video

Index

290 × 250 mm
11³⁄₈ × 9⁷⁄₈ inches
160 pp
c.120 col, 30 b&w illus.

Paperback
0 7148 3754 7

£ 24.95 UK
$ 39.95 US
€ 39.95 EUR
$ 59.95 CAN
$ 69.95 AUS

Jenny Holzer

Survey by David Joselit, Interview by Joan Simon, Focus by Renata Salecl, Artist's choice texts by Samuel Beckett and Elias Canetti, Writings by Jenny Holzer

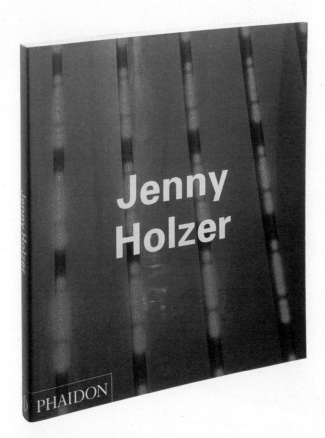

- Among America's best-known artists, Jenny Holzer (b.1950) examines the power of language through glowing, disembodied texts
- In addition to having written many oft-quoted truisms ('Abuse of Power Comes as No Surprise'), she has found visually stunning means of conveying them – from the anonymous posters hung in the streets of Manhattan to a giant installation spiralling up the Guggenheim Museum interior
- Holzer, awarded the Leone d'Oro prize for her contribution to the 1990 Venice Biennale, fuses influences ranging from advertising to Minimalism's use of industrial materials in an innovative form of public art

David Joselit is a Assistant Professor of Art History at the University of California
Joan Simon is a Paris-based, American-born writer, curator and arts administrator
Renata Salecl is a Slovenian cultural theorist and philosopher
Samuel Beckett was an Irish-born playwright, poet and novelist
Elias Canetti was a Bulgarian writer

General
Non-Fiction

Art
Contemporary
Artists

Photography

Collector's
Editions

Film

Architecture

290 × 250 mm
11³⁄₈ × 9⁷⁄₈ inches
160 pp
c.120 col, 30 b&w illus.

Paperback
0 7148 3865 9

£ **24.95** UK
$ **39.95** US
€ **39.95** EUR
$ **59.95** CAN
$ **69.95** AUS

Roni Horn

Survey by Louise Neri, Interview by Lynne Cooke, Focus by Thierry de Duve, Artist's choice text by Clarice Lispector, Writings by Roni Horn

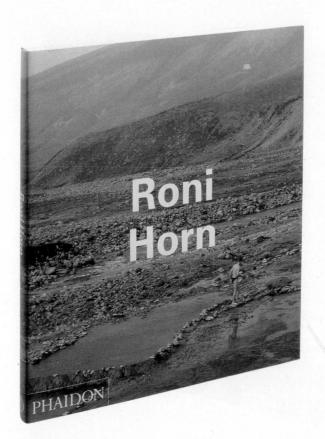

- American artist Roni Horn (b.1955) is admired internationally for the quiet seriousness of her exquisitely conceived artworks
- Horn has concentrated on a small, highly personal selection of subjects in her work: the tradition of Minimal sculpture, and our response to it; Iceland, a place she has visited regularly for many years; and the poetry of Wallace Stevens and Emily Dickinson
- Groupings of sculptures and photographs are often presented together in large installations which invite the viewer's full, prolonged attention in the observation of precise, subtle shifts of detail or mood, offering a heightened sense of environment and presence in the world

Louise Neri is an independent curator and editor based in New York
Lynne Cooke is Curator at Dia Center for the Arts, New York
Thierry de Duve is an art critic and author
Clarice Lispector (1920–77) was a Brazilian writer

290 × 250 mm
11³⁄₈ × 9⁷⁄₈ inches
160 pp
c.120 col, 30 b&w illus.

Paperback
0 7148 3797 0

£ **24.95** UK
$ **39.95** US
€ **39.95** EUR
$ **59.95** CAN
$ **69.95** AUS

Ilya Kabakov

Survey by Boris Groys, Interview by David A Ross, Focus by Iwona Blazwick, Artist's choice text by Anton Chekhov, Writings by Ilya Kabakov

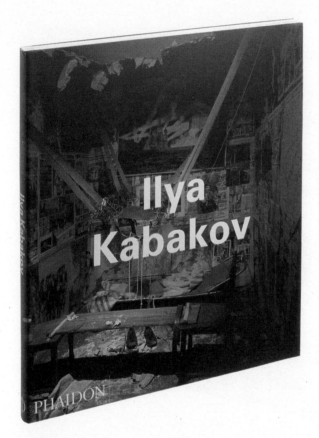

- After some 30 years as an 'unofficial' artist in the former Soviet Union, Ilya Kabakov (b.1933) first came to international recognition in the late 1980s; now based in New York, he is considered the most important Russian artist of the late 20th century
- His installations are akin to theatrical mise-en-scènes or comedies on human frustration and doomed aspirations, presenting, for example, a cramped communal apartment or a flooded art museum
- Alternating between irony and tragedy, Kabakov evokes a shadowy world in which fable-like miracles might occur: a homespun cosmonaut may fly into space or an ordinary aerial may spell out a poem against the sky

Boris Groys is Professor of Aesthetics and Media Theory at ZKM (Centre for Art and Media Technology), Karlsruhe, Germany
David A Ross is Director of the San Francisco Museum of Modern Art
Iwona Blazwick is Director at the Whitechapel Art Gallery, London
Anton Chekhov (1860–1904) was a Russian playwright

General
Non-Fiction

Art
Contemporary
Artists

Photography

Collector's
Editions

Film

Architecture

290 × 250 mm
11³⁄₈ × 9⁷⁄₈ inches
160 pp
c.120 col, 30 b&w illus.

Paperback
0 7148 4104 8

£ **24.95** UK
$ **39.95** US
€ **39.95** EUR
$ **59.95** CAN
$ **69.95** AUS

On Kawara

Survey by Jonathan Watkins, Tribute by various authors, Focus by René Denizot, Artist's choice texts by Stuart Hameroff and Roger Penrose, Writings by On Kawara

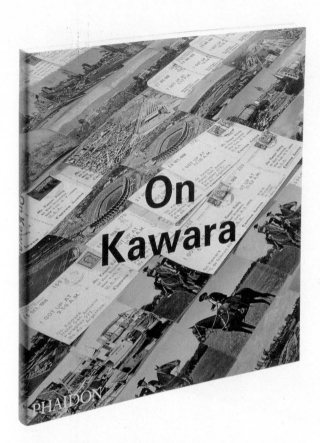

- Japanese-born, New York-based On Kawara (b.1933) is one of the world's best-known Conceptual artists, a major international figure since the 1960s
- Best known are his Date Paintings (1965–ongoing), in which he methodically creates a single painting a day, with simply the date written upon it
- A unique feature of this book is the Tribute section, which reflects the artist's lifelong commitment never to be personally documented in his own words
- This collection of short statements by 30 individuals selected by Kawara creates an indirect 'portrait of the artist'

Jonathan Watkins is Director of the Ikon Gallery, Birmingham
René Denizot is Director of the École Supérieure des Beaux-Arts, Nîmes
Stuart Hameroff is Professor in the Departments of Anesthesiology and Psychology, and Associate Director at the Center for Consciousness Studies, at the University of Arizona, Tucson
Roger Penrose is Rouse Ball Professor of Mathematics at the University of Oxford

Design

Fashion & Contemporary Culture

Decorative Arts

Music & Performing Arts

Video

Index

290 × 250 mm
11³⁄₈ × 9⁷⁄₈ inches
160 pp
c.120 col, 30 b&w illus.

Paperback
0 7148 3834 9

£ 24.95 UK
$ 39.95 US
€ 39.95 EUR
$ 59.95 CAN
$ 69.95 AUS

Mike Kelley

Survey by John C Welchman, Interview by Isabelle Graw, Focus by Anthony Vidler, Artist's choice texts by Georges Bataille and Charles Fort, Writings by Mike Kelley

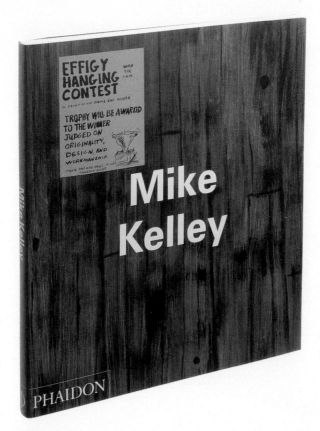

- Los Angeles-based sculptor, performance and installation artist Mike Kelley (b.1954) is one of the most important American artists to have emerged in the 1980s
- Best known for his assemblage sculptures made from stuffed children's toys, Kelley draws from popular culture as well as the Modernist traditions of the found object and collage to comment on late 20th-century American society
- Mike Kelley's audience is very broad, ranging from academics and teenage comic-book cultists to curators of the world's most prestigious museums

John C Welchman is Associate Professor in the Visual Arts Department of the University of California, San Diego
Isabelle Graw is the founder and Editor of the Cologne-based art journal *Texte zur Kunst*
Anthony Vidler is Professor of Art History and Architecture at the University of California, Los Angeles
Georges Bataille (1897–1962) was a French writer

General
Non-Fiction

Art
Contemporary
Artists

Photography

Collector's
Editions

Film

Architecture

290 × 250 mm
11³⁄₈ × 9⁷⁄₈ inches
160 pp
c.120 col, 30 b&w illus.

Paperback
0 7148 3661 3

£ **24.95** UK
$ **39.95** US
€ **39.95** EUR
$ **59.95** CAN
$ **69.95** AUS

Mary Kelly

Survey by Margaret Iversen, Interview by Douglas Crimp, Focus by Homi K Bhabha, Artist's choice texts by Julia Kristeva and Lynne Tillman, Writings by Mary Kelly

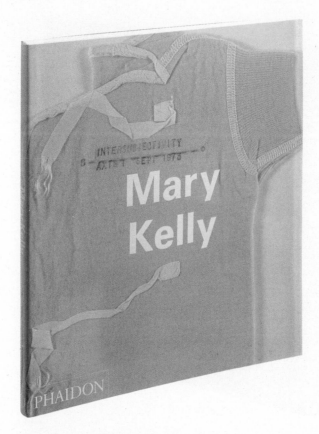

- Among the most influential feminist artists working today, Mary Kelly (b.1941) first came to prominence in 1976 with her epic series, Post Partum Document
- This work, exploring the artist's relationship with her infant son through a combination of texts, images and found objects, was pivotal not only to Conceptual art, but also to late 20th-century feminism
- Her richly textured narratives and images have received international attention for over 20 years and were the subject of a major US museum tour in 1997–8

Margaret Iversen is a Reader in the Department of Art History and Theory at the University of Essex
Douglas Crimp is Professor of Visual and Cultural Studies at the University of Rochester
Homi K Bhabha is Chair in the Humanities at the University of Chicago
Julia Kristeva is a Bulgarian-born writer and psychoanalyst based in Paris
Lynne Tillman is a New York-based writer and critic

'Crucial rememberings of a past that, far from being riddled with nostalgia, allow for an understanding of the diverse possibilities of feminist art in the present.' *(Art Monthly)*

Design

Fashion &
Contemporary
Culture

Decorative Arts

Music &
Performing Arts

Video

Index

290 × 250 mm
11³⁄₈ × 9⁷⁄₈ inches
160 pp
c.120 col, 30 b&w illus.

Paperback
0 7148 3829 2

£ **24.95** UK
$ **39.95** US
€ **39.95** EUR
$ **59.95** CAN
$ **69.95** AUS

William Kentridge

Survey by Dan Cameron, Interview by Carolyn Christov-Bakargiev, Focus by J M Coetzee,
Artist's choice text by Italo Svevo, Writings by William Kentridge

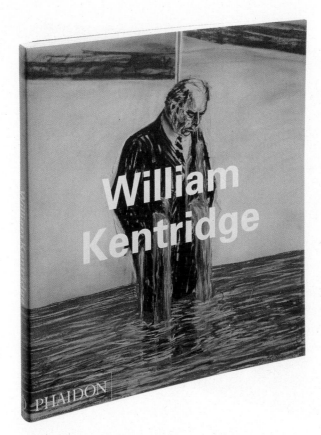

- **The first major publication on internationally acclaimed South African artist William Kentridge (b.1955)**
- **Kentridge's work has navigated between the personal and the political through an innovative use of animation in drawings, film and theatre**
- **His writings and lectures present considered meditations on the process of drawing and the dilemmas of politically engaged art**
- **Kentridge's animated films offer a unique view of South Africa's past and present**

Carolyn Christov-Bakargiev is Curator at the Castello di Rivoli, Turin and former Senior Curator at PS 1, New York
Dan Cameron is Senior Curator at the New Museum of Contemporary Art, New York
J M Coetzee is one of South Africa's most distinguished authors and winner of the Booker Prize (1983)
Italo Svevo (1861–1928) was an Italian novelist of German-Jewish descent whose largely autobiographical novels were much admired by James Joyce

'Illuminating ... presents this extraordinary body of work – drawing, film and theatre – as a cohesive whole' *(Contemporary Visual Arts)*
'A magnificent book, appealingly designed and filled with valuable information.'
(Mail & Guardian, South Africa)

General
Non-Fiction

Art
Contemporary
Artists

Photography

Collector's
Editions

Film

Architecture

290 × 250 mm
11³⁄₈ × 9⁷⁄₈ inches
160 pp
c.120 col, 30 b&w illus.

Paperback
0 7148 3920 5

£ **24.95** UK
$ **39.95** US
€ **39.95** EUR
$ **59.95** CAN
$ **69.95** AUS

Yayoi Kusama

Survey by Laura Hoptman, Interview by Akira Tatehata, Focus by Udo Kultermann, Artist's choice text by Ishikawa Takuboki, Writings by Yayoi Kusama

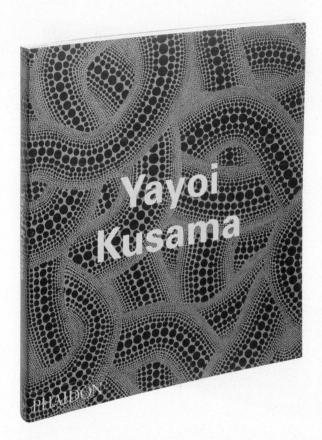

- Japanese artist Yayoi Kusama (b.1929) has pursued her themes of infinite repetition, self-image and sexuality since she took the New York art world by storm in the late 1950s
- Compulsively covering all surfaces in dots and repeated patterns or forms, Kusama has worked in painting, collage and assemblage and was a pioneer of installation art
- This is the first monograph on the 40-year career of this distinguished, highly innovative artist who has also been a writer, fashion designer and film-maker

Akira Tatehata is a Japanese art critic and poet
Laura Hoptman is the Curator of Contemporary Art at the Carnegie Museum of Art, Pittsburgh
Udo Kultermann is a German-born art historian and critic based in New York
Ishikawa Takuboku (1886–1912) was a Japanese poet and novelist

'This book is a fine collection of her influential and beautifully turbulent work.' (*Creative Review*)
'A handsome monograph.' (*Modern Painters*)

Design

Fashion &
Contemporary
Culture

Decorative Arts

Music &
Performing Arts

Video

Index

290 × 250 mm
11³⁄₈ × 9⁷⁄₈ inches
160 pp
c.120 col, 30 b&w illus.

Paperback
0 7148 3552 8

£ **24.95** UK
$ **39.95** US
€ **39.95** EUR
$ **59.95** CAN
$ **69.95** AUS

Paul McCarthy

Survey by Ralph Rugoff, Interview by Kristine Stiles, Focus by Giacinto Di Pietrantonio, Artist's choice text by Jean-Paul Sartre, Writings by Paul McCarthy

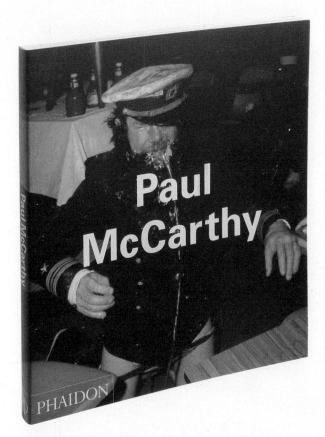

- In works which are equally hilarious and disturbing, American artist Paul McCarthy (b.1945) evokes unconscious, repressed undercurrents in art and human relationships
- In live performance, videos and uncanny sculptural environments, he peels back urban society's veneers of sophistication with a viscerality reminiscent of Viennese Aktionism
- This is the first comprehensive survey of over 20 years of work by a profoundly influential artist

Kristine Stiles is an artist and Associate Professor of Art and Art History at Duke University, North Carolina
Ralph Rugoff is a Los Angeles-based critic and curator
Giacinto Di Pietrantonio is a critic and curator and Associate Professor in Art History at the Brera Academy of Fine Arts, Milan
Jean-Paul Sartre was a French philosopher and writer and the leading exponent of Existentialism

'The first comprehensive survey of over 20 years of work, this excellent publication explores McCarthy's Disneyesque installations and slapstick performances.' *(Stills)*

General
Non-Fiction

Art
Contemporary
Artists

Photography

Collector's
Editions

Film

Architecture

290 × 250 mm
11³⁄₈ × 9⁷⁄₈ inches
160 pp
c.120 col, 30 b&w illus.

Paperback
0 7148 3858 6

£ **24.95** UK
$ **39.95** US
€ **39.95** EUR
$ **59.95** CAN
$ **69.95** AUS

Cildo Meireles

Survey by Paulo Herkenhoff, Interview by Gerardo Mosquera, Focus by Dan Cameron, Artist's choice text by Jorge Luis Borges, Writings by Cildo Meireles

- **A pioneer of installation art in the 1960s, Brazilian Cildo Meireles (b.1948) has influenced generations of international artists**
- **Best known for his dramatic and politically charged environments which incorporate sound, smell and touch, Meireles envelops viewers in his installations and offers an alternative – visual, political and sensual – to the less-than-perfect world around us**
- **This is the only major monograph on this innovative artist**

Gerardo Mosquera is Adjunct Curator at the New Museum of Contemporary Art, New York
Paulo Herkenhoff is a curator at The Museum of Modern Art, New York, and was formerly Chief Curator of the Biennial of São Paulo
Dan Cameron is Senior Curator at the New Museum of Contemporary Art, New York
Jorge Luis Borges (1899–1986) was a short story writer, essayist and poet, and one of Argentina's most acclaimed writers

Design

Fashion & Contemporary Culture

Decorative Arts

Music & Performing Arts

Video

Index

290 × 250 mm
11³⁄₈ × 9⁷⁄₈ inches
160 pp
c.120 col, 30 b&w illus.

Paperback
0 7148 3919 1

£ **24.95** UK
$ **39.95** US
€ **39.95** EUR
$ **59.95** CAN
$ **69.95** AUS

Raymond Pettibon

Survey by Robert Storr, Interview by Dennis Cooper, Focus by Ulrich Loock, Artist's choice text by George Puttenham, John Ruskin and Laurence Sterne, Writings by Raymond Pettibon

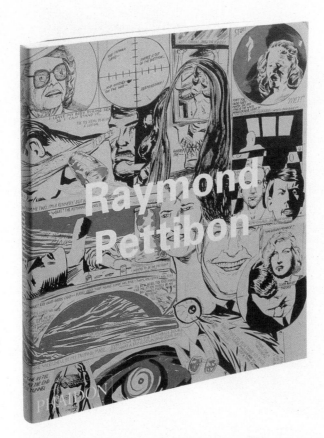

- California-based artist Raymond Pettibon (b.1957) is known internationally for his signature ink-wash drawings which combine cartoon-like images with short, enigmatic texts
- His irresistibly compelling and witty drawings reveal all the deviations within American culture – in film, crime, TV, sex, art, religion, sports, comic books and more
- From late 1970s underground fanzine artist and designer of record covers for Sonic Youth and Black Flag, Pettibon has risen to become a world renowned figure. Retrospectives include The Museum of Contemporary Art, Los Angeles (1994)

Dennis Cooper is a Los Angeles-based novelist, poet and art critic
Robert Storr is Professor of Modern Art, Institute of Fine Arts, New York University
Ulrich Loock is Chief Curator at the Museu Serralves, Oporto
George Puttenham (1529–90) was a man of letters in Tudor England, attributed as the author of *The Arte of English Poesie* (1589)
Laurence Sterne (1713–68) was the Irish-born author of the novel *Tristram Shandy* (1759–67)
John Ruskin (1819–1900) was Victorian England's pre-eminent critical writer on art and architecture

'Apart from the obvious delights of the images … there are essays, interviews, as well as never before published video screenplays, song lyrics and an LSD derived homage to beatnik poetry. Refreshment for body and mind.' *(Sleaze Nation)*

General Non-Fiction

Art Contemporary Artists

Photography

Collector's Editions

Film

Architecture

290 × 250 mm
11³⁄₈ × 9⁷⁄₈ inches
160 pp
c.120 col, 30 b&w illus.

Paperback
0 7148 4164 1

£ **24.95** UK
$ **39.95** US
€ **39.95** EUR
$ **59.95** CAN
$ **69.95** AUS

Richard Prince

*Survey by Rosetta Brooks, Interview by Jeff Rian, Focus by Luc Sante, Artist's choice text
by Sheila Nicholls, Writings by Richard Prince*

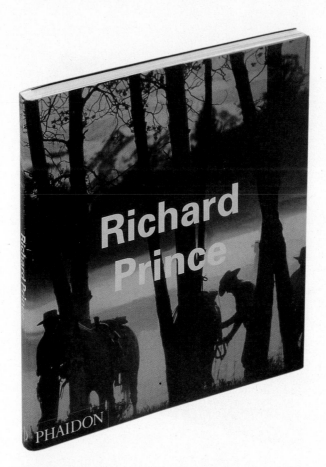

- Richard Prince (b.1949) is one of the US's best known and most popular artists
- Along with Cindy Sherman and others, he defined the 'postmodern' generation, appropriating
  and re-presenting images from sources that range from joke cartoons to girls in biker
  magazines to cowboys in Marlboro advertising campaigns
- Now including painting, Prince's work remains as original and inspiring as ever. This is the first
  major survey of his work since his 1992 retrospective at the Whitney Museum of American Art,
  New York

Jeff Rian is a writer and professor at the École des Beaux-Arts, Paris. His books include *Lewis
Baltz* (2001)
Rosetta Brooks is an art critic and curator based in California and an authority on Prince's work
Luc Sante is a widely published writer on photography and film and a contributor to the
New York Review of Books
Sheila Nicholls is a Los Angeles-based singer and songwriter

290 × 250 mm
11³⁄₈ × 9⁷⁄₈ inches
160 pp
c.120 col, 30 b&w illus.

Paperback
0 7148 3965 5

£ 24.95 UK
$ 39.95 US
€ 39.95 EUR
$ 59.95 CAN
$ 69.95 AUS

Pipilotti Rist

Survey by Peggy Phelan, Interview by Hans Ulrich Obrist, Focus by Elisabeth Bronfen, Artist's choice texts by Anne Sexton and Richard Brautigan, Writings by Pipilotti Rist

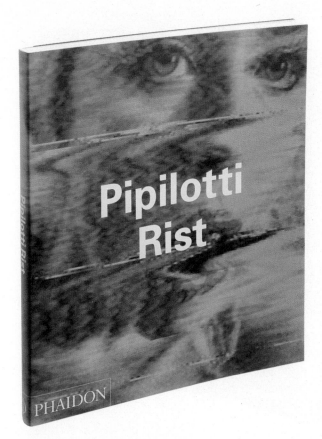

- Swiss-born artist Pipilotti Rist's (b.1962) colourful multi-screen video works invent new possibilities for poetry, feminine identity and the traditional genre of portraiture
- Since the late 1980s, her skilful and unprecedented fusions of film, music, sculpture and performance have established Rist among the world's best-known video artists
- This is the first comprehensive monograph on this vibrantly talented and influential artist

Hans Ulrich Obrist is an art critic and curator who has run the Migrateurs programme at the Musée d'Art Moderne de la Ville de Paris since 1993
Peggy Phelan is among the best-known feminist theorists of contemporary art and performance. Her books include *Unmarked: The Politics of Performance* (1993)
Elisabeth Bronfen is the author of *Over Her Dead Body: Death, Femininity and the Aesthetic* (1992)
Anne Sexton (1928–74) was one of America's most respected post-war poets, awarded the Pulitzer Prize in 1965
Richard Brautigan (1935–84) was an American novelist, short story writer and poet who emerged from the 1950s Beat generation

General
Non-Fiction

Art
Contemporary
Artists

Photography

Collector's
Editions

Film

Architecture

290 × 250 mm
11³⁄₈ × 9⁷⁄₈ inches
160 pp
c.120 col, 30 b&w illus.

Paperback
0 7148 3929 9

£ **24.95** UK
$ **39.95** US
€ **39.95** EUR
$ **59.95** CAN
$ **69.95** AUS

Doris Salcedo

Survey by Nancy Princenthal, Interview by Carlos Basualdo, Focus by Andreas Huyssen, Artist's choice texts by Paul Celan and Emmanuel Levinas, Writings by Doris Salcedo

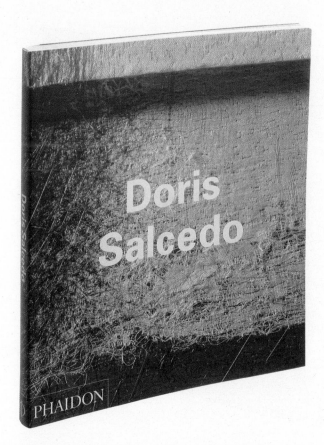

- **Doris Salcedo (b.1958) is one of today's most internationally respected South American sculptors, represented in museum collections around the world**
- **Inspired as much by poetry and philosophy as by the affecting material qualities of sculpture, Salcedo subtly and painstakingly transforms the everyday object such as a door, a table, a chair or a bed into a universally affecting symbol of vanished existence and of the human tragedies that were its cause**

Carlos Basualdo is a poet and curator based in New York. He is a regular contributor to *Artforum*
Nancy Princenthal is an American art critic, the author of numerous catalogues and monographs and a contributor to *Art in America*, *Parkett* and *Artforum*
Andreas Huyssen is the author of *Twilight Memories: Marking Time in a Culture of Amnesia* (1995) and an editor of the journal *New German Critique*
Paul Celan (1920–70) was a German-born Jewish poet whose work evokes the moral horror of the Holocaust, of which he was a survivor
Emmanuel Levinas is a French philosopher whose writing addresses the conditions of memory, loss and our relation to others

Design

Fashion & Contemporary Culture

Decorative Arts

Music & Performing Arts

Video

Index

290 × 250 mm
11⅜ × 9⅞ inches
160 pp
c.120 col, 30 b&w illus.

Paperback
0 7148 3714 8

£ **24.95** UK
$ **39.95** US
€ **39.95** EUR
$ **59.95** CAN
$ **69.95** AUS

Thomas Schütte

Writings by Julian Heynen, Interview by James Lingwood, Focus by Angela Vettese, Artist's choice text by Seneca, Writings by Thomas Schütte

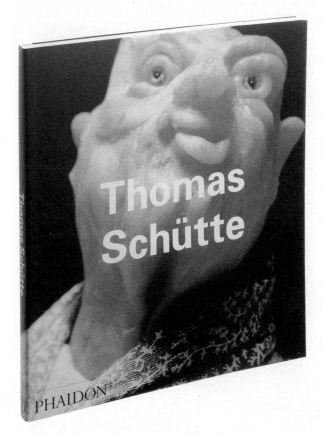

- German artist Thomas Schütte (b.1954) makes sculptures which range from giant cherries to miniature castles, manipulating size and materials like a master juggler
- His bizarre worlds of shifting scale create a universe replete with food and shelter yet full of false promise: a museum that incinerates art; bronze potatoes; or his very own 'audience' of metal-clad robots assembled before his work
- This is the only major English language monograph on one of Germany's most important contemporary sculptors

James Lingwood is an independent curator and writer and Co-Director of Artangel, the London-based arts organization
Julian Heynen is Director of Exhibitions at the Haus Lange, Haus Esters and Kaiser Wilhelm Museums, Krefeld, Germany
Angela Vettese is a Milan-based critic and curator, and the author of *Capire l'arte contemporanea* (*Understanding Contemporary Art*, 1996)
Seneca was one of ancient Rome's most influential statesmen and philosophers

General Non-Fiction

Art Contemporary Artists

Photography

Collector's Editions

Film

Architecture

290 × 250 mm
11³⁄₈ × 9⁷⁄₈ inches
160 pp
c.120 col, 30 b&w illus.

Paperback
0 7148 4038 6

£ **24.95** UK
$ **39.95** US
€ **39.95** EUR
$ **59.95** CAN
$ **69.95** AUS

Lorna Simpson

Survey by Kellie Jones, Interview by Thelma Golden, Focus by Chrissie Iles, Artist's choice text by Suzan Lori Parks, Writings by Lorna Simpson

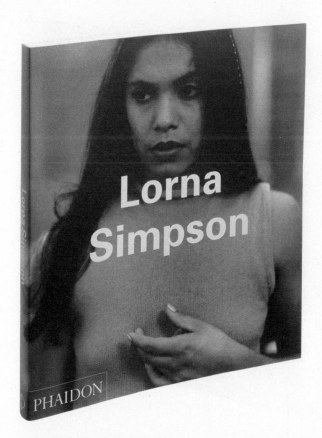

- Lorna Simpson (b.1960) is one of the United States' leading African-American artists
- Using photography and texts and more recently film, Simpson raises profound questions about how we represent, see and communicate with each other and ourselves
- This is the first comprehensive monograph on Simpson's work, published to coincide with her solo exhibitions at the Whitney Museum of American Art, New York, the Studio Museum, Harlem, New York, and Documenta 11, Kassel, Germany, in 2002

Thelma Golden is Chief Curator at the Studio Museum, Harlem, New York
Kellie Jones is a New York-based art historian and a professor in the departments of History of Art and African-American Studies at Yale University
Chrissie Iles is Curator of Film and Video at the Whitney Museum of American Art, New York
Suzan-Lori Parks is an American playwright, awarded the Pulitzer Prize in 2002

290 × 250 mm
11³⁄₈ × 9⁷⁄₈ inches
160 pp
c.120 col, 30 b&w illus.

Paperback
0 7148 3340 1

£ 24.95 UK
$ 39.95 US
€ 39.95 EUR
$ 59.95 CAN
$ 69.95 AUS

Nancy Spero

Survey by Jon Bird, Interview by Jo Anna Isaak, Focus by Sylvère Lotringer, Artist's choice texts by Stanley Kubrick, Alice Jardine, Writings by Nancy Spero

- Nancy Spero (b.1926) is one of the world's most significant and inspiring feminist artists and activists
- Her subject matter, which has ranged from depictions of goddesses from the ancient world to protests against modern war, mirrors her life, from Paris in the cultural ferment of the 1960s to New York in the 1970s
- Since the 1980s she has attracted international acclaim, her exquisite works giving form to feminist issues and new critical discourses

Jo Anna Isaak is a New York-based writer and curator whose books include *Feminism and Contemporary Art: The Revolutionary Power of Women's Laughter* (1996)
Jon Bird is Professor of Art and Critical Theory at Middlesex University, London
Sylvère Lotringer is Professor of French and Comparative Literature at Columbia University, New York
Alice Jardine is the author of *Gynesis: Configurations of Woman and Modernity* (1985)
Stanley Kubrick (1928–99) was one of the world's most acclaimed film directors whose work included *Dr Strangelove* (1963) and *A Clockwork Orange* (1971)

General
Non-Fiction

Art
Contemporary
Artists

Photography

Collector's
Editions

Film

Architecture

290 × 250 mm
11³⁄₈ × 9⁷⁄₈ inches
160 pp
c.120 col, 30 b&w illus.

Paperback
0 7148 3406 8

£ **24.95** UK
$ **39.95** US
€ **39.95** EUR
$ **59.95** CAN
$ **69.95** AUS

Jessica Stockholder

Survey by Barry Schwabsky, Interview by Lynne Tillman, Focus by Lynne Cooke, Artist's choice text by Julian Jaynes and Cornelius Castoriadis, Writings by Jessica Stockholder

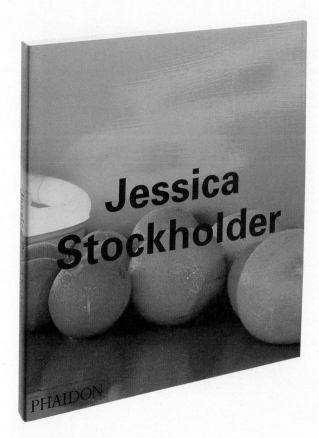

- Among the most exciting of a new generation of North American artists, Jessica Stockholder (b.1959) explodes the boundaries between painting, sculpture and architecture
- Found objects, ranging from oranges to neon tubes, discarded household fabrics and building materials are massed and intertwined with profusions of vivid colour
- Her architectonic installations recall Kurt Schwitters' Dadaist collages, spliced with the formal concerns of 1950s abstract painting and a postmodern sensibility

Lynne Tillman is a New York-based critic and novelist
Barry Schwabsky is an art critic and poet living in New York, and a former Editor of *Arts Magazine* and Managing Editor of *Flash Art*
Lynne Cooke is Curator at the Dia Center for the Arts, New York, and the author of numerous catalogues and monographs
Julian Jaynes (1920–97) was a renowned psychologist, author of *The Origin of Consciousness in the Breakdown of the Bicameral Mind* (1976)
Cornelius Castoriadis (1922–97) was a social philosopher, author of *The Imaginary Institution of Society* (1994)

290 × 250 mm
11³⁄₈ × 9⁷⁄₈ inches
160 pp
c.120 col, 30 b&w illus.

Paperback
0 7148 4192 7

£ 24.95 UK
$ 39.95 US
€ 39.95 EUR
$ 59.95 CAN
$ 69.95 AUS

Wolfgang Tillmans

Survey by Jan Verwoert, Interview by Peter Halley, Focus by Midori Matsuri, Artist's choice text by Caroline Stephen, Writings by Wolfgang Tillmans

- Wolfgang Tillmans (b.1968) is one of the most internationally recognized young photographers, whose unique style is often imitated but seldom matched
- This is the only book to cover his entire career, from his best-selling debut portraits in 1995 at the age of 24 to his most recent, abstract works installed in major museums
- Tillmans's explorations of portraiture, landscape and abstract genres are uniquely recognizable emblems of our times
- Awarded the Turner Prize in 2000, Tillmans has presented his work in museums around the world and is the subject of a retrospective at Tate Britain in 2003

Peter Halley is a widely acclaimed New York artist and critic, and the publisher of *index* magazine
Jan Verwoert is a critic based in Hamburg who is a regular contributor to *Parkett* and *frieze* magazines
Midori Matsuri is an art critic and scholar based in Tokyo
Caroline Stephen (1834–1909) was a British theologian whose *Quaker Strongholds* (1890) is a classic text

General Non-Fiction

Art Contemporary Artists

Photography

Collector's Editions

Film

Architecture

Revised and expanded edition
290 × 250 mm
11³⁄₈ × 9⁷⁄₈ inches
212 pp
c.180 col, 40 b&w illus.

Paperback
0 7148 3951 5

£ 24.95 UK
$ 39.95 US
€ 39.95 EUR
$ 59.95 CAN
$ 69.95 AUS

Jeff Wall

Survey by Thierry de Duve, Update by Jean-François Chevrier, Interview by Arielle Pelenc, Focus by Boris Groys, Artist's choice texts by Blaise Pascal and Franz Kafka, Writings by Jeff Wall

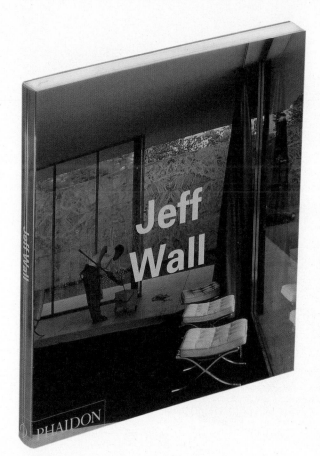

- Jeff Wall (b.1946) is foremost among the artists who since the late 1970s have brought photography to the forefront of contemporary art
- His images employ the latest technology to create tableaux which dramatically evoke subjects ranging from Hollywood cinema to 19th-century history painting
- This revised and expanded edition includes a new fully illustrated essay on Wall's recent work by the French historian of art and photography Jean-François Chevrier, in addition to the artist's recent writings

Thierry de Duve is an art historian and philosopher based in Belgium
Jean-François Chevrier is Professor of Contemporary Art at the École des Beaux-Arts in Paris
Ariella Pelenc is a French art critic and curator
Boris Groys is Professor at the Centre for Art and Media Technology in Karlsruhe
Blaise Pascal was a mathematician, physicist and philosopher
Franz Kafka was a writer born in Prague

Design

Fashion & Contemporary Culture

Decorative Arts

Music & Performing Arts

Video

Index

290 × 250 mm
11³⁄₈ × 9⁷⁄₈ inches
160 pp
c.120 col, 30 b&w illus.

Paperback
0 7148 3824 1

£ 24.95 UK
$ 39.95 US
€ 39.95 EUR
$ 59.95 CAN
$ 69.95 AUS

Gillian Wearing

Survey by Russell Ferguson, Interview by Donna De Salvo, Focus by John Slyce, Artist's choice text by Michael Apted, Writings by Gillian Wearing

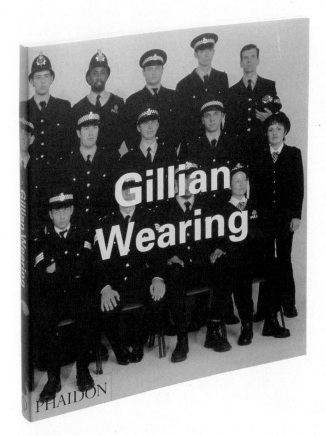

- Whether asking people to display their own message in her famous *Signs* series or making videos that evoke experimental documentary, British artist Gillian Wearing (b.1963) uses photography and video to produce direct, revealing records of the complexities of contemporary life
- Winner of the 1997 Turner Prize, Wearing is among the most international of the recent generation of British artists
- This is the only comprehensive monograph on this remarkable artist's work

Donna De Salvo is a Senior Curator at Tate Modern, London, and formerly held curatorial positions at the Dia Center for the Arts, New York and the Andy Warhol Museum, Pittsburgh
Russell Ferguson is an Associate Curator at The Museum of Contemporary Art, Los Angeles, and has written on the work of many contemporary artists
John Slyce is a writer, critic, lecturer and the London correspondent for *Flash Art*
Michael Apted is an acclaimed television documentary maker and film producer

290 × 250 mm
11³⁸ × 9⁷⁸ inches
160 pp
c.120 col, 30 b&w illus.

Paperback
0 7148 3755 5

£ **24.95** UK
$ **39.95** US
€ **39.95** EUR
$ **59.95** CAN
$ **69.95** AUS

Lawrence Weiner

Survey by Alexander Alberro and Alice Zimmerman, Interview by Benjamin H D Buchloh, Focus by David Batchelor, Artist's choice texts by Kenneth Patchen and W B Yeats, Writings by Lawrence Weiner

- Lawrence Weiner's (b.1942) language-based art can appear painted across an entire building, floating inside a souvenir biro or sung as a lyric by a Country and Western band
- One of the most important of the New York artists who emerged in the late 1960s, he explores how language can make available to us sculptural propositions about our relationship to objects and places
- Weiner's typographic presentation is also much admired by designers internationally
- This is the only comprehensive monograph on Weiner's work

Benjamin H D Buchloh is a renowned writer on 20th-century art who teaches at Columbia University, New York
Alexander Alberro is Professor of Modern Art at the University of Florida and a historian of conceptual art
Alice Zimmerman is an artist and writer and an authority on Weiner's work
David Batchelor is a London-based artist and writer whose books include *Minimalism* (1997)
Kenneth Patchen (1911–72) was a poet associated with the Beat generation
W B Yeats (1865–1939) was one of Ireland's greatest poets of the 20th century

Design

Fashion & Contemporary Culture

Decorative Arts

Music & Performing Arts

Video

Index

290 × 250 mm
11³⁄₈ × 9⁷⁄₈ inches
160 pp
c.120 col, 30 b&w illus.

Paperback
0 7148 3825 X

£ **24.95** UK
$ **39.95** US
€ **39.95** EUR
$ **59.95** CAN
$ **69.95** AUS

Franz West

Survey by Robert Fleck, Interview by Bice Curiger, Focus by Neal Benezra, Artist's choice text by Kathryn Norberg, Writings by Franz West

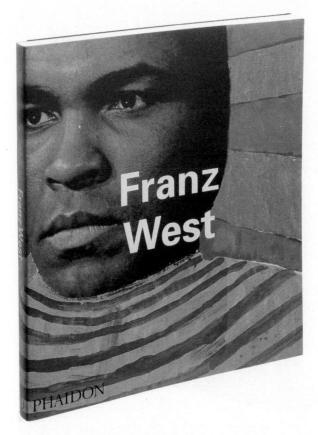

- Franz West (b.1947) is an internationally renowned Austrian sculptor who emerged from the 1960s generation of Viennese Aktionists, who used their own bodies in their art
- Often inviting visitors to participate in or even wear his sculptures, West encourages us to explore our involvement in contemporary art and its presentation
- Packed with wonderful photographs, this book is an indispensible guide to the diverse, allusive, witty structures, collages and installations of this important and prolific artist

Bice Curiger is founding Editor of *Parkett* magazine and Curator of the Kunsthaus, Zürich
Robert Fleck is a Viennese critic and curator based in France. He has published widely in contemporary art magazines, such as *Artforum* and *Parkett*
Neal Benezra is Director of the San Francisco Museum of Modern Art
Kathryn Norberg is Associate Professor of History at the University of California, Los Angeles, and Director of the UCLA Center for the Study of Women

General
Non-Fiction

Art
Contemporary
& Modern

Photography

Collector's
Editions

Film

Architecture

290 × 250 mm
11³⁄₈ × 9⁷⁄₈ inches
512 pp
536 col illus.

Paperback
0 7148 3888 8

£ **29.95** UK
$ **45.00** US
€ **49.95** EUR
$ **69.95** CAN
$ **89.95** AUS

Art Today

Edward Lucie-Smith

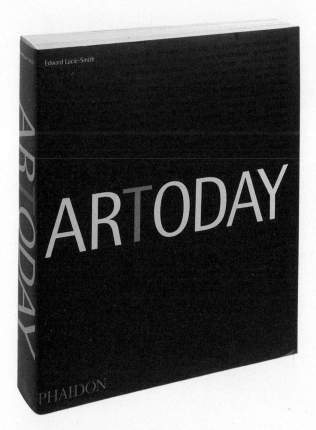

- A seminal survey of the visual arts from the 1960s to the present, written by a leading authority on the subject
- Navigates the reader through this period of extraordinary creativity and controversy
- The work of more than 500 key artists is analysed and illustrated in full colour
- Internationally recognized as an indispensable introduction to contemporary art

Edward Lucie-Smith is well known as a poet, critic, broadcaster and writer on art. He is the author of *Art Deco Painting*, also published by Phaidon

'Written with authority, perception and challenging judgement … an invaluable vessel of reliable reference in a sea of confusion.' *(Scotland on Sunday)*

Design

Fashion & Contemporary Culture

Decorative Arts

Music & Performing Arts

Video

Index

290 × 250 mm
11³⁄₈ × 9⁷⁄₈ inches
352 pp
c.490 col illus.

Hardback
0 7148 4246 X

£ **39.95** UK
$ **69.95** US
€ **69.95** EUR
$ **95.00** CAN
$ **120.00** AUS

Vitamin P

New Perspectives in Painting
Introduction by Barry Schwabsky

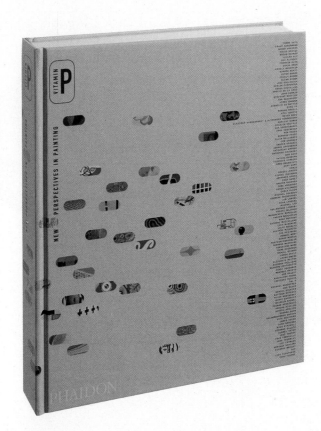

- A global, up-to-the-minute survey of painting today
- Features the work of 114 emerging and eminent painters on the international art scene, as nominated by influential critics and curators from around the world
- Almost 500 illustrations demonstrate the myriad ways in which these painters use their chosen medium – on everything from canvas to street curbs
- Both sourcebook and reference work for art world professionals and newcomers

Barry Schwabsky writes regularly for *Artforum*. He is currently Visiting Lecturer at Goldsmiths' College in London

General Non-Fiction

Art Contemporary & Modern

Photography

Collector's Editions

Film

Architecture

297 × 148.5 mm
12 × 6 inches
656 pp
869 col, 68 b&w illus.

Hardback
0 7148 3924 8

£ **35.00** UK
$ **59.95** US
€ **59.95** EUR
$ **89.95** CAN
$ **95.00** AUS

Awards

I.D.
I.D. award

print
Print magazine award

Fresh Cream

Contemporary Art in Culture
Curated by Iwona Blazwick, Amada Cruz, Bice Curiger, Vasif Kortun, Maria Lind, Viktor Misiano, Gerardo Mosquera, Olu Oguibe, Apinan Poshyananda and Octavio Zaya

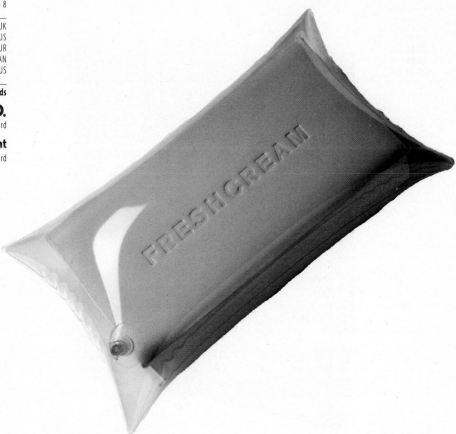

- An indispensable guide to the 100 artists from around the world who rose to prominence between 1995 and 2000
- A biennale in a book curated by an international panel of influential curators
- Contains the enormous breadth of ideas and forms in contemporary art
- An essential source of reference for both art professionals and art newcomers
- Each artist's work is represented by a generous selection of colour images, an introductory text, and an exhibition history and bibliography

'Accessible, intellectual, low brow, humorous, serious … the essence of the 21st century is distilled in this volume.' *(Blueprint)*
'*Fresh Cream* presents an extraordinary worldwide survey of art, present and future, indispensable to anyone interested in the cutting edge of contemporary culture.' *(Creative Review)*
'Does more than any blockbuster exhibition in exposing the work of a great many artists to fresh new audiences.' *(Art Newspaper)*
'A volume of the best in very young, very hip contemporary art … this book is fine art finely packaged.' *(Black Book, New York)*

Design

Fashion & Contemporary Culture

Decorative Arts

Music & Performing Arts

Video

Index

290 × 250 mm
11³⁄₈ × 9⁷⁄₈ inches
448 pp
c.700 col, 40 b&w illus.

Hardback
0 7148 4311 3

£ **39.95** UK
$ **59.95** US
€ **65.00** EUR
$ **89.95** CAN
$ **120.00** AUS

CREAM 3

100 Artists, 10 Curators, 10 Source Artists
Curated by Carolyn Christov Bakargiev, Charles Esche, Rubén Gallo, Yuko Hasegawa, Udo Kittelmann, Adriano Pedrosa, Beatrix Ruf, Nancy Spector, Hamza Walker and Igor Zabel

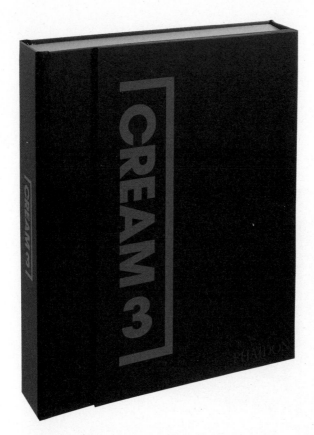

· **The latest biennale-in-a-book: a survey of 100 of the world's most significant and emerging artists, as selected by internationally renowned experts on contemporary art**
· **Each artist's work is represented by a generous selection of colour images, an introductory text, and an exhibition history and bibliography**
· **Follows the award-winning *cream* – now a collector's item – and *Fresh Cream***
· **New feature – each curator selects a source artist who has inspired or influenced the younger generation, providing readers with a broader historical perspective**
· **A must-have for art world insiders, a crash course for beginners and an authoritative reference book for years to come**

Carolyn Christov Bakargiev is Senior Curator at the Museo di Rivoli, Turin
Charles Esche is Director of the Rooseum Centre for Contemporary Art, Malmö
Rubén Gallo teaches Latin-American Literature and Cultural Studies at Princeton University
Yuko Hasegawa is Chief Curator at the 21st Century Museum of Contemporary Art, Kanazawa
Udo Kittelmann is Director of the Museum of Modern Art, Frankfurt
Adriano Pedrosa is a former co-curator of the São Paulo Biennale
Beatrix Ruf is Director of the Kunsthalle Zürich
Nancy Spector is Curator of Contemporary Art at the Solomon R Guggenheim Museum, New York
Hamza Walker is Director of Education for the Renaissance Society at the University of Chicago
Igor Zabel is Senior Curator at the Moderna galerija (Museum of Modern Art), Ljubljana

123 × 185 mm
4⁷₈ × 7¹₄ inches
580 pp
575 col illus.

Hardback
0 7148 4011 4

£ **14.95** UK
$ **19.95** US
€ **24.95** EUR
$ **29.95** CAN
$ **39.95** AUS

They Called Her Styrene, Etc.

Ed Ruscha

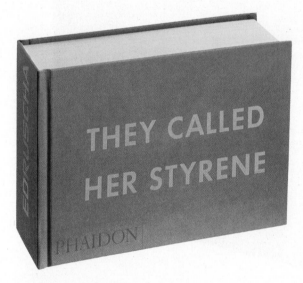

- Reproduces close to 600 'word' artworks by Los Angeles-based artist Ruscha (b.1937), one of the seminal American artists of the past 30 years
- The only book devoted solely to Ruscha's hundreds of 'word' prints, drawings and paintings, which have become a hallmark of his stellar career
- Works are assembled page-by-page in the form of a thick block, making the book an art 'object' in itself
- These images are evidence of the artist's fascination with wordplay and the animated power of the letterforms that surround us daily

Ed Ruscha began making prints and drawings consisting of one word on an often monochromatic, abstract background in the late 1950s. Since then his work is characterized by the exploration of language-based imagery and can be found in major museum collections around the world

'Ambiguous, often hilarious and with no narrative to explain their presence, the words become objects or landscapes all to themselves.' *(V magazine)*

Design

Fashion & Contemporary Culture

Decorative Arts

Music & Performing Arts

Video

Index

290 × 250 mm
11³⁄₈ × 9⁷⁄₈ inches
272 pp
c.324 col illus.

Hardback
0 7148 3908 6

£ **45.00** UK
$ **75.00** US
€ **75.00** EUR
$ **99.95** CAN
$ **140.00** AUS

Ed Ruscha

Richard D. Marshall

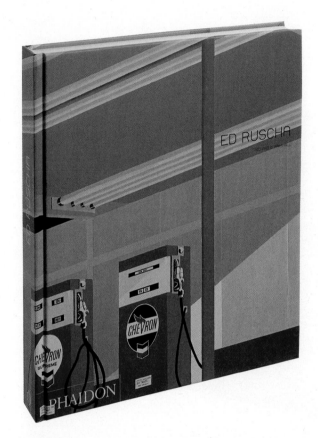

- The first monograph on Ruscha (b. 1937) looks at the prolific and many-faceted career of an artist whose work has been variously described as Pop, Conceptual or Surrealist
- Ruscha initially gained attention in the early 1960s with paintings, drawings and photographic books that focused on his fascination with his adopted home of Los Angeles
- Wealth of quotes by Ruscha himself, allowing him to speak about his art in his own words
- Includes more than 250 works by Ruscha, all reproduced in colour

Richard D. Marshall is an independent curator and critic who, during his 20-year tenure as Curator at the Whitney Museum of American Art worked extensively with Ruscha. He is the author of *Edward Ruscha: Los Angeles Apartments*, and has published many other books and exhibition catalogues

General Non-Fiction

Art Contemporary & Modern

Photography

Collector's Editions

Film

Architecture

250 × 210 mm
9⁷⁄₈ × 8¹⁄₄ inches
144 pp
68 col and b&w illus.

Paperback
0 7148 3459 9

£ **17.95** UK
$ **24.95** US
€ **29.95** EUR
$ **35.00** CAN
$ **49.95** AUS

Rachel Whiteread's House

Edited by James Lingwood, with essays by Jon Bird, Doreen Massey, Iain Sinclair, Richard Shone, Anthony Vidler and Simon Watney

- Fully documents a remarkable work hailed as one of the greatest public sculptures made by an English artist in the 20th century
- Chronicles the house's life, from its conception through to completion and eventual destruction – and the remarkable responses from the local and international communities
- Essays by key figures in art journalism are illustrated by photographs, drawings, cartoons and press clippings
- A lasting record of this Turner Prize-winning artist's first-ever public project

Jon Bird is Cultural Studies Lecturer at Middlesex University and a founder of *Block* magazine
James Lingwood is Co-Director of Artangel
Doreen Massey is Professor of Cultural Geography at the Open University
Richard Shone is Associate Editor of the *Burlington Magazine*
Iain Sinclair, a poet and novelist, has often written on London's history
Neil Thomas is a partner in Atelier One Structural Engineers
Anthony Vidler is Professor of Art History at UCLA, Los Angeles
Simon Watney is a writer and broadcaster

Design

Fashion & Contemporary Culture

Decorative Arts

Music & Performing Arts

Video

Index

245 × 355 mm
9⅝ × 14 inches
80 pp
38 col illus.

Paperback
0 7148 3707 5

£ **14.95** UK
$ **19.95** US
€ **24.95** EUR
$ **29.95** CAN
$ **39.95** AUS

Award

Bustamante's 1997
contribution to
Documenta X

Amandes Amères

Bitter Almonds
Jean-Marc Bustamante

- An artwork in its own right, this beautifully designed and printed book by acclaimed photographer and sculptor Jean-Marc Bustamante was his contribution to the international art event Documenta X (Kassel, Germany, 1997)
- Vivid colour photographs present intense yet contemplative images of the cityscape, from Tel Aviv to Buenos Aires
- Bustamante's art includes both photography and sculpture, often placed in relation to each other in installations that explore memories and associations triggered by urban architecture and the landscape

Jean-Marc Bustamante, born in Toulouse in 1952, lives and works in Paris. A retrospective of his photographic works was presented at the Centre National de la Photographie, Paris, in 1999

General
Non-Fiction

Art
Contemporary
& Modern

Photography

Collector's
Editions

Film

Architecture

170 × 240 mm
6³₄ × 9¹₂ inches
128 pp
88 duotone photos

Hardback
0 7148 3779 2

£ **12.95** UK
$ **19.95** US
€ **22.95** EUR
$ **29.95** CAN
$ **35.00** AUS

Richard Long: Mirage

Introduction by Alison Sleeman, interviews with Geórgia Lobacheff and Mario Codognato

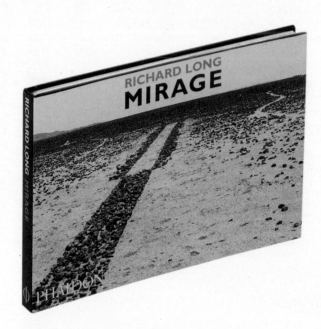

- In this book, celebrated contemporary artist Richard Long presents chosen works from some 30 years of his interactions with landscape
- Long is admired worldwide for the integrity, purity and formal beauty of his art, which is based on the activity of walking
- Includes a selection of pieces from his recent exhibitions
- Stunning photographs allow readers to contemplate the relationship between artist and environment

Alison Sleeman lectures in Art History and Art Theory at the Slade School of Fine Art, London
Geórgia Lobacheff is art critic of *Jornal da Tarde*
Mario Codognato is an Italian critic and curator

Design
Fashion & Contemporary Culture
Decorative Arts
Music & Performing Arts
Video
Index

250 × 250 mm
9⁷⁄₈ × 9⁷⁄₈ inches
332 pp
260 col, 63 b&w illus.

Hardback
0 7148 3819 5

£ **45.00** UK
$ **69.95** US
€ **75.00** EUR
$ **98.00** CAN
$ **125.00** AUS

Robert Mangold

Essays by Richard Shiff, Robert Storr, Arthur C Danto, Nancy Princenthal and an interview with Sylvia Plimack Mangold

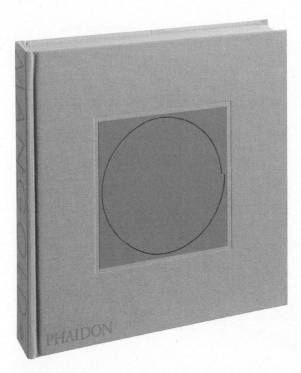

- A timely retrospective on the career of Robert Mangold (b.1937), whose large, gently curving paintings are among the most majestically beautiful abstract works of the last century
- The first comprehensive assessment of Mangold's contribution to painting, with essays by some of the most distinguished writers on contemporary art
- Mangold is often associated with Minimalism, but his subtle colours and soft, hand-drawn geometries set him apart from the sober austerity of the movement
- The book's unique design reflects the singularity of Mangold's work, which is widely collected and exhibited internationally

Arthur C Danto is Johnsonian Professor Emeritus of Philosophy at Columbia University, New York and the art critic of *The Nation*
Sylvia Plimack Mangold is a painter and has been married to Robert Mangold since 1961
Nancy Princenthal is a noted American art critic
Richard Shiff is an art historian and the Effie Marie Cain Regents Chair in Art
Robert Storr is Curator in the Department of Painting and Sculpture at the Museum of Modern Art, New York

'One of the most beautifully designed and comprehensively thoughtful works to come along for some time.' *(Art Book)*

General Non-Fiction

Art Contemporary & Modern

Photography

Collector's Editions

Film

Architecture

250 × 250 mm
9⁷⁄₈ × 9⁷⁄₈ inches
240 pp
c.120 col, 100 b&w illus.

Hardback
0 7148 3916 7

£ **45.00** UK
$ **75.00** US
€ **75.00** EUR
$ **99.95** CAN
$ **140.00** AUS

Gordon Matta-Clark

Thomas Crow, Corinne Diserens (ed.), Judith Russi Kirshner, Christian Kravagna

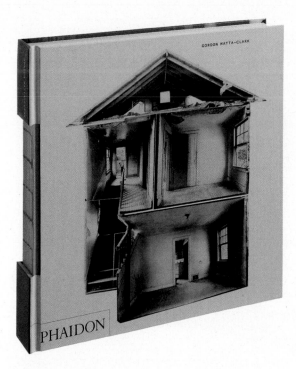

- The first and definitive monograph on one of the great heroes of late 20th century art, a cult figure as much in the contemporary art world as on the architecture scene
- Gordon Matta-Clark (1943–78) is most famous for 'deconstructing' derelict buildings by slicing through their façades, walls and floors – the inspiration for the book's distinctive design
- Many never-before-published images and documents chronicle Matta-Clark's short but remarkable career
- Author's survey text is the most comprehensive commentary published to date on the life and works of the artist

Thomas Crow is Director of the Getty Research Institute at the Getty Center, Los Angeles, and Professor of Art History at the University of Southern California, Los Angeles

Design

Fashion &
Contemporary
Culture

Decorative Arts

Music &
Performing Arts

Video

Index

'Gordon's work spotlights and pinpoints one of the crucial ideas of modern art – actually doing and redoing an absurd idea. This might sound strange, but he was both a Minimalist and a Surrealist.'

John Baldessari, artist

General
Non-Fiction

Art
Contemporary
& Modern

Photography

Collector's
Editions

Film

Architecture

250 × 290 mm
9⁷⁸ × 11³⁸ inches
512 pp
696 col, 131 b&w illus.

Hardback
0 7148 4086 6

£ **150.00** UK
$ **250.00** US
€ **250.00** EUR
$ **375.00** CAN
$ **450.00** AUS

Andy Warhol Catalogue Raisonné Volume 1

Paintings and Sculpture 1961–1963
Edited by Georg Frei and Neil Printz

- The first volume in a multi-volume series presents the most accurate and authoritative data on Andy Warhol (1928–87) ever assembled, including eagerly awaited new scholarship
- Includes 546 catalogued works, documenting his early paintings and sculpture made between 1961 and 1963 and incorporating newly discovered works as well as some previously thought to be lost
- Features the Campbell Soup paintings, serial works representing cultural icons, photobooth portraits of Warhol's friends and idols, and early self-portraits
- Works are accompanied by some 280 images of source material – from newspaper clippings to movie star publicity stills

Georg Frei is a curator and art critic who has been affiliated with Thomas Ammann Fine Art AG in Zurich since 1988, producing exhibits and publications
Neil Printz, a specialist in 20th-century American art, is currently Editor of the Isamu Noguchi Catalogue Raisonné. He is Professor of Art History at Caldwell College in Caldwell, New Jersey

'Magnificently produced ... Evidence of thoroughness appears on every page.' *(Art & Auction)*

Design

Fashion &
Contemporary
Culture

Decorative Arts

Music &
Performing Arts

Video

Index

'One does not ordinarily read catalogue raisonneés for fun, but the volume on Andy Warhol that deals with his paintings and sculptures from 1961 to 1963 takes you as close as I think you could get to the way his mind worked in that extraordinarily creative period. The mystery of Warhol's mind is undissolved, but how that mind worked on a day-to-day basis is thrilling to observe.' Arthur C Danto, Emeritus Johnsonian Professor of Philosophy, Columbia University, *The Art Newspaper*.

General
Non-Fiction

Art
Contemporary
& Modern

Photography

Collector's
Editions

Film

Architecture

305 × 238 mm
12¹₄ × 9³₈ inches
224 pp
142 col, 86 b&w illus.

Paperback
0 7148 3891 8

£ **24.95** UK
$ **39.95** US
€ **39.95** EUR
$ **59.95** CAN
$ **65.00** AUS

Kitaj

3rd edition
Marco Livingstone

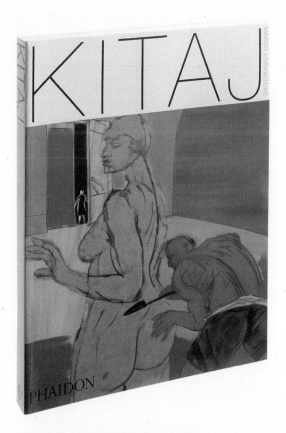

- An expanded new edition of the definitive monograph on R B Kitaj (b.1932), offering a fresh account of a productive and turbulent phase in the modern master's career
- Kitaj's powerful figurative paintings evoke both the art of the past and current political issues, while exploring his own Jewish identity
- Full-colour visual documentation of Kitaj's work to date, including his highly personal paintings, pastels and drawings
- With a new chapter by the author and three new 'prefaces' by Kitaj himself

Marco Livingstone is an independent art historian, critic and curator who writes extensively on modern and contemporary art

Design

Fashion &
Contemporary
Culture

Decorative Arts

Music &
Performing Arts

Video

Index

290 × 250 mm
11³⁄₈ × 9⁷⁄₈ inches
272 pp
233 col, 51 b&w illus.

Paperback
0 7148 3444 0

£ **22.95** UK
$ **35.00** US
€ **39.95** EUR
$ **49.95** CAN
$ **59.95** AUS

Patrick Heron

Mel Gooding

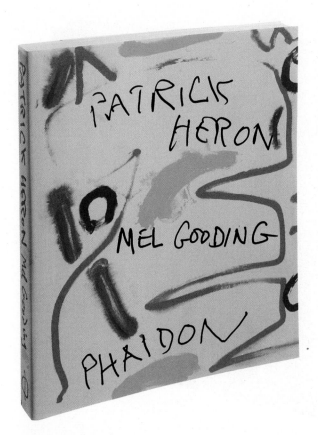

- The first book to examine the dynamic work of Patrick Heron (1920–99), a leading figure in the development of post-war abstract art in Britain
- Heron is renowned for his sensuous manipulation of colour, space and shape that recalls his idols Matisse, Bonnard and Braque
- Discusses the influence of American Abstract Expressionism on Heron's evolution as an artist and critic
- Explores his relationships with his fellow St Ives artists Ben Nicholson, William Scott and Roger Hilton

Mel Gooding is an author and journalist who has written extensively on contemporary art and artists

'The most complete and fascinating record of Heron's work to date. Gooding's analysis helps us to see even more and better, and very enjoyably.' (Marina Vaizey, *Country Living*)

General Non-Fiction

Art Contemporary & Modern

Photography

Collector's Editions

Film

Architecture

290 × 250 mm
11³⁄₈ × 9⁷⁄₈ inches
240 pp
251 col, 62 b&w illus.

Hardback
0 7148 3614 1

£ **39.95** UK
$ **59.95** US
€ **65.00** EUR
$ **98.00** CAN
$ **99.95** AUS

Bill Jacklin

John Russell Taylor

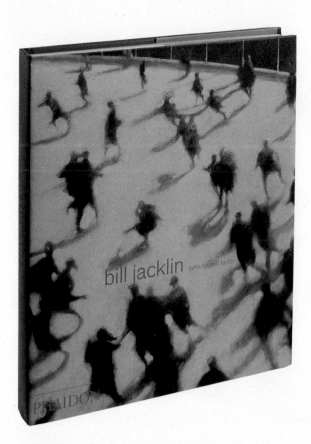

- The definitive mid-career survey of the British-American artist Bill Jacklin (b.1943)
- Traces Jacklin's evolution, from his rise to prominence in the 1960s as an abstract artist in the era of Pop Art to his return to a form of realistic representation
- Both biographical and critical, the text is based on a detailed study of Jacklin's work and on conversations with the artist
- Includes his series of 'urban portraits' of late 1980s to early 1990s New York City

John Russell Taylor is Art Critic of *The Times* and the author of several books on Impressionism, Art Nouveau and contemporary artists

'This volume is everything an art book should be.' *(Contemporary Visual Arts)*

Design

Fashion &
Contemporary
Culture

Decorative Arts

Music &
Performing Arts

Video

Index

290 × 250 mm
11³⁄₈ × 9⁷⁄₈ inches
256 pp
201 col, 14 b&w illus.

Paperback
0 7148 3521 8

£ 22.95 UK
$ 35.00 US
€ 39.95 EUR
$ 49.95 CAN
$ 59.95 AUS

Arikha

Duncan Thomson

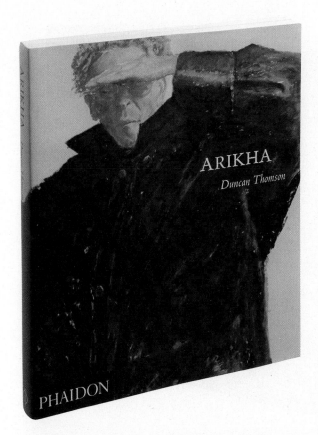

- Authoritative monograph on Romanian-born Israeli artist Avigdor Arikha (b.1929), one of the most original and independent-minded of contemporary figurative artists
- Surveys Arikha's entire body of work, from the drawings he made as a child in a Nazi concentration camp to the abstract work that won him acclaim in the 1960s, to the carefully composed portraits, nudes and still lifes of his recent career
- More than 200 illustrations document Arikha's paintings, drawings and graphics
- Winner of the Scottish Arts Council Book Award for Excellence, 1995

Duncan Thomson is Keeper of the Scottish National Portrait Gallery in Edinburgh

'A perceptive, stunningly illustrated biographical-critical study.' *(Publishers Weekly)*

General
Non-Fiction

Art
Contemporary
& Modern

Photography

Collector's
Editions

Film

Architecture

290 × 250 mm
11³⁄₈ × 9⁷⁄₈ inches
288 pp
188 col, 65 b&w illus.

Paperback
0 7148 3622 2

£ **22.95** UK
$ **35.00** US
€ **39.95** EUR
$ **49.95** CAN
$ **59.95** AUS

Paula Rego

2nd edition
John McEwen

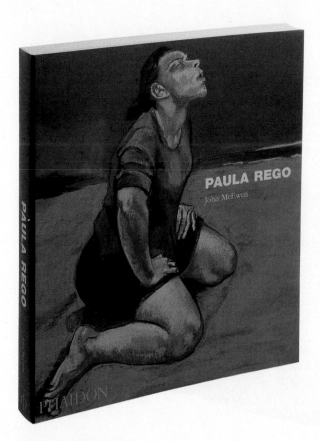

- **The first monograph to treat the complete works of Paula Rego (b.1935), one of today's most important figurative painters**
- **Influenced by Surrealism, folklore, dreams and animation, Rego creates strongly narrative works imbued with a sense of subversive mystery**
- **A wealth of full-colour illustrations documents Rego's career, including her celebrated etchings based on her dark interpretations of *Peter Pan* and other nursery rhymes**
- **This updated edition includes three new chapters and a revised chronology, bibliography and list of exhibitions**

John McEwen is the art critic of the *Sunday Telegraph* and writes extensively on 20th century art

'This is an excellently produced book, more strengthened than stifled by the close presence of its subject.' *(Times Literary Supplement)*

Design
Fashion & Contemporary Culture
Decorative Arts
Music & Performing Arts
Video
Index

220 × 156 mm
8²₃ × 6¹₈ inches
192 pp
24 col, 12 b&w illus.

Paperback
0 7148 2983 8

£ **9.95** UK
$ **14.95** US
€ **16.95** EUR
$ **24.95** CAN
$ **27.95** AUS

Francis Bacon

In Conversation with Michel Archimbaud

- A collection of revealing interviews with legendary painter Francis Bacon (1909–92), conducted by his close friend shortly before Bacon's death
- Discussions range across painting, literature and music, with candid disclosures about Bacon's childhood, his friends and his art – including comments on such key figures as Rubens, Blake, Monet, Cézanne, Picasso, Balthus and Giacometti
- Photographs depict Bacon in his studio
- A rare, intimate glimpse of the man behind the paintings

Michel Archimbaud has had a long and distinguished career in publishing as well as in television, radio, film and theatre production

General
Non-Fiction

Art
Contemporary
& Modern

Photography

Collector's
Editions

Film

Architecture

Stanley Spencer

Keith Bell

**Complete catalogue
of the paintings**
290 × 250 mm
11³⁄₈ × 9⁷⁄₈ inches
544 pp
314 col, 150 b&w illus.

Hardback
0 7148 2735 5

£ **125.00** UK
$ **195.00** US
€ **195.00** EUR
$ **285.00** CAN
$ **345.00** AUS

Abridged edition
290 × 250 mm
11³⁄₈ × 9⁷⁄₈ inches
408 pp
314 col, 10 b&w illus.

Paperback
0 7148 3890 X

£ **27.95** UK
$ **45.00** US
€ **49.95** EUR
$ **69.95** CAN
$ **75.00** AUS

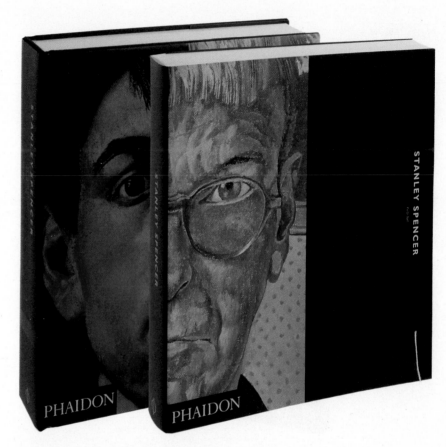

- Two volumes on Stanley Spencer (1891–1959), an eccentric visionary and one of Britain's most influential painters
- The catalogue raisonné is the essential reference cataloguing his entire oeuvre
- Abridged paperback version includes the entire narrative text from the catalogue, illustrated with more than 300 colour plates
- Both books examine his highly personal philosophy, his eroticism and religiosity in the context of his work

Keith Bell teaches Art History at the University of Saskatchewan in Saskatoon

'There can be no question that this unusually handsome, well illustrated and meticulously researched volume will be the point of departure for all subsequent evaluations of Spencer.' (*The Times*)

Design

Fashion & Contemporary Culture

Decorative Arts

Music & Performing Arts

Video

Index

280 × 240 mm
11 × 9¹₂ inches
128 pp
55 col, 45 b&w illus.

Paperback
0 7148 2810 6

£ **16.95** UK
$ **24.95** US
€ **29.95** EUR
$ **59.95** CAN
$ **45.00** AUS

Stanley Spencer

Duncan Robinson

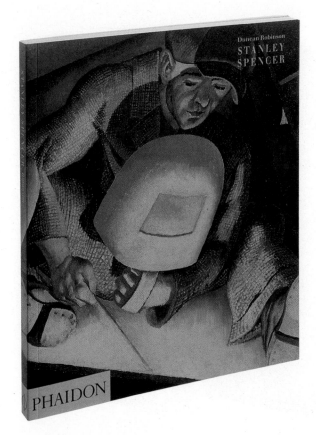

- An entertaining survey of the career of Stanley Spencer (1891–1959), one of Britain's foremost painters of the 20th century
- Renowned for his eccentric vision
- Discusses the full range of his work and places him in the wider context of 20th century European art

Duncan Robinson is Director of the Yale Center for British Art and Professor of the History of Art at Yale University

'A better short introduction to Spencer and his work would be hard to find.' *(The New York Times)*

General
Non-Fiction

Art
Contemporary
& Modern

Photography

Collector's
Editions

Film

Architecture

290 × 250 mm
11³⁄₈ × 9⁷⁄₈ inches
352 pp
292 col, 30 b&w illus.

Paperback
0 7148 3980 9

£ 24.95 UK
$ 39.95 US
€ 39.95 EUR
$ 59.95 CAN
$ 65.00 AUS

Hardback
0 7148 3210 3

£ 49.95 UK
$ 69.95 US
€ 79.95 EUR
$ 98.00 CAN
$ 125.00 AUS

Latin American Art in the Twentieth Century

Edited by Edward Sullivan

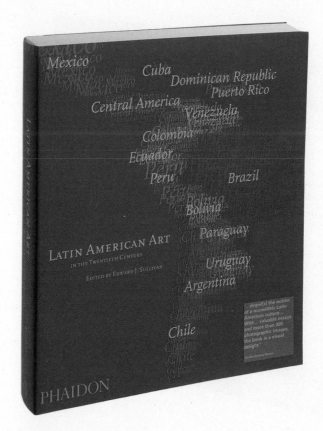

- This is the first comprehensive and authoritative survey of an increasingly popular and important field, edited by one of its most respected scholars
- Springing from complex cultural roots, Latin American art is extraordinarily diverse and often startling in its originality
- Written by a team of experts, each of whom writes about the art of his or her own country, providing a genuinely Latin American viewpoint
- The first English-language publication to do full justice to the richness and complexity of the Latin American art traditions

Edward Sullivan is Professor and Chairman of the Department of Fine Arts at New York University

Design

Fashion &
Contemporary
Culture

Decorative Arts

Music &
Performing Arts

Video

Index

290 × 250 mm
11³⁄₈ × 9⁷⁄₈ inches
240 pp
352 col, 72 b&w illus.

Paperback
0 7148 4009 2

£ **22.95** UK
$ **35.00** US
€ **39.95** EUR
$ **49.95** CAN
$ **59.95** AUS

Hardback
0 7148 3149 2

£ **45.00** UK
$ **69.95** US
€ **75.00** EUR
$ **98.00** CAN
$ **125.00** AUS

Raw Creation

Outsider Art and Beyond
Text by John Maizels, introduction by Roger Cardinal

- Pioneering study of 'Outsider Art and its seminal influence on modern art
- The art of visionaries, folk creators, spiritualists, recluses, the insane and the socially marginalized, once scorned, is now recognized as speaking with great immediacy and power
- Author looks at a wide range of work by self-taught and 'Outsider' artists, offering a fascinating account of human creativity
- Examines in particular the inspiration it provided for Jean Dubuffet and his Art Brut movement

John Maizels is Editor of *Raw Vision* magazine.
Roger Cardinal is Professor of Literary and Visual Studies at the University of Kent at Canterbury

'The definitive book on this vastly misunderstood, endlessly fascinating art.' *(Buzz)*
'A compendium worthy of the vibrant range of human creativity it documents.' *(Time Out, New York)*

General Non-Fiction
Art Contemporary & Modern
Photography
Collector's Editions
Film
Architecture

290 × 250 mm
11³⁄₈ × 9⁷⁄₈ inches
400 pp
239 col, 259 b&w illus.

Hardback
0 7148 8078 7

£ **125.00** UK
$ **195.00** US
€ **195.00** EUR
$ **295.00** CAN
$ **345.00** AUS

The Prints of Stanley William Hayter

A Complete Catalogue
Peter Black and Désirée Moorhead

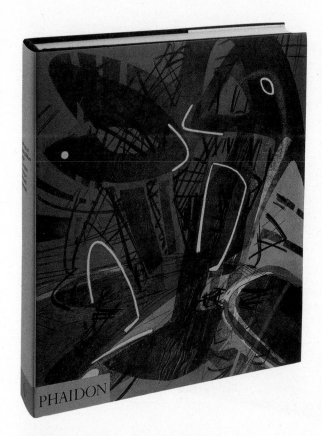

- The definitive catalogue of the work of Stanley William Hayter (1901–88), the most influential printmaker of the 20th century
- As the inventor of simultaneous colour printing, Hayter had contact with the major Cubist, Surrealist and Abstract Expressionist painters of his day
- Almost 500 illustrations cover Hayter's entire canon of work
- A vital reference work for readers concerned with 20th-century art and printmaking

Peter Black is a freelance writer and dealer
Désirée Moorhead is the artist's widow

290 × 250 mm
11³⁄₈ × 9⁷⁄₈ inches
240 pp
120 col, 40 b&w illus.

Paperback
0 7148 3167 0

£ **22.95** . UK
$ **35.00** US
€ **39.95** EUR
$ **49.95** CAN
$ **59.95** AUS

Mondrian

John Milner

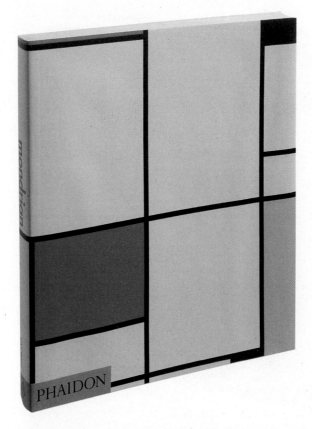

- A masterful account of the life and work of Dutch artist Piet Mondrian (1872–1944), whose abstract compositions are landmarks of Modernist painting
- Illustrates all of Mondrian's key works, from his early studies of landscapes and flowers to his experiments with pointillist colour and spare seascapes, to his discovery of Cubism and beyond
- Examines the artist's working process and explores the tension between the brilliantly disciplined compositions and their underlying subject matter
- More than a monograph, it's an essential study of the evolution of abstract art in the 20th century

John Milner is Professor in the Department of Fine Art at the University of Newcastle upon Tyne

General
Non-Fiction

Art
Contemporary
& Modern

Photography

Collector's
Editions

Film

Architecture

290 × 250 mm
11³⁄₈ × 9⁷⁄₈ inches
472 pp
419 col, 27 b&w illus.

Hardback
0 7148 2813 0

£ 79.95 UK
$ 125.00 US
€ 125.00 EUR
$ 180.00 CAN
$ 225.00 AUS

Award

Silver Award for the
most outstanding
Complete Book

Ben Nicholson

Norbert Lynton

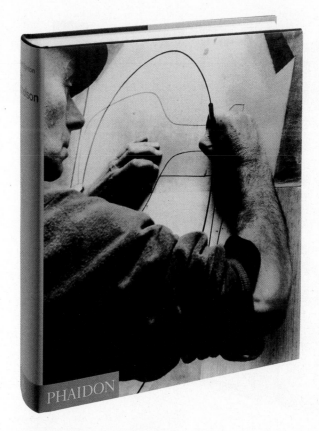

- The first comprehensive monograph on the life and work of Ben Nicholson (1894-1982),
  one of the pioneers of abstract art in the 20th century
- Explores each phase of Nicholson's creativity as he played with the elements of landscape
  and still life, explored the eloquence of limitations in his famous white reliefs, and
  experimented with colour, surface texture and transparency
- Author's acquaintance with Nicholson allows him to craft an exceptionally well-rounded
  portrait of the artist's 60-year career

Norbert Lynton is a distinguished art historian, lecturer and critic. From 1975 to 1989 he was
Professor of the History of Art at the University of Sussex. He is the author of *The Story of
Modern Art*, also published by Phaidon

'Intelligent, subtle and magisterial. A masterpiece, a model of its kind.' *(Modern Painters)*
'The ultimate reference source on Britain's most important abstract artist.' *(San Francisco
Chronicle)*

Design

Fashion & Contemporary Culture

Decorative Arts

Music & Performing Arts

Video

Index

290 × 250 mm
11³⁄₈ × 9⁷⁄₈ inches
252 pp
183 col, 8 b&w illus.

Paperback
0 7148 3750 4

£ **22.95** UK
$ **35.00** US
€ **39.95** EUR
$ **49.95** CAN
$ **59.95** AUS

Ben Nicholson

Abridged edition
Norbert Lynton

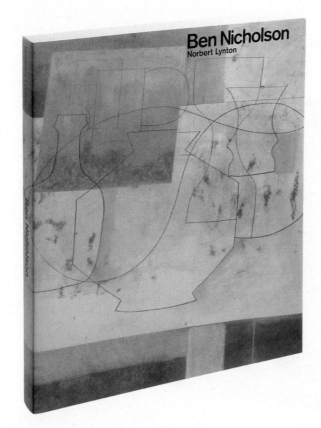

- A subtle and sensitive study of the work and life of Ben Nicholson (1894–1982), a pioneer of abstract art
- Examines his revolutionary white reliefs as well as his attachment to landscape and still life
- Covers his entire career
- Originally published in 1993 in a larger edition with many suplementary illustrations (see p.122), this abridged version has been reissued at a highly competitive price

Norbert Lynton is a distinguished art historian, lecturer and critic. From 1975 to 1989 he was Professor of the History of Art at the University of Sussex. He is the author of *The Story of Modern Art*, also published by Phaidon

General
Non-Fiction

Art
Contemporary
& Modern

Photography

Collector's
Editions

Film

Architecture

245 × 210 mm
9⅝ × 8¼ inches
672 pp
c.500 col, 100 b&w illus.

Hardback
0 7148 2950 1

£ **75.00** UK
$ **125.00** US
€ **125.00** EUR
$ **195.00** CAN
$ **225.00** AUS

Picasso: Style and Meaning

Elizabeth Cowling

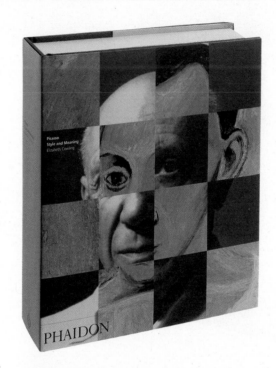

- **Groundbreaking new study of Pablo Picasso (1881–1973) examines how he deliberately used style as a means of expression, in order to avoid the sterility he equated with consistency**
- **Weaves biography and analysis into a compelling, eloquent narrative that supersedes all other introductions to Picasso's art**
- **More than 600 illustrations document all of Picasso's major works up to the beginning of World War II, juxtaposing them with their sources**
- **Represents more than ten years of research by the author, a Picasso specialist**

Elizabeth Cowling teaches art history at the University of Edinburgh. A curator of the exhibition 'Picasso: Sculptor/Painter' (Tate Gallery, London, 1994), she is also Co-Curator of the 'Matisse/Picasso' exhibition (Tate Modern, London; Grand Palais, Paris; MoMA, New York, 2002–3)

'A genuinely nuanced approach to the intimidating enormity of Picasso's achievement ... page-turningly gripping ...' (*Apollo*)
'Ms Cowling's virtue is a well-judged combination of detail and synthesis. She provides beautifully clear and close analysis of almost every aspect of Picasso's output ...' (*The Art Newspaper*)
'I have read no book on Picasso that is a greater aid to understanding him.' (Brian Sewell, *Evening Standard*)

Design

Fashion & Contemporary Culture

Decorative Arts

Music & Performing Arts

Video

Index

246 × 173 mm
9²₃ × 6⁷₈ inches
320 pp
170 col, 204 b&w illus.

Paperback
0 7148 3242 1

£ **14.95** UK
€ **24.95** EUR
$ **24.95** US
$ **39.95** CAN
$ **45.00** AUS

The Cubist Epoch

Douglas Cooper

- Illustrated with over 300 photographs, this book presents a vivid personal evocation of Cubism as a historic and aesthetic force
- First published to accompany a now legendary exhibition in 1970–1, it is based on first-hand documentary sources
- Douglas Cooper was a personal friend of the main protagonists, including Picasso, Braque and Léger
- The book now has permanent value as a documentary sourcebook

Douglas Cooper (1911–84), a close confidant of many cubist artist, was one of the foremost critics and art collectors of his generation

'This book has achieved classic status during the last quarter century.' *(Chicago Tribune)*

General
Non-Fiction

Art
Contemporary
& Modern

Photography

Collector's
Editions

Film

Architecture

280 × 215 mm
11 × 8¹₂ inches
270 pp
64 col, 16 duotone
and 93 b&w illus.

Paperback
0 7148 2862 9

£ **19.95** UK
$ **29.95** US
€ **35.00** EUR
$ **45.00** CAN
$ **55.00** AUS

Egon Schiele

Erwin Mitsch

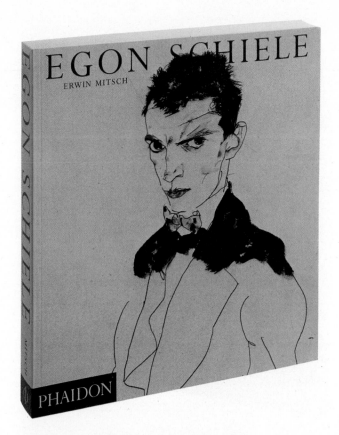

- A fundamental study of the character and development of Austrian artist Egon Schiele (1890–1918), a major figure in the birth of modern art
- Schiele's distinctive and original Expressionism reaffirmed the unrecognized role of Vienna as one of the leading centres of the fine arts
- Fully examines Schiele's paintings and drawings, illustrating a representative selection of his nudes, portraits, allegories and landscapes
- Explores Schiele's relationships with his contemporaries on the European art scene, including Munch, Rodin and Klimt

Erwin Mitsch was for many years on the staff of the Albertina, Vienna

Design

Fashion &
Contemporary
Culture

Decorative Arts

Music &
Performing Arts

Video

Index

280 × 215 mm
11 × 8½ inches
80 pp
30 col, 48 b&w illus.

Paperback
0 7148 2927 7

£ **9.95** UK
$ **14.95** US
€ **16.95** EUR
$ **21.95** CAN
$ **27.95** AUS

Egon Schiele

Simon Wilson

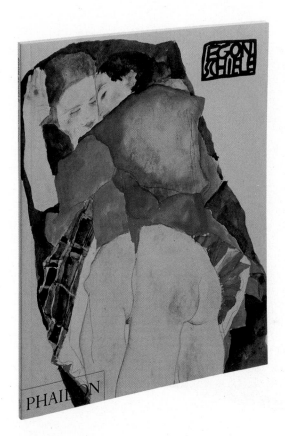

- Explores the influences that helped shape the art of Austrian Expressionist Egon Schiele (1890–1918)
- Discusses Schiele's role in the development of Expressionism, his vision of the artist in society and his obsessions with sex, life and death
- Puts Schiele in the context of his time, demonstrating how the painter's style of expression gave form to the anxieties that beset turn-of-the-century European culture
- Illustrates key works, from his famous female nudes and nude self-portraits to his lesser-known landscapes and portraits

Simon Wilson is Consultant Curator at Tate Britain, London

General
Non-Fiction

Art
Contemporary
& Modern

Photography

Collector's
Editions

Film

Architecture

280 × 215 mm
11 × 8¹₂ inches
256 pp
78 col, 137 b&w illus.

Paperback
0 7148 2967 6

£ **19.95** UK
$ **29.95** US
€ **35.00** EUR
$ **45.00** CAN
$ **55.00** AUS

Art In Vienna 1898–1918

Klimt, Kokoschka, Schiele and Their Contemporaries
3rd edition
Peter Vergo

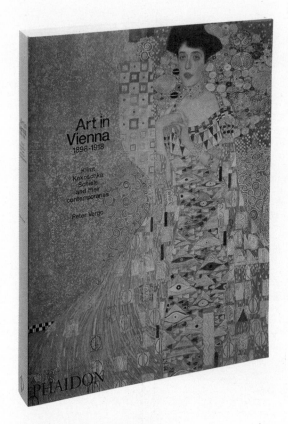

- A classic text, now in its third edition
- Brilliantly traces the course of both the Viennese Secession and the Wiener Werkstätte that followed
- Provides a fascinating documentary study of the successes and failures, hopes and fears of the members of an artistic movement that is much admired today
- Author is a specialist in early 20th century German and Russian art

Peter Vergo is Professor of Art History and Theory, University of Essex

Design

Fashion &
Contemporary
Culture

Decorative Arts

Music &
Performing Arts

Video

Index

280 × 240 mm,
11 × 9¹⁄₂ inches
160 pp
108 col illus.

Paperback
0 7148 3576 5

£ **16.95** UK
$ **24.95** US
€ **29.95** EUR
$ **35.00** CAN
$ **45.00** AUS

Art Deco Painting

Edward Lucie-Smith

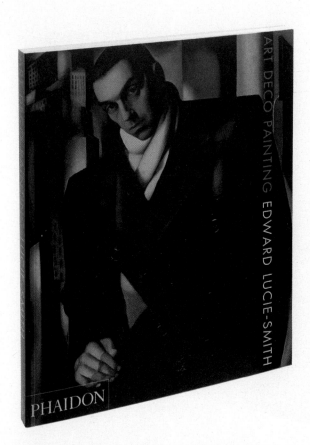

- **The first book to focus specifically on Art Deco painting**
- **Demonstrates that in the 1920s and 1930s there was a distinctive Art Deco style in painting as well as in the decorative arts**
- **French, American, Russian, British and Italian painters are all represented, including Tamara de Lempicka, Jean Dupas and Glyn Philpot**
- **Written by a leading authority on 20th-century art**

Edward Lucie-Smith is well known as a poet, critic, broadcaster and writer on art. He is the author of *Art Today*, also published by Phaidon

General
Non-Fiction

Art
Impressionism
& 19th Century

Photography

Collector's
Editions

Film

Architecture

290 × 250 mm
11³⁄₈ × 9⁷⁄₈ inches
240 pp
130 col, 40 b&w illus.

Paperback
0 7148 3892 6

£ 22.95 UK
$ 35.00 US
€ 39.95 EUR
$ 49.95 CAN
$ 59.95 AUS

Hardback
0 7148 2687 1

£ 35.00 UK
$ 55.00 US
€ 59.95 EUR
$ 79.95 CAN
$ 95.00 AUS

Sisley

Richard Shone

- The most detailed and authoritative survey yet to appear of the life and works of Alfred Sisley (1839–99)
- Sisley was one of the greatest landscape painters of the 19th century and a leading figure in the Impressionist movement
- Includes important series of paintings never before reproduced together in such quantity
- Author's extensive research uncovers new biographical details

Richard Shone is Editor of the *Burlington Magazine* and the author of *Bloomsbury Portraits*, also published by Phaidon

'Richard Shone's *Sisley* is a work of distinction: knowledgeable, thoughtful and very well written. This is the book to buy.' *(Daily Telegraph)*

Design

Fashion &
Contemporary
Culture

Decorative Arts

Music &
Performing Arts

Video

Index

290 × 250 mm
11³⁄₈ × 9⁷⁄₈ inches
240 pp
151 col, 22 b&w illus.

Paperback
0 7148 3451 3

£ **22.95** UK
$ **35.00** US
€ **39.95** EUR
$ **49.95** CAN
$ **59.95** AUS

Bonnard

Nicholas Watkins

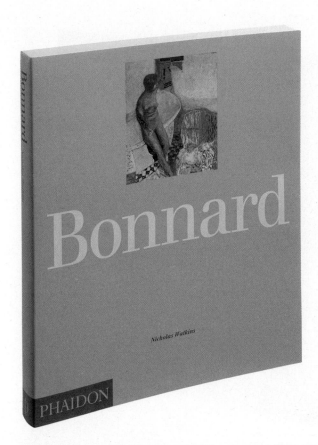

- A definitive survey of the life and work of Pierre Bonnard (1867–1947), one of the 20th century's great colourists
- Best known as a painter of intimate, domestic interiors, Bonnard was also a highly accomplished draughtsman and graphic artist – this book reproduces a wealth of paintings, sketches and lithographs
- The author offers an important reassessment of Bonnard's role in the context of Impressionism and Post-Impressionism, and explores his legacy of innovation

Nicholas Watkins is Reader in the History of Art at the University of Leicester

General
Non-Fiction

Art
Impressionism
& 19th Century

Photography

Collector's
Editions

Film

Architecture

280 × 240 mm
11 × 9¹₂ inches
160 pp
76 col, 64 b&w illus.

Paperback
0 7148 2955 2

£ **14.95** UK
$ **19.95** US
€ **22.95** EUR
$ **29.95** CAN
$ **39.95** AUS

Vuillard

Belinda Thomson

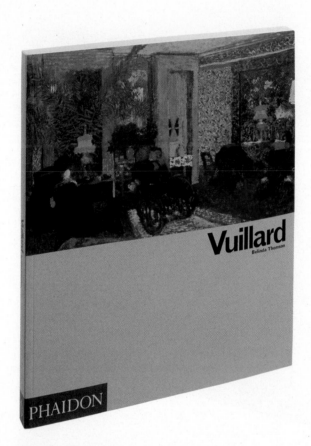

- Original and authoritative monograph on one of France's best-loved painters
- Edouard Vuillard (1868–1940), an Intimist painter and member of the Nabi group, was a master of colour and rich pattern
- Lively and well-written text presenting much previously unpublished information
- The standard introduction to a much-admired artist

Belinda Thomson is an independent scholar and Honorary Fellow in the History of Art at the University of Edinburgh. She is the author of *The Post-Impressionists*, also published by Phaidon

'Belinda Thomson's excellent and skilled biography is the finest analysis of Vuillard's life we have … This sympathetic, vivid and detailed account is exemplary.' (Marina Vaizey)

Design

Fashion &
Contemporary
Culture

Decorative Arts

Music &
Performing Arts

Video

Index

280 × 240 mm
11 × 9½ inches
128 pp
49 col, 50 b&w illus.

Paperback
0 7148 3479 3

£ **16.95** UK
$ **24.95** US
€ **29.95** EUR
$ **35.00** CAN
$ **45.00** AUS

Berthe Morisot

Kathleen Adler and Tamar Garb

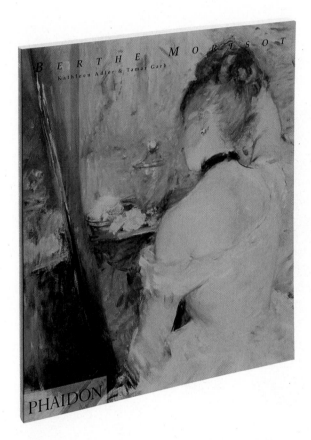

- A seminal study of the key female artist in the Impressionist movement, Berthe Morisot (1841–95)
- Considers her work in the context of the era's artistic and social debates, taking into account gender and class issues in 19th-century Paris
- Examines her relationships with contemporaries Monet, Renoir, Pissarro and Degas
- Features all of her finest work in full-colour detail

Kathleen Adler is an independent writer and critic
Tamar Garb is a professor in the Art History department, University College, London

'The authors admirably set Morisot in the artistic milieu of the period and explain the severely limiting restrictions of painting seriously for a middle-class woman.' *(World of Interiors)*

General
Non-Fiction

Art
Impressionism
& 19th Century

Photography

Collector's
Editions

Film

Architecture

305 × 225 mm
12 × 8⁶⁸ inches
128 pp
95 b&w illus.

Paperback
0 7148 3577 3

£ **12.95** UK
$ **19.95** US
€ **22.95** EUR
$ **29.95** CAN
$ **35.00** AUS

Rodin

Sculptures
10th edition
Selected by Ludwig Goldscheider

- First published in 1939, this is the classic monograph on legendary sculptor Auguste Rodin (1840–1917)
- Stunning photographs of Rodin's masterpieces, all specially commissioned for this edition, depict his most significant works in great detail
- Reveals how Rodin's early Modernist art drew on the artistic traditions of ancient Greece, Egypt, the Far East and the Renaissance
- Places Rodin alongside the finest painters of his generation, including Manet and Cézanne

Ludwig Goldscheider (1896–1973) was a distinguished art historian and book designer, and co-founder of Phaidon Press in Vienna in 1923

Design

Fashion &
Contemporary
Culture

Decorative Arts

Music &
Performing Arts

Video

Index

290 × 250 mm
11³⁄₈ × 9⁷⁄₈ inches
520 pp
c.500 col, c.200 b&w illus.

Hardback
0 7148 4304 0

£ **59.95** UK
$ **95.00** US
€ **95.00** EUR
$ **145.00** CAN
$ **180.00** AUS

Hokusai

Gian Carlo Calza

· **A stunning new volume on the life and work of Katsushika Hokusai (1769–1849), one of
the greatest of the Japanese printmakers, painters and book illustrators**
· **Hundreds of illustrations give a full picture of his entire career, from his most beloved
seascapes and mountain views to rarely seen works from private collections**
· **Explores Western influences on Hokusai, and his own influence on the art of the West**
· **Author is a distinguished authority on Hokusai and Japanese art**

Gian Carlo Calza is Professor of East Asian Art History at the University of Venice, and Director of
the International Hokusai Research Centre in Milan. He has published many books, exhibition
catalogues and articles on Hokusai, and is currently preparing a catalogue raisonné of Hokusai's
paintings

General
Non-Fiction

Art
Impressionism
& 19th Century

Photography

Collector's
Editions

Film

Architecture

305 × 225 mm
12 × 8⅞ inches
192 pp
80 col, 100 b&w illus.

Paperback
0 7148 2662 6

£ **7.95** UK
$ **12.95** US
€ **12.95** EUR
$ **19.95** CAN
$ **22.95** AUS

The Post-Impressionists

Belinda Thomson

- A lively survey of French painting in the 1880s and 1890s – a period of avant-garde experimentation
- Discusses and illustrates major and minor artists, including Cézanne, Gauguin, Van Gogh, Bonnard and their contemporaries
- Tells a story of personal rivalry, commercial pressures, individual enterprises and shifting alliances
- A vital contribution to the scholarship on the subject of Post-Impressionist art

Belinda Thomson is an independent scholar and an Honorary Fellow in the History of Art at the University of Edinburgh. She is the author of *Vuillard*, also published by Phaidon

Design

Fashion &
Contemporary
Culture

Decorative Arts

Music &
Performing Arts

Video

Index

310 × 245 mm
12¼ × 9½ inches
80 pp
37 col, 5 b&w illus.

Paperback
0 7148 3814 4

£ **6.95** UK
$ **9.95** US
€ **11.95** EUR
$ **14.95** CAN
$ **16.95** AUS

Van Gogh's Flowers

Judith Bumpus

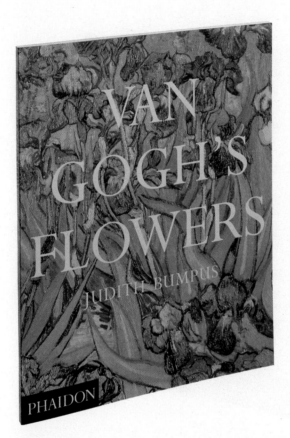

- Celebrates Van Gogh's fascination with flowers, which inspired some of his most remarkable paintings
- Illustrations are complemented by the artist's pen-and-ink drawings
- The text draws on the artist's own letters to show the profound influence of nature on his work
- An essential addition to the literature on Van Gogh

Judith Bumpus is an independent art historian and writer, and the author of *Impressionist Gardens*, also published by Phaidon

General
Non-Fiction

Art
Impressionism
& 19th Century

Photography

Collector's
Editions

Film

Architecture

305 × 225 mm
12 × 8⁷⁄₈ inches
192 pp
77 col, 104 b&w illus.

Paperback
0 7148 2661 8

£ **7.95** UK
$ **12.95** US
€ **12.95** EUR
$ **19.95** CAN
$ **22.95** AUS

The Impressionists

Michael Wilson

- Recounts the story of the Impressionist fellowship and how it scandalized the Paris art world, from the first encounters in 1861–2 to the last group exhibition in 1886
- Covers the key figures of the Impressionist movement, among them Monet, Pissarro, Degas, Sisley, Cézanne, Manet and Renoir
- Examines the personal and professional relationships between the artists, and their individual and collective struggles for recognition
- Illustrations showcase the most important of the Impressionist works

Michael Wilson is Head of Exhibitions and Displays at the National Gallery, London

Design

Fashion &
Contemporary
Culture

Decorative Arts

Music &
Performing Arts

Video

Index

310 × 245 mm
12¹₄ × 9⁵₈ inches
80 pp
45 col, 5 b&w illus.

Paperback
0 7148 3813 6

£ **6.95** UK
$ **9.95** US
€ **11.95** EUR
$ **14.95** CAN
$ **16.95** AUS

Impressionist Gardens

Judith Bumpus

- Explores the Impressionists' shared passion for painting gardens and flowers
- Features well-known works by Monet, Renoir, Pissarro and Sisley
- Full-colour illustrations include many close-up details, revealing the artists' techniques
- A must for art lovers and nature enthusiasts alike

Judith Bumpus is an independent art historian and writer, and the author of *Van Gogh's Flowers*, also published by Phaidon

General Non-Fiction

Art Impressionism & 19th Century

Photography

Collector's Editions

Film

Architecture

290 × 250 mm
11³⁄₈ × 9⁷⁄₈ inches
240 pp
137 col, 63 b&w illus.

Paperback
0 7148 3623 0

£ 22.95 UK
$ 35.00 US
€ 39.95 EUR
$ 49.95 CAN
$ 59.95 AUS

Hardback
0 7148 2919 6

£ 35.00 UK
$ 55.00 US
€ 59.95 EUR
$ 79.95 CAN
$ 95.00 AUS

The Barbizon School and the Origins of Impressionism

Steven Adams

- Re-evaluates French landscape painting in the half-century before Impressionism
- Places the Barbizon painters' 'return to nature' against the background of rapid industrialization and political turmoil
- Includes paintings by Corot, Millet, Rousseau and their contemporaries

Steven Adams teaches at the School of Art and Design at the University of Hertfordshire and lectures at the Victoria & Albert Museum and National Gallery in London

'A superb investigation of a long-overshadowed subject.' *(Library Journal)*

Design

Fashion &
Contemporary
Culture

Decorative Arts

Music &
Performing Arts

Video

Index

280 × 240 mm
11 × 9½ inches
160 pp
70 col, 62 b&w illus.

Paperback
0 7148 2956 0

£ **16.95** UK
$ **24.95** US
€ **29.95** EUR
$ **35.00** CAN
$ **45.00** AUS

British Impressionism

Kenneth McConkey

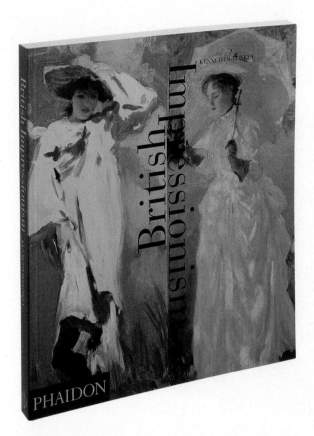

- A comprehensive survey of the distinctly British version of Impressionism
- Traces the debates and personalities that emerged as the style travelled across the English Channel and collided with the academic Victorian art world
- Artists discussed include Sargent, Forbes, Lavery, Sickert, Steer and Clausen

Kenneth McConkey is Professor of Art History and Dean of the Faculty of Arts and Design, University of Northumbria at Newcastle

General
Non-Fiction

Art
Impressionism
& 19th Century

Photography

Collector's
Editions

Film

Architecture

245 × 210 mm
9⅝ × 8¼ inches
272 pp
84 col, 103 b&w illus.

Paperback
0 7148 2961 7

£ **19.95** UK
$ **29.95** US
€ **35.00** EUR
$ **45.00** CAN
$ **55.00** AUS

Bloomsbury Portraits

Vanessa Bell, Duncan Grant and Their Circle
Richard Shone

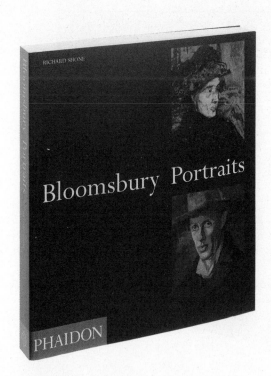

- A rare glimpse inside the Bloomsbury group – the circle of artists and writers that dominated English cultural life in the early 20th century
- Profiles the lives and careers of Vanessa Bell (1879–1961) and Duncan Grant (1885–1978), the two painters in the Bloomsbury group
- Examines their work both within the context of Bloomsbury and from the wider perspective of modern British art
- Discusses their interactions with the personalities of their time, from Virginia Woolf and Lytton Strachey to Picasso, Derain and Sickert

Richard Shone is Editor of the *Burlington Magazine* and the author of *Sisley*, also published by Phaidon

Design

Fashion &
Contemporary
Culture

Decorative Arts

Music &
Performing Arts

Video

Index

290 × 250 mm
11³⁄₈ × 9⁷⁄₈ inches
240 pp
c.200 col, 20 b&w illus.

Hardback
0 7148 4232 X

£ **29.95** UK
$ **49.95** US
€ **49.95** EUR
$ **75.00** CAN
$ **89.95** AUS

J W Waterhouse

Peter Trippi

- This major new monograph presents a fresh appraisal of John William Waterhouse (1849–1917)
- A timely re-evaluation of Waterhouse's imagery, focusing on his depictions of women, which reflect the troubled relations between the sexes in Victorian England
- Explores the artist's stylistic influences, his studio practice and his dealings with collectors, dealers, critics and curators
- Outstanding colour reproductions, some never previously published

Peter Trippi is Director of the Dahesh Museum of Art, New York

General
Non-Fiction

Art
Impressionism
& 19th Century

Photography

Collector's
Editions

Film

Architecture

280 × 240 mm
11 × 9½ inches
128 pp
58 col, 38 b&w illus.

Paperback
0 7148 2864 5

£ **16.95** UK
$ **24.95** US
€ **29.95** EUR
$ **35.00** CAN
$ **45.00** AUS

J W Waterhouse

Anthony Hobson

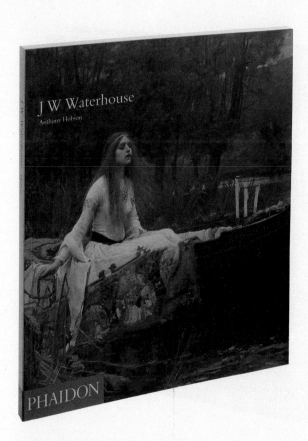

- An accessible introduction to the works of John William Waterhouse (1849–1917)
- The author, himself a painter, presents an artist's appreciation of Waterhouse as a master of Romantic classicism
- Includes his paintings of Ophelia, the Lady of Shalott and Pandora – some of the most archetypal Victorian images

Anthony Hobson (1920–99) taught History of Art at Coventry Polytechnic, and was also a practising artist

Design

Fashion &
Contemporary
Culture

Decorative Arts

Music &
Performing Arts

Video

Index

290 × 250 mm
11³⁄₈ × 9⁷⁄₈ inches
240 pp
135 col, 61 b&w illus.

Hardback
0 7148 3846 2

£ **35.00** UK
$ **59.95** US
€ **59.95** EUR
$ **89.95** CAN
$ **95.00** AUS

Albert Moore

Robyn Asleson

- The first monograph to be published on key Victorian painter Albert Moore (1841–93) for more than 100 years
- Moore created many celebrated icons of his time, yet his radical ideas, anticipating Modernism, have remained little known
- New evidence throws fresh light on Moore's hitherto mysterious personality and lifestyle, and reveals his close relationship with James McNeil Whistler

Robyn Asleson won Yale University's prestigious Frances Blanshard Prize for her doctoral thesis on late Victorian classical painting. She has lectured and published extensively on British art

General
Non-Fiction

Art
Impressionism
& 19th Century

Photography

Collector's
Editions

Film

Architecture

280 × 240 mm
11 × 9½ inches
144 pp
60 col, 43 b&w illus.

Paperback
0 7148 2957 9

£ **16.95** UK
$ **24.95** US
€ **29.95** EUR
$ **35.00** CAN
$ **45.00** AUS

The Art of Lord Leighton

Christopher Newall

- A critical survey of the works of Frederic, Lord Leighton (1830–96), one of the most widely admired artists in Victorian public life
- Leighton is best known for his elaborate figurative paintings, inspired by both ancient and classical art
- The author concentrates on the works themselves, exploring their narratives and constructions and examining the initial reactions of the public upon their exhibition
- Paintings, drawings, sculptures and photographs complement the text

Christopher Newall is an independent scholar and writer, and author of *Victorian Watercolours*, also published by Phaidon

Design

Fashion &
Contemporary
Culture

Decorative Arts

Music &
Performing Arts

Video

Index

280 × 240 mm
11 × 9½ inches
128 pp
Over 100 illus.

Paperback
0 7148 3575 7

£ **16.95** UK
$ **24.95** US
€ **29.95** EUR
$ **35.00** CAN
$ **45.00** AUS

Atkinson Grimshaw

Alexander Robertson

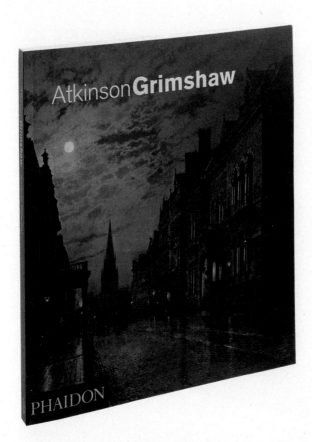

- The first comprehensive study of English painter Atkinson Grimshaw (1836–93)
- Covers the full scope of Grimshaw's career, from his early landscapes to the urban and industrial scenes that became his hallmark
- Discusses the techniques of Grimshaw's art, and places him in the context of Victorian art and society among such contemporaries as Alma-Tadema and Tissot
- Many of Grimshaw's paintings are in private collections and are reproduced here for the first time

Alexander Robertson is Senior Curator at Leeds City Art Gallery

'Alexander Robertson's handsome and most readable biography is a fitting tribute to a brilliant artist.' *(Yorkshire Evening Press)*

General Non-Fiction

Art Impressionism & 19th Century

Photography

Collector's Editions

Film

Architecture

280 × 240 mm
11 × 9¹₂ inches
144 pp
101 col illus.

Paperback
0 7148 2811 4

£ **16.95** UK
$ **24.95** US
€ **29.95** EUR
$ **35.00** CAN
$ **45.00** AUS

Victorian Watercolours

Christopher Newall

- The first general introduction to a popular Victorian-era medium – the preferred form of expression for many Victorian artists
- Features full-colour masterworks by such major figures as Ruskin, Burne-Jones and Rossetti, along with many lesser-known but respected talents
- Analyses both the art's subject matter and the artists' stylistic developments
- A valuable addition to the scholarship on Victorian art

Christopher Newall is an independent scholar, writer and curator, and the author of *The Art of Lord Leighton*, also published by Phaidon

'A jewel-box of a book … a commanding overview of the subject.' *(BBC Homes and Antiques)*

Design

Fashion & Contemporary Culture

Decorative Arts

Music & Performing Arts

Video

Index

300 × 240 mm
11³⁄₄ × 9¹⁄₂ inches
160 pp
50 col, 85 b&w illus.

Hardback
0 7148 2518 2

£ **45.00** UK
$ **75.00** US
€ **75.00** EUR
$ **110.00** CAN
$ **145.00** AUS

Bonington

Malcolm Cormack

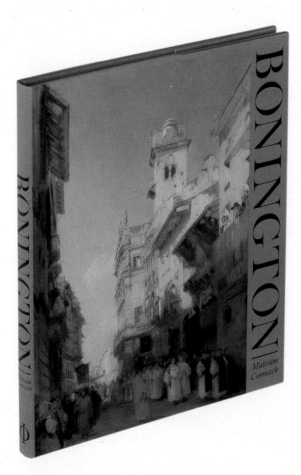

- Standard monograph on one of the finest Romantic watercolour painters
- Precocious and short-lived, Richard Parkes Bonington (1802–28) achieved a European reputation for his brilliant and poetic landscapes
- Rich and detailed biographical and critical study re-establishes Bonington as one of the greatest of landscape artists

Malcolm Cormack is Curator of Paintings at the Yale Center for British Art, New Haven, and author of *Constable* (1986)

General
Non-Fiction

Art
Impressionism
& 19th Century

Photography

Collector's
Editions

Film

Architecture

280 × 215 mm
11 × 8¹₂ inches
144 pp
40 col, 200 b&w illus.

Paperback
0 7148 3244 8

£ **14.95** UK
$ **19.95** US
€ **24.95** EUR
$ **29.95** CAN
$ **39.95** AUS

L S Lowry

Michael Leber and Judith Sandling

- A classic monograph on popular British painter L S Lowry (1887–1976), best known for his atmospheric urban and industrial landscapes
- Features his paintings and drawings of the mill life in Manchester, which document an important period in English social history
- Includes a series of interviews with the artist

Michael Leber was formerly Principal Museums Officer at Salford Museum and Art Gallery and is now Cultural Strategy Manager, Salford Culture and Heritage Department
Judith Sandling was Keeper of Art at Salford Museum and Art Gallery before her retirement

Design

Fashion & Contemporary Culture

Decorative Arts

Music & Performing Arts

Video

Index

240 × 240 mm
9¹₂ × 9¹₂ inches
96 pp
32 col, 45 b&w illus.

Paperback
0 7148 3811 X

£ **9.95** UK
$ **14.95** US
€ **16.95** EUR
$ **24.95** CAN
$ **27.95** AUS

Hugh Casson's Cambridge
Hugh Casson's Oxford

Hugh Casson

- The two companion volumes are a distinguished architect's pictorial celebration of two of Britain's most famous cities
- Sir Hugh Casson's enchanting watercolours and text capture the essence of both cities, exploring their imposing and impressive structures and their more intimate and unusual locations
- These keenly observed watercolours and witty, informative text prompt us to take a fresh look at two of the world's greatest tourist attractions

Sir Hugh Casson (1910–99) was educated at St John's College, Cambridge, and had a long and distinguished career as an architect. He was Director of Architecture for the Festival of Britain in 1951, and President of the Royal Academy, 1976–84

General
Non-Fiction

Art
Impressionism
& 19th Century

Photography

Collector's
Editions

Film

Architecture

Phaidon Miniature Editions

Each volume
120 × 100 mm
4³₄ × 4 inches
c.160 pp
c.90 col illus.

Paperback

£ **5.95** UK
$ **8.95** US
€ **9.95** EUR
$ **12.95** CAN
$ **16.95** AUS

Point of sale
10-copy counterpack
available
0 7148 3275 8

'Real little treasures.'

World of Interiors

- Pocket-sized books on a range of perennially popular and accessible subjects
- Includes a range of subjects from the romance of J W Waterhouse to the eroticism of Georgia O'Keeffe
- Ideal source books to inspire designers and artists
- With short introductions on each subject
- Perfect stocking-fillers

Design

Fashion &
Contemporary
Culture

Decorative Arts

Music &
Performing Arts

Video

Index

The Age of Elegance
The paintings
of John Singer Sargent
0 7148 3544 7

• The stylish portraits of
John Singer Sargent
(1856–1925) reflect the
charm, opulence and
assurance of the
late Victorian and Edwardian
eras
• Quotations from Sargent's
friend and mentor, the
novelist Henry James, provide
poignant commentary

Books of Hours
0 7148 3464 5

• The most famous of all
medieval manuscripts, a
Book of Hours is a glittering
compendium of illustrated
and embellished devotional
texts
• This book brings together
exquisite examples from
collections around the world

A Child is Born
0 7148 3253 7

• Motherhood is celebrated
in this collection of
beautiful paintings and
drawings from all periods
in art
• Complemented by a
selection of poetry
by women poets

**The Designs of
William Morris**
0 7148 3465 3

• William Morris (1834–96) is
the designer of some of the
finest wallpapers and fabrics
of the nineteenth century
• This extensive selection of
Morris's drawings and
designs evokes its genius
and perennial charm

**Georgia O'Keeffe
One Hundred Flowers**
Edited by Nicholas Callaway
0 7148 2696 0

• One hundred of the
extraordinary and
internationally admired
flower paintings of Georgia
O'Keeffe (1887–1986) are
reproduced in the delicate
colours of the originals

The Pre-Raphaelite Vision
0 7148 3252 9

• The famously evocative and
graceful female portraits
of the Pre-Raphaelites are
presented alongside the
poetry of their late
nineteenth-century
contemporaries

Myth and Romance
The art of J W Waterhouse
0 7148 3264 2

• This collection brings
together the perennially
popular paintings of J W
Waterhouse (1849–1917),
depicting legends of the
Middle Ages and myths of
the ancient world

General
Non-Fiction

Art
Old Masters
& Ancient Art

Photography

Collector's
Editions

Film

Architecture

280 × 240 mm
11 × 9½ inches
288 pp
201 b&w illus.

Hardback
0 7148 2553 0

£ 59.95 UK
$ 95.00 US
€ 95.00 EUR
$ 139.95 CAN
$ 175.00 AUS

Turner Prints

The Engraved Work of J M W Turner
Luke Herrmann

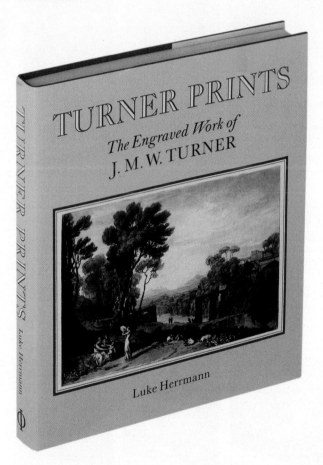

· Comprehensive, authoritative study of Turner's polific output of engravings and other prints
· Analyses Turner's relations with his engravers, and their role in his development as an artist
· Assesses the role of the prints in establishing Turner's contemporary reputation
· Includes a full checklist of over 800 prints

Luke Herrmann is Professor Emeritus in the History of Art at the University of Leicester

Design

Fashion &
Contemporary
Culture

Decorative Arts

Music &
Performing Arts

Video

Index

290 × 250 mm
11³⁄₈ × 9⁷⁄₈ inches
320 pp
167 col, 82 b&w illus.

Paperback
0 7148 3844 6

£ **24.95** UK
$ **39.95** US
€ **39.95** EUR
$ **59.95** CAN
$ **65.00** AUS

Winner of the Eleanor Tufts
Award from the American
Association of Hispanic
Art Studies, 1996

Goya

Janis Tomlinson

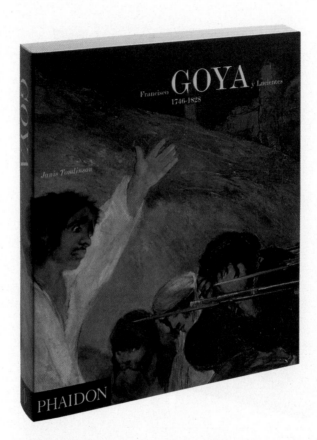

- A celebrated account of the life and work of Francisco Goya (1746–1828)
- Goya is considered to be the last of the Old Masters and the first of the Moderns; his diverse body of work includes both formal royal portraits of the Spanish court and some of the most compelling images of social unrest and personal anguish ever painted
- Places Goya in the social and political context of his time, addresses the contradictions of his art and discusses his drive to experiment with new media

Janis Tomlinson has taught at Columbia University, New York, and Williams College, Massachusetts

'The best monograph on Goya yet written.' *(Times Literary Supplement)*
'Beyond being a clear-eyed, historically alert reading of Goya's art, Tomlinson's book is a full and dazzling record of it.' *(San Francisco Chronicle)*

General
Non-Fiction

Art
Old Masters
& Ancient Art

Photography

Collector's
Editions

Film

Architecture

290 × 250 mm
11⅜ × 9⅞ inches
256 pp
160 col, 52 b&w illus.

Paperback
0 7148 3843 8

£ 22.95 UK
$ 35.00 US
€ 39.95 EUR
$ 49.95 CAN
$ 59.95 AUS

Canaletto

J G Links

- The definitive monograph on Canaletto (1697–1768), one of the most renowned Old Master painters
- Canaletto is celebrated for his views of Venice, Rome and London, which display both his technical skill and his unrivalled ability to evoke the atmosphere of a scene
- Explores Canaletto's life and career, relating his art to that of his predecessors, rivals and followers
- Generously illustrated with paintings, sketches, etchings and manuscripts

J G Links, who died in 1997 aged 92, was the world's leading authority on Canaletto

'Mr Links writes with clarity and elegance … *Canaletto* deserves to be read by everyone who loves Venice and Venetian Art.' *(Spectator)*

Design

Fashion &
Contemporary
Culture

Decorative Arts

Music &
Performing Arts

Video

Index

245 × 210 mm
9⅝ × 8¼ inches
448 pp
182 col, 36 b&w illus.

Paperback
0 7148 3966 3

£ **24.95** UK
$ **39.95** US
€ **39.95** EUR
$ **59.95** CAN
$ **69.95** AUS

Caravaggio

Catherine Puglisi

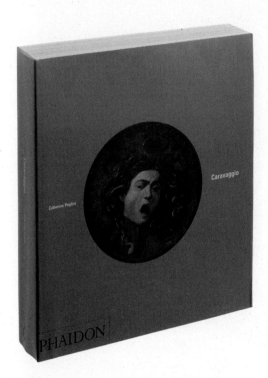

- Chronicles the controversial life of Michelangelo Merisi da Caravaggio (1571–1610), and offers the most penetrating analysis available of his art
- Illustrates all of Caravaggio's works in full colour, from his sexually provocative nude figures to the dramatic compositions and lighting of his religious paintings
- Author uses recent archival research and technical investigation to produce the most up-to-date and accurate study available
- An appendix of documents dating back to the 16th century positions Caravaggio in the context of his time

Catherine Puglisi is Associate Professor of Art History at Rutgers University, New Jersey

General
Non-Fiction

Art
Old Masters
& Ancient Art

Photography

Collector's
Editions

Film

Architecture

280 × 250 mm
11 × 9⅞ inches
320 pp
30 col, 331 b&w illus.

Paperback
0 7148 3715 6

£ **22.95** UK
$ **35.00** US
€ **39.95** EUR
$ **49.95** CAN
$ **59.95** AUS

Bernini

The Sculptor of the Roman Baroque
4th edition
Rudolf Wittkower

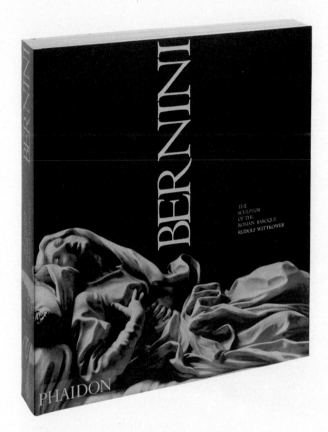

- Updated, expanded edition of the classic 1955 monograph and catalogue raisonné of Italian master sculptor Gian Lorenzo Bernini (1598–1680)
- A survey provides an introduction to all aspects of Bernini's sculpture, while the full catalogue gives detailed information on his complete oeuvre
- A wealth of photographs document his work in detail, from his religious-themed figures to his remarkable portraits and renowned Roman fountains

Rudolf Wittkower was one of the most distinguished art historians of the 20th century

'Wittkower's *Bernini* rightly enjoys almost canonical status among studies of the artist and his age, as an elegant survey which provides deep insights and rests lightly on profound scholarship.' *(Burlington Magazine)*

Design

Fashion & Contemporary Culture

Decorative Arts

Music & Performing Arts

Video

Index

304 × 238 mm
12 × 9³⁄₈ inches
288 pp
16 col, 326 b&w illus.

Paperback
0 7148 2953 6

£ **24.95** UK
$ **39.95** US
€ **39.95** EUR
$ **59.95** CAN
$ **69.95** AUS

Giambologna

The Complete Sculpture
Charles Avery, with photographs by David Finn

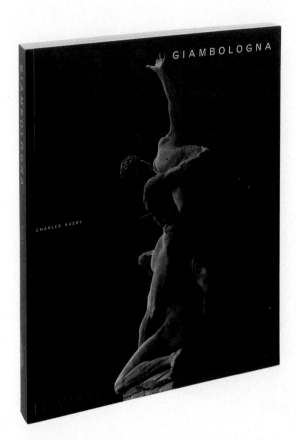

- A survey and critical analysis of Giambologna (1529–1608), the greatest sculptor of the age of Mannerism
- Covers the full range of his work, from bronze statuettes to equestrian monuments, while emphasizing his influence on the development of European sculpture
- Richly illustrated with photographs by renowned sculpture photographer David Finn

Charles Avery was formerly Director of the Department of European Sculpture at Christie's, London, and is now an independent scholar and writer

'An outstanding book.' *(Daily Telegraph)*
'A lucid and subtle account … complemented by superb photographs.' *(The Times)*

General
Non-Fiction

Art
Old Masters
& Ancient Art

Photography

Collector's
Editions

Film

Architecture

304 × 224 mm
12 × 8⅞ inches
280 pp
11 col, 390 b&w illus.

Paperback
0 7148 3296 0

£ **19.95** UK
$ **29.95** US
€ **35.00** EUR
$ **45.00** CAN
$ **55.00** AUS

Michelangelo

Paintings, Sculpture, Architecture
6th edition
Ludwig Goldscheider

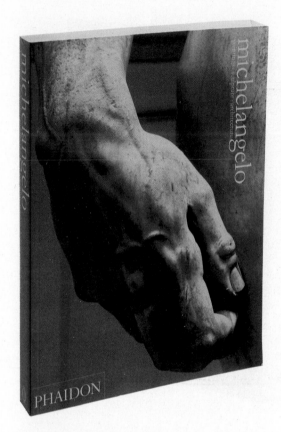

- First published in 1953, this book remains a classic of the literature on Michelangelo (1475–1564)
- The only volume to feature illustrations of all of his paintings, sculpture and architecture
- Photographs depict the works in unusual, close-up detail
- Includes a complete visual documentation of the Sistine Chapel before and after its controversial restoration

Ludwig Goldscheider (1896–1973) was a distinguished art historian and book designer, and co-founder of Phaidon Press in Vienna in 1923

Design

Fashion & Contemporary Culture

Decorative Arts

Music & Performing Arts

Video

Index

290 × 250 mm
11³⁄₈ × 9⁷⁄₈ inches
560 pp
160 col, 260 b&w illus.

Hardback
0 7148 2362 7

£ **125.00** UK
$ **195.00** US
€ **195.00** EUR
$ **295.00** CAN
$ **345.00** AUS

Fra Filippo Lippi

Life and Work, with a complete catalogue
Jeffrey Ruda

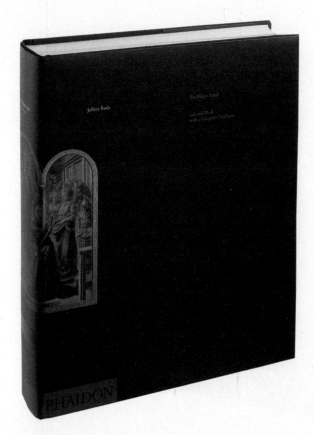

- Complete catalogue raisonné of the work of Fra Filippo Lippi (c.1406–69), one of the finest artists of the early Renaissance in Italy
- Author provides an important reassessment of Lippi's break from medieval traditions and his pioneering use of psychological realism
- A visual document of Lippi's entire oeuvre, with many works published here for the first time

Jeffrey Ruda is Associate Professor of Art History at the University of California, Davis

'This scholarly book, with its many fine illustrations, restores Fra Filippo Lippi to a position of pre-eminence among his peers.' *(Art Review)*

General
Non-Fiction

Art
Old Masters
& Ancient Art

Photography

Collector's
Editions

Film

Architecture

290 × 250 mm
11³⁄₈ × 9⁷⁄₈ inches
352 pp
151 col, 26 b&w illus.

Paperback
0 7148 3889 6

£ **29.95** UK
$ **45.00** US
€ **49.95** EUR
$ **69.95** CAN
$ **89.95** AUS

Fra Filippo Lippi

Life and Work
Abridged edition
Jeffrey Ruda

- A narrative monograph on Fra Filippo Lippi (c.1406–69), one of the greatest artists of early Renaissance Italy
- Contains an absorbing and penetrating examination of Lippi's life and work, and his place in the history of Renaissance art
- Outstanding colour illustrations of all Lippi's major works
- Includes full notes and bibliography, and a checklist of all Lippi's works
- Originally published in 1993, as a catalogue raisonné (see p.161), this abridged edition has been reissued as a more introductory volume for a wider audience

Design

Fashion &
Contemporary
Culture

Decorative Arts

Music &
Performing Arts

Video

Index

290 × 250 mm
11³⁄₈ × 9⁷⁄₈ inches
488 pp
161 col, 319 b&w illus.

Hardback
0 7148 2398 8

£ **125.00** UK
$ **195.00** US
€ **195.00** EUR
$ **285.00** CAN
$ **345.00** AUS

Masaccio and Masolino

A Complete Catalogue
Paul Joannides

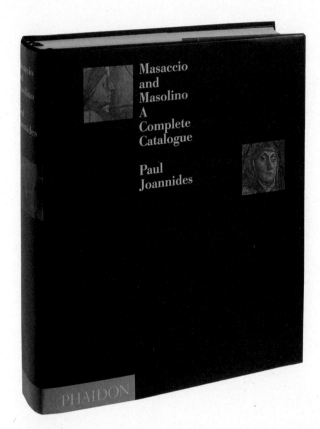

- This richly illustrated catalogue raisonné is an authoritative study of the complete oeuvre of both Masaccio (1401–28) and his colleague and collaborator Masolino (1383–1440)
- Masaccio is a key figure in early Renaissance painting, as a pioneer in the rigorous use of perspective – his collaborative frescos with Masolino make their names inseparable
- Author addresses long-standing problems of dating, development, influence and authenticity
- Generous illustrations showcase the artists' individual and joint projects

Paul Joannides is a lecturer in the Department of History of Art at the University of Cambridge

'This book contains almost everything one needs to know about Masaccio and Masolino, and is likely to prove a hard act to follow.' *(The Times)*

General
Non-Fiction

Art
Old Masters
& Ancient Art

Photography

Collector's
Editions

Film

Architecture

Introduction to Italian Sculpture Volumes I–III

John Pope-Hennessy

'No book on art is more intelligent, more learned and unpretentious, or more infused with passion; it is a tremendously exciting education in art, history, society, the advancement of thought and craft – in a word, in civilization.'

New York Times

- First published in 1955–63, Sir John Pope-Hennessy's classic *Introduction to Italian Sculpture* still stands as the definitive introduction to the subject
- Its three volumes bring order to a huge mass of material, and present a magisterial survey of one of the most creative phases in Western art
- These books have long been indispensable for scholars, students, curators, collectors and dealers
- Fourth edition, thoroughly revised and updated by the author shortly before his death

Sir John Pope-Hennessy (1913–94) was one of the 20th century's most distinguished art historians and museum directors. He was Director of the Victoria & Albert Museum (1967–73), Director of the British Museum (1974–6) and Consultative Chairman of the Department of European Paintings, Metropolitan Museum, New York (1977–86)

290 × 250 mm
11³⁄₈ × 9⁷⁄₈ inches
288 pp
226 duotone illus.

Paperback
0 7148 3881 0

£ **29.95** UK
$ **49.95** US
€ **49.95** EUR
$ **75.00** CAN
$ **89.95** AUS

Volume I: Italian Gothic Sculpture

4th edition
John Pope-Hennessy

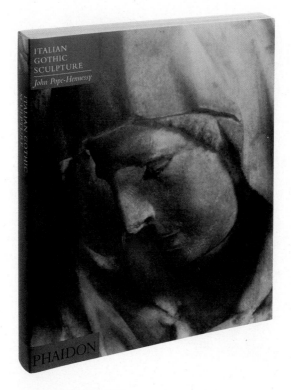

- The groundbreaking first volume was the first to give a coherent account of the formative period from 1150 to 1400
- Lucid and inspiring narrative text, with detailed scholarly notes and bibliography
- Includes the work of Nicola Pisano, Jacopo della Quercia and Lorenzo Ghiberti

General
Non-Fiction

Art
Old Masters
& Ancient Art

Photography

Collector's
Editions

Film

Architecture

Volume II: Italian Renaissance Sculpture

4th edition
John Pope-Hennessy

290 × 250 mm
11³⁄₈ × 9⁷⁄₈ inches
444 pp
329 duotone illus.

Paperback
0 7148 3882 9

£ 35.00 UK
$ 59.95 US
€ 59.95 EUR
$ 89.95 CAN
$ 99.95 AUS

Hardback
0 7148 3015 1

£ 80.00 UK
$ 125.00 US
€ 125.00 EUR
$ 175.00 CAN
$ 245.00 AUS

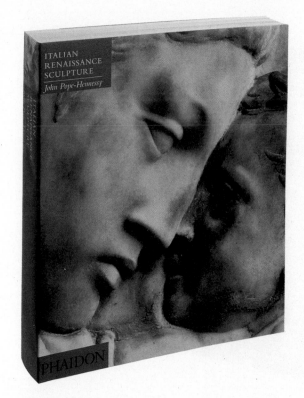

- The second volume covers the fifteenth century, one of the great creative periods of Italian sculpture
- With its clarity and sure judgement, the author's brilliant narrative is recognized as a classic art-historical text
- Includes comprehensive and up-to-date bibliographical data
- Covers the work of Donatello, Luca della Robbia, Verrocchio and Antonio Pollaiuolo, among many others

290 × 250 mm
11³⁄₈ × 9⁷⁄₈ inches
560 pp
350 duotone illus.

Paperback
0 7148 3883 7

£ 39.95 UK
$ 69.95 US
€ 69.95 EUR
$ 95.00 CAN
$ 120.00 AUS

Hardback
0 7148 3016 X

£ 95.00 UK
$ 150.00 US
€ 150.00 EUR
$ 220.00 CAN
$ 295.00 AUS

Volume III: Italian High Renaissance and Baroque Sculpture

4th edition
John Pope-Hennessy

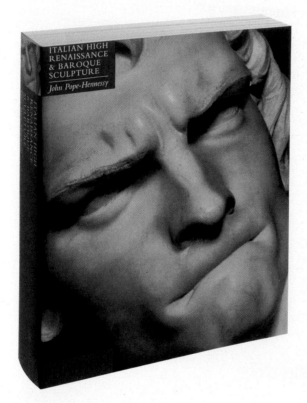

- The concluding volume deals with the immensely fruitful period from 1500 to the late seventeenth century
- The masterly narrative is a triumph of clear organization, aesthetic judgement and sustained scholarship
- Provides a lucid account of a rich and complex period, with a vast mass of well-organized scholarly bibliography
- Includes the work of the three great masters of the High Renaissance, Mannerism and the Baroque: Michelangelo, Giambologna and Bernini

General
Non-Fiction

Art
Old Masters
& Ancient Art

Photography

Collector's
Editions

Film

Architecture

290 × 250 mm
11³⁄₈ × 9⁷⁄₈ inches
208 pp
124 col, 71 b&w illus.

Hardback
0 7148 2933 1

£ 75.00 UK
$ 125.00 US
€ 125.00 EUR
$ 185.00 CAN
$ 225.00 AUS

The Devonshire Collection of Italian Drawings

A Complete Catalogue
Michael Jaffé
Volume 1: Tuscan and Umbrian Schools

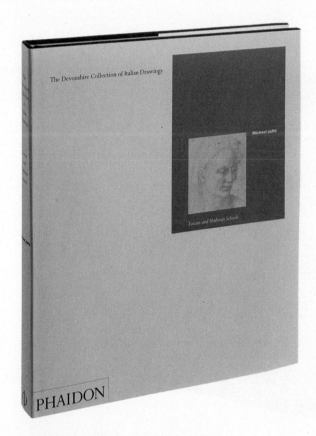

- A catalogue raisonné of one of the world's premier collections of Old Master drawings
- Four volumes, each dedicated to works from different regions of Italy
- Detailed entries for nearly 1,000 works in total, dating from the 15th century to the 18th
- The collection at Chatsworth House in Derbyshire, home of the Dukes of Devonshire, ranks with the Royal Collection at Windsor Castle as the finest privately owned group of such drawings in Britain
- *Volume 1, Tuscan and Umbrian Schools,* catalogues 151 drawings, mainly from the fifteenth and sixteenth centuries, including works by Barocci, Botticelli, Filippo Lippi, Pontormo and Andrea del Sarto

Michael Jaffé (1923–97) was Professor of the History of Western Art at the University of Cambridge

'Without a doubt the four volumes constitute the most lavish catalogue of any drawings collection published in living memory.' *(Burlington Magazine)*

Design
Fashion & Contemporary Culture
Decorative Arts
Music & Performing Arts
Video
Index

290 × 250 mm
11³⁄₈ × 9⁷⁄₈ inches
304 pp
228 col, 116 b&w illus.

Hardback
0 7148 2934 X

£ **95.00** UK
$ **150.00** US
€ **150.00** EUR
$ **225.00** CAN
$ **275.00** AUS

The Devonshire Collection of Italian Drawings

A Complete Catalogue
Michael Jaffé
Volume 2: Roman and Neapolitan Schools

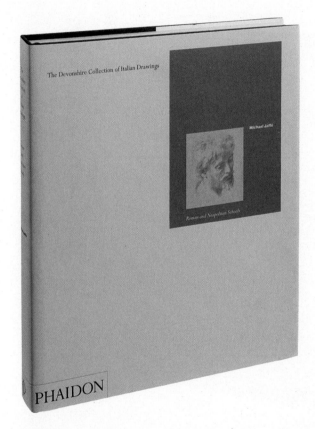

- Volume 2 catalogues 281 drawings from the sixteenth to the eighteenth century
- Each drawing beautifully illustrated in colour and with full scholarly apparatus
- Includes works by Pietro da Cortona, Giulio Romano, Raphael and other artists

General
Non-Fiction

Art
Old Masters
& Ancient Art

Photography

Collector's
Editions

Film

Architecture

290 × 250 mm
11³⁄₈ × 9⁷⁄₈ inches
320 pp
253 col, 124 b&w illus.

Hardback
0 7148 2935 8

£ **95.00** UK
$ **150.00** US
€ **150.00** EUR
$ **225.00** CAN
$ **275.00** AUS

The Devonshire Collection of Italian Drawings

A Complete Catalogue
Michael Jaffé
Volume 3: Bolognese and Emilian Schools

- Volume 3 catalogues 301 drawings, mainly from the sixteenth and seventeenth centuries
- Each drawing beautifully illustrated in colour, with full scholarly apparatus
- Includes works by the Carracci, Domenichino, Guercino, Guido Reni, Parmigianino and Correggio

Design

Fashion & Contemporary Culture

Decorative Arts

Music & Performing Arts

Video

Index

290 × 250 mm
11³⁄₈ × 9⁷⁄₈ inches
256 pp
181 col, 103 b&w illus.

Hardback
0 7148 2936 6

£ **75.00** UK
$ **125.00** US
€ **125.00** EUR
$ **195.00** CAN
$ **225.00** AUS

The Devonshire Collection of Italian Drawings

A Complete Catalogue
Michael Jaffé
Volume 4: Venetian and North Italian Schools

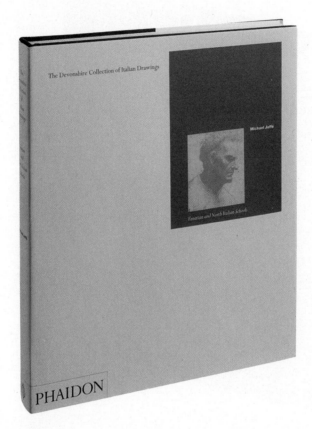

- Volume 4 catalogues 219 drawings, from the fifteenth to the eighteenth century
- Each drawing beautifully illustrated in colour, with full scholarly apparatus
- Includes works by Tintoretto, Titian and Leonardo da Vinci

General
Non-Fiction

Art
Old Masters
& Ancient Art

Photography

Collector's
Editions

Film

Architecture

280 × 215 mm
11 × 8½ inches
256 pp
16 col, 160 b&w illus.

Hardback
0 7148 2395 3

£ **99.95** UK
$ **150.00** US
€ **150.00** EUR
$ **220.00** CAN
$ **295.00** AUS

Simone Martini

Complete Edition
Andrew Martindale

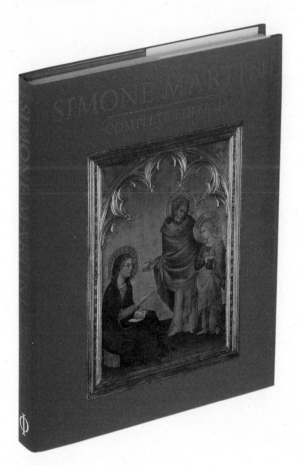

- Comprehensive monograph and catalogue raisonné of the work of this major early Italian painter
- Simone Martini (c.1284–1344) was the greatest master of the Sienese school, admired for the beauty, pathos and supreme technical skill of his works
- Professor Martindale examines in detail the historical evidence, sums up existing scholarship and proposes new solutions to old and new problems

Andrew Martindale (1932–99) was Professor of Visual Arts at the University of East Anglia

Design

Fashion & Contemporary Culture

Decorative Arts

Music & Performing Arts

Video

Index

245 × 175 mm
9⁵⁄₈ × 6⁷⁄₈ inches
320 pp
35 col, 209 b&w illus.

Paperback
0 7148 2301 5

£ **14.95** UK
$ **19.95** US
€ **24.95** EUR
$ **29.95** CAN
$ **39.95** AUS

A Handbook of Roman Art

A Survey of the Visual Arts of the Roman World
Edited by Martin Henig

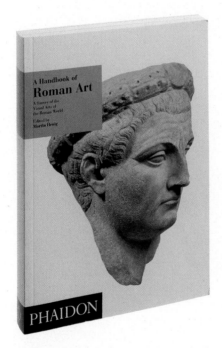

- An indispensable guide to the creative output of the Roman empire
- Spans a vast range from early Rome to late antiquity and from Rome and Italy to the provinces
- Written by a team of experts, each authoritative in his or her field
- Covers architecture, painting, sculpture, metalwork, ceramics, mosaics, jewellery and furniture
- A must-have for all students of Roman art and civilization

Martin Henig lectures on Roman art and archaeology at the University of Oxford

General
Non-Fiction

Art
Old Masters
& Ancient Art

Photography

Collector's
Editions

Film

Architecture

245 × 175 mm
9⁵⁄₈ × 6⁷⁄₈ inches
432 pp
520 b&w illus.

Paperback
0 7148 2496 8

£ **14.95** UK
$ **19.95** US
€ **24.95** EUR
$ **29.95** CAN
$ **39.95** AUS

A Handbook of Greek Art

A Survey of the Visual Arts of Ancient Greece
9th edition
Gisela M A Richter

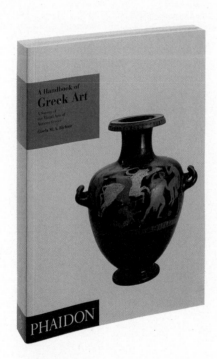

- Recognized since its first publication in 1959 as the authoritative survey of the subject
- Detailed chapters examine Greek art and architecture from myriad angles, taking in everything from urban planning to coins and jewellery
- Copious illustrations and extensive appendices combine to create an invaluable reference work
- The author was one of the great scholars of her generation – her book remains the best introduction and sourcebook

Gisela Richter was for many years Curator of Greek and Roman Art, Metropolitan Museum of Art, New York

Design

Fashion &
Contemporary
Culture

Decorative Arts

Music &
Performing Arts

Video

Index

245 × 210 mm
9⁵⁄₈ × 8¹⁄₄ inches
368 pp
c.300 col illus.

Hardback
0 7148 4200 1

£ **24.95** UK
$ **39.95** US
€ **39.95** EUR
$ **59.95** CAN
$ **69.95** AUS

Point of Sale
Book tower available

Egypt

4000 Years of Art
Jaromir Malek

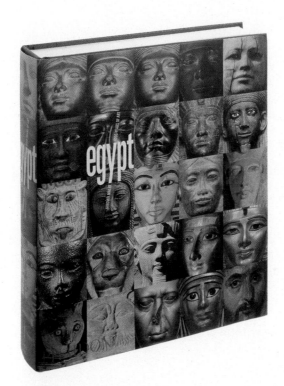

- A self-contained and accessible introduction to the history of Egyptian art written by a authority on the subject
- Presents a carefully chosen sequence of masterpieces ranging in date from c.4000 BC to c.200 AD
- All media are represented, from monumental architecture to exquisite jewellery and personal ornaments
- The introduction, captions, chronological chart, map, glossary and index provide the essential background for understanding why Egyptian art and architecture took the forms they did

Jaromir Malek is Keeper of the Archive at the Griffith Institute, Ashmolean Museum, Oxford. His books include *Egyptian Art* (1999), published in Phaidon's Art & Ideas series

General
Non-Fiction

Art
Art & Ideas

Photography

Collector's
Editions

Film

Architecture

Art & Ideas

'Art & Ideas has broken new ground in making accessible authoritative views on periods, movements and concepts in art. As a series it represents a real advance in publishing.' Sir Nicholas Serota, Director, Tate

'This is an invaluable series of introductory texts – accessible, authoritative and vividly illustrated.' Mark Haworth-Booth, Curator of Photographs, Victoria & Albert Museum

'The format is wonderful and offers what had long been missing in academic studies: usable manuals for specific themes or periods … I am definitely not alone in welcoming Art & Ideas as a precious set of teaching tools.' Joachim Pissarro, Yale University

'Inexpensive, well-produced and well-constructed art historical texts … writings here are erudite, informative, current and not at all pretentious or abstruse. Recent art historical methodologies are incorporated, especially in broadening the historical, literary and social context beyond the art itself, but never losing sight of the objects in question.' Art Libraries Journal

Each title:
• A comprehensive publishing program of up-to-date, authoritative, enjoyable and thought-provoking books on every aspect of the history of art around the world
• Place the art and architecture firmly in the context of the culture and ideas in which they were created
• Written by internationally respected scholars
• Enjoyable to read and free from jargon
• Ideal for students and anyone curious about art
• With glossaries, biographies and comparative chronologies

220 × 160 mm
8³⁄₄ × 6¹⁄₄ inches
448 pp
240 col, 38 b&w illus.

Paperback
0 7148 3752 0

£ **14.95** UK
$ **24.95** US
€ **24.95** EUR
$ **35.00** CAN
$ **39.95** AUS

Aboriginal Art

Howard Morphy

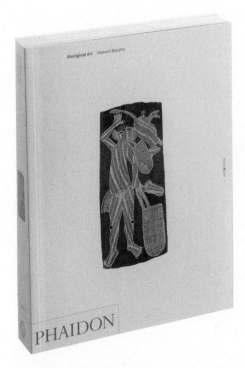

- A manifestation of the creative forces of Dreamtime, Australian Aborigines have been making art for thousands of years
- Surveys the great variety of Aboriginal art – paintings, sculptures, weapons and utensils – from across Australia, bringing out common themes but also highlighting regional diversity
- Many examples of Aboriginal art published here for the first time

Howard Morphy is Director of the Centre for Cross-Cultural Research at the Australian National University, Canberra

'This is a wonderful book by the pre-eminent scholar of Aboriginal art. For anyone who wants to know about Aboriginal art and the people who make it, this is the most important, indeed brilliant, book in 20 years.' (Fred Myers, Department of Anthropology, New York University)
'Howard Morphy's *Aboriginal Art* is far and away the best survey of this subject to have appeared to date.' (Luke Taylor, Senior Curator, National Museum of Australia)

General
Non-Fiction

Art
Art & Ideas

Photography

Collector's
Editions

Film

Architecture

220 × 160 mm
8³⁄₄ × 6¹⁄₄ inches
448 pp
217 col, 44 b&w illus.

Paperback
0 7148 3822 5

£ **14.95** UK
$ **24.95** US
€ **24.95** EUR
$ **35.00** CAN
$ **39.95** AUS

Art Nouveau

Stephen Escritt

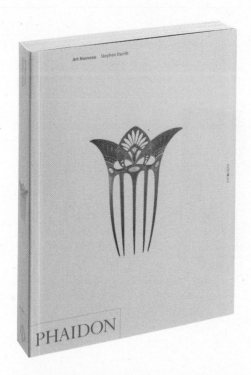

- The sinuous forms of Art Nouveau were the hallmark of Europe's and America's boldest and most fashionable style at the turn of the 19th century
- Art Nouveau brought a new decorative language to furniture, jewellery, graphic arts, architecture, sculpture and painting
- The first book to examine Art Nouveau worldwide in the context of the issues of the age, from the pressures of modern life to nationalism, spiritualism and the emancipation of women

Stephen Escritt, who was educated at Cambridge University, is a specialist in 19th- and 20th-century decorative arts. He is co-author of *Art Deco Style*, also published by Phaidon

'Escritt … travels with easy assurance from Western Europe to Scandinavia and on to Russia and America, incorporating new research material along the way. His training as a historian is evident in the passages of social history which illuminate the text.' *(Crafts)*
'Lucid and concise … well organized and well written.' *(Times Literary Supplement)*

Design

Fashion &
Contemporary
Culture

Decorative Arts

Music &
Performing Arts

Video

Index

220 × 160 mm
8³⁄₄ × 6¹⁄₄ inches
352 pp
152 col, 48 b&w illus.

Paperback
0 7148 3974 4

£ **12.95** UK
$ **19.95** US
€ **22.95** EUR
$ **29.95** CAN
$ **35.00** AUS

Bosch

Laurinda Dixon

- One of the most intriguing and enigmatic figures of art history, Hieronymus Bosch (c.1450–1516) is known as the creator of disturbing demons and spectacular hellscapes
- Adopted by the Surrealists as their predecessor, who saw his work as the imagery of dream, fantasy and the subconscious
- Illustrates all the signed and attributed works
- Author draws on popular culture, religious texts and contemporary medicine, astrology, astronomy and chemistry to investigate the meaning of Bosch's art

Laurinda Dixon is Professor of Art History at Syracuse University, New York. Her books include *Alchemical Imagery in Bosch's 'Garden of Delights'* and *Perilous Chastity: Women and Illness in Pre-Enlightenment Art and Medicine*

General
Non-Fiction

Art
Art & Ideas

Photography

Collector's
Editions

Film

Architecture

220 × 160 mm
8³⁄₄ × 6¹⁄₄ inches
352 pp
193 col, 13 b&w illus.

Paperback
0 7148 3515 3

£ **12.95** UK
$ **19.95** US
€ **22.95** EUR
$ **29.95** CAN
$ **35.00** AUS

Cézanne

Mary Tompkins Lewis

- With his distinctive paintings of landscapes, figures, nudes and still lifes, Paul Cézanne (1839–1906) profoundly influenced the Cubists and 20th-century art
- The first study to bring biographical, formal and larger contextual approaches to bear on his whole career
- Author argues that his legacy can be fully understood only in the context of the social and historical circumstances of France in conjunction with the regional tensions of his native Provence

Mary Tompkins Lewis teaches art history at Trinity College, Hartford, Connecticut.
Her publications include *Cézanne's Early Imagery*

'Lewis takes the mandate to address the general reader as an occasion to frame Cezanne's life in the kind of broad terms that will be of interest to the most sophisticated reader … She deals with tricky questions of interpretation while never losing track of the ultimate autonomy of the work.' (Jed Perl, *New Republic*)

Design

Fashion & Contemporary Culture

Decorative Arts

Music & Performing Arts

Video

Index

220 × 160 mm
8³⁄₄ × 6¹⁄₄ inches
352 pp
181 col, 47 b&w illus.

Paperback
0 7148 3160 3

£ **12.95** UK
$ **19.95** US
€ **22.95** EUR
$ **29.95** CAN
$ **35.00** AUS

Chagall

Monica Bohm-Duchen

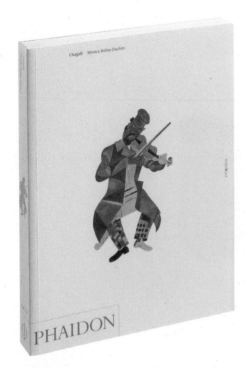

- A lively and comprehensive examination of the prodigious output of Marc Chagall (1887–1985), not only in painting but also book illustration, theatre design, stained glass and poetry
- The first survey of Chagall's work to take full advantage of new material available to the West since *glasnost*
- Follows Chagall from his Russian–Jewish childhood, through his encounter with the Parisian avant-garde and his activities in revolutionary Russia, to his later years in America and the South of France

Monica Bohm-Duchen is the author of *Understanding Modern Art* and was a contributor to the catalogue of *Chagall: Love and the Stage* (Royal Academy of Arts, London, 1998)

'Immediately becomes the most useful introduction to Chagall.' *(Independent on Sunday)*
'This book is the most even-handed to date in dealing with the later work.' *(Burlington Magazine)*

General
Non-Fiction

Art
Art & Ideas

Photography

Collector's
Editions

Film

Architecture

220 × 160 mm
8³⁄₄ × 6¹⁄₄ inches
448 pp
171 col, 85 b&w illus.

Paperback
0 7148 3388 6

£ **14.95** UK
$ **24.95** US
€ **24.95** EUR
$ **35.00** CAN
$ **39.95** AUS

Conceptual Art

Tony Godfrey

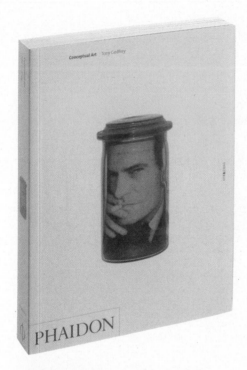

- A clear and engaging account of art where the idea behind the work is as important, if not more, than its physical existence
- The first truly international account of Conceptual art, considering works from as far afield as Japan and Argentina, as well as the more well-known locations of Europe and America
- Covers the many forms of Conceptual art: photographs, videos, posters, billboards, charts, plans and even language itself
- Traces its origins to the anti-art gestures of Dada, as well as considering how artists have continued to adapt Conceptual strategies up to the present day

Tony Godfrey is Programme Director of the MA in Contemporary Art at Sotheby's Institute, London

'Tony Godfrey's book is the intelligent, well argued, comprehensive and beautifully presented survey of Conceptual art we have been waiting on for years ... [It is] both accessible and easily readable while at the same time conceding little intellectual high ground ... This is that rare thing – an indispensable classic that is a must for anyone interested in understanding the roots of contemporary art.' *(Contemporary Visual Arts)*

Design

Fashion & Contemporary Culture

Decorative Arts

Music & Performing Arts

Video

Index

220 × 160 mm
8³⁄₄ × 6¹⁄₄ inches
352 pp
159 col, 56 b&w illus.

Paperback
0 7148 3180 8

£ **12.95** UK
$ **19.95** US
€ **22.95** EUR
$ **29.95** CAN
$ **35.00** AUS

Courbet

James H Rubin

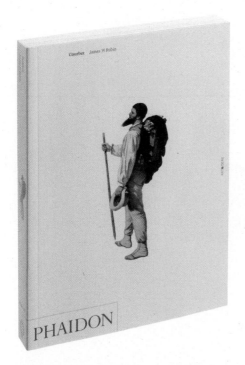

- Gustave Courbet's (1819–77) unconventional paintings of real people in everyday scenes came to embody values with radical implication
- Addresses the entire range of his work, including landscapes, portraits and erotic nudes
- Combines a clear reading of the paintings with a discussion of the personal, political and social framework in which they were created
- Written by an acknowledged scholar of 19th-century French art

James Rubin is Professor of Art History at Stony Brook, State University of New York, and also teaches at The Cooper Union in New York City. His books include *Impressionism, Realism and Social Vision in Courbet and Proudhon* and *Manet's Silence and the Poetics of Bouquets*, and, in the Art & Ideas series, *Impressionism*

'An eloquent and intelligent account of Courbet's work. Rubin manages to find a level which makes the book relevant to present scholarship on Courbet, but also eminently accessible to undergraduate students.' (John Kear, Department of the History and Theory of Art, University of Kent at Canterbury)

General
Non-Fiction

Art
Art & Ideas

Photography

Collector's
Editions

Film

Architecture

220 × 160 mm
8³⁄₄ × 6¹⁄₄ inches
448 pp
189 col, 67 b&w illus.

Paperback
0 7148 4010 6

£ **14.95** UK
$ **24.95** US
€ **24.95** EUR
$ **35.00** CAN
$ **39.95** AUS

Cubism

Neil Cox

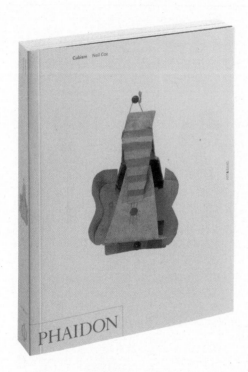

- An up-to-date, engaging survey of the most important revolution in early 20th-century art
- Examines the work of Braque and Picasso, how their invention became an avant-garde movement and spread through the work of the artists who followed them
- Emphasizes the historical background to Cubism, on a local as well as national and international scale
- Guides the reader through the complex strands of thought about Cubist art and the numerous areas of debate about Cubism

Neil Cox is Senior Lecturer in the Department of Art History and Theory at the University of Essex and has taught at the University of California at Berkeley. He is co-author of *A Picasso Bestiary* and *Marcel Duchamp*

'This comprehensive survey is a judicious and accessible account of Cubism and the remarkable imaginative possibilities contained within it … Cox offers a thoughtful and even-handed commentary on critical debate … The full range of Cubist activity is described, with analysis of international developments … exemplifying Cubism's capacity for transformation and reinvention.' (Sophie Bowness, *Burlington Magazine*)

Design

Fashion & Contemporary Culture

Decorative Arts

Music & Performing Arts

Video

Index

220 × 160 mm
8³₄ × 6¹₄ inches
448 pp
183 col, 48 b&w illus.

Paperback
0 7148 3261 8

£ **14.95** UK
$ **24.95** US
€ **24.95** EUR
$ **35.00** CAN
$ **39.95** AUS

Dada & Surrealism

Matthew Gale

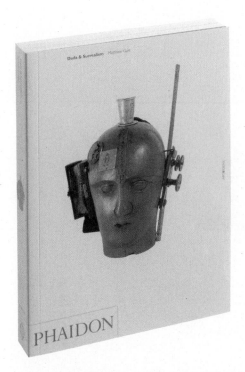

- A stimulating introduction to this movement in 20th-century art that emerged from the disillusionment and questioning of accepted values
- Explores the work of a wide range of artists, from Marcel Duchamp and Raoul Hausmann to Max Ernst, René Magritte and Salvador Dalí
- Uses paintings, collages, sculptures, assemblages, photographs, photomontages, film stills and graphics to illustrate the rich variety of Dada and Surrealist art
- The first book to illustrate many of these works in colour

Matthew Gale, a specialist in 20th-century art, is a curator at the Tate, London

'Anyone who wants to get their bearings in Duchamp and Dalí's worlds should read Matthew Gale's *Dada & Surrealism*. Gale provides an extremely clear, up-to-date and thorough account of all the movements' different strands around the world … Should become the standard general survey.' *(Independent)*

'Gale brilliantly manages the challenge of delivering a huge wealth of facts on events, groups and a great number of players, while never losing sight of the big picture. It will remain a must on lists of assigned readings for years to come.' (Joachim Pissarro, Yale University)

General
Non-Fiction

Art
Art & Ideas

Photography

Collector's
Editions

Film

Architecture

220 × 160 mm
8³⁄₄ × 6¹⁄₄ inches
352 pp
146 col, 61 b&w illus.

Paperback
0 7148 3411 4

£ **12.95** UK
$ **19.95** US
€ **22.95** EUR
$ **29.95** CAN
$ **35.00** AUS

Dalí

Robert Radford

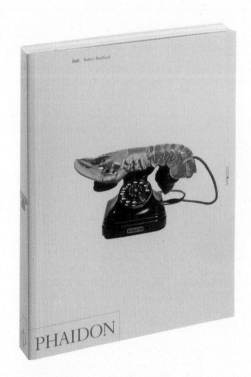

- Re-evaluates the work of Salvador Dalí (1904–89), one of the best-known and most visually influential artists of the 20th century
- Gives proper recognition not only to Dalí the painter but also to the writer, film-maker, illustrator, object-maker, jewellery designer, myth-maker and performance artist
- Sets the artist's complex personality and varied work against the background of ideological and political conflict that erupted in the Spanish Civil War and World War II

Robert Radford is well known as a lecturer, writer and exhibition curator, and taught art history for many years at Winchester School of Art, University of Southampton

'This book condenses Dalí's career into a highly readable narrative, with a judicious mixture of historical and biographical facts, entertaining autobiographical detail and critical comment on the artist's creative output.' (Roger Cardinal, School of Drama, Film and Visual Arts, University of Kent at Canterbury)

Design

Fashion & Contemporary Culture

Decorative Arts

Music & Performing Arts

Video

Index

220 × 160 mm
8³⁄₄ × 6¹⁄₄ inches
352 pp
167 col, 38 b&w illus.

Paperback
0 7148 3804 7

£ **12.95** UK
$ **19.95** US
€ **22.95** EUR
$ **29.95** CAN
$ **35.00** AUS

David

Simon Lee

- **Argues that Jacques-Louis David (1748–1825), participant in and chronicler of the French Revolution and painter to Napoleon, was the single most important painter of the age**
- **The first book to trace all aspects of David's career, from his intellectual interests to his entrepreneurial skills and his relationships with patrons**
- **Sets the artist in the context of Bourbon, Revolutionary, Napoleonic and Restoration France and discusses all the current scholarly debates about David**

Simon Lee is Senior Lecturer in the History of Art at the University of Reading

'Appropriate to its subject, this up-to-date overview of David is a seamless fusion of art and history. Filled with unfamiliar facts, observations and corollary images, it rejuvenates the father of modern French painting within the drama of Revolution, Empire and Restoration.' (Robert Rosenblum, Department of Fine Arts, New York University)

General
Non-Fiction

Art
Art & Ideas

Photography

Collector's
Editions

Film

Architecture

220 × 160 mm
8³⁄₄ × 6¹⁄₄ inches
448 pp
223 col, 46 b&w illus.

Paperback
0 7148 3168 9

£ **14.95** UK
$ **24.95** US
€ **24.95** EUR
$ **35.00** CAN
$ **39.95** AUS

Early Christian & Byzantine Art

John Lowden

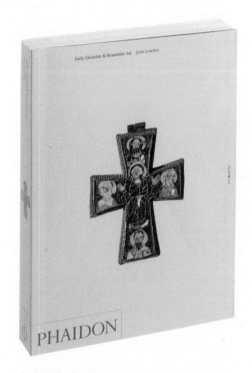

- Explains how and why Early Christian and Byzantine art was made and used from the 3rd century AD to the fall of Constantinople in 1453
- Situates the art within the controversies of its time
- Discusses the artists who invented and defined the Christian tradition in visual representation that dominated European art until recent times

John Lowden is Professor of the History of Art at the Courtauld Institute of Art, University of London

'One could not praise too highly its lucidity and balance. If it were a novel, one would even speak of its un-put-downability.' (Sister Wendy Beckett)
'Authoritative, clearly written and up-to-date.' (W Eugene Kleinbauer, Indiana University, Bloomington)
'The best short study in English. Compact in style and beautiful to look at, this is a likeable as well as a learned book.' *(Catholic Herald)*

Design

Fashion & Contemporary Culture

Decorative Arts

Music & Performing Arts

Video

Index

220 × 160 mm
8³⁄₄ × 6¹⁄₄ inches
448 pp
255 col, 17 b&w illus.

Paperback
0 7148 3627 3

£ **14.95** UK
$ **24.95** US
€ **24.95** EUR
$ **35.00** CAN
$ **39.95** AUS

Egyptian Art

Jaromir Malek

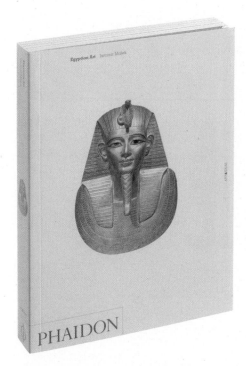

- Deftly traces Egyptian art from its prehistoric origins through three thousand years of astonishing achievements in the era of the pharaohs to the conquest of Egypt by the Romans
- Outlines artistic trends in each period, linking them to economic, political and spiritual developments
- Discusses the full range of artistic output: monumental architecture, sculpture, wall-reliefs, paintings, furniture, jewellery, papyri and pottery

Jaromir Malek is Keeper of the Archive at the Griffith Institute, Ashmolean Museum, Oxford. His books include *In the Shadow of the Pyramids: Egypt during the Old Kingdom* and *Egypt: 4000 Years of Art*, also published by Phaidon

'Dr Malek's intimate knowledge of Egyptian culture and history informs his approach to art. A fascinating survey of how Egypt's own history influenced its art forms and genres over three thousand years.' (Betsy Bryan, Department of Near Eastern Studies, Johns Hopkins University, Baltimore)

'Useful for students, scholars and others ... Provides an excellent, readable and very fresh survey of Egyptian art in context.' (Denis M Doxey, Museum of Fine Arts, Boston, *Religious Studies Review*)

220 × 160 mm
8³⁄₄ × 6¹⁄₄ inches
448 pp
223 col, 38 b&w illus.

Paperback
0 7148 3480 7

£ **14.95** UK
$ **24.95** US
€ **24.95** EUR
$ **35.00** CAN
$ **39.95** AUS

The Gothic Revival

Chris Brooks

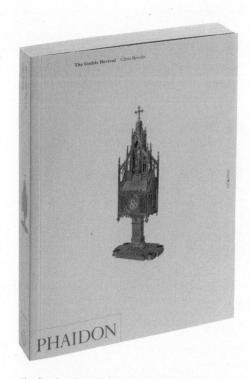

- The first book to deal comprehensively with the whole scope of the Gothic Revival
- Reveals the layers of meaning that Gothic held for its many reinventors
- Examines why Gothic became a dominant cultural and architectural force not only in 19th-century Britain but across Europe, in the United States and in the countries of the British Empire
- Discusses poetry and fiction, painting and sculpture, movies and video games, Gothic music and Gothic punk as well as buildings

Chris Brooks was Professor of Victorian Culture at Exeter University and served as Chairman of the Victorian Society

'This breathtaking and stimulating survey … offers, in one grand, sweeping narrative, an entirely new interpretation, at a stroke advancing a field that has been stagnant too long.' (*Burlington Magazine*)
'Anyone involved in studying or teaching 18th- or 19th-century British culture should read this book.' (Tim Barringer, Yale University, *Journal of Design History*)
'This is the most complete study available, and Brooks is a confident and reliable guide.' (*Independent*)

Design

Fashion & Contemporary Culture

Decorative Arts

Music & Performing Arts

Video

Index

220 × 160 mm
8¾ × 6¼ inches
352 pp
186 col, 27 b&w illus.

Paperback
0 7148 3751 2

£ **12.95** UK
$ **19.95** US
€ **22.95** EUR
$ **29.95** CAN
$ **35.00** AUS

Goya

Sarah Symmons

- Places Francisco Goya (1746–1828) within the context of his Spanish heritage and traces the immense influence of his work throughout Europe
- Written by an international authority on Spanish art of the Romantic period
- Covers the full range of Goya's pictorial expression: oil and fresco paintings, drawings, tapestry designs and prints

Sarah Symmons is Senior Lecturer in the Department of Art History and Theory at the University of Essex

'Sarah Symmons has done a deft job contextualizing Goya.' *(Independent)*
'Symmons gathers together the most up-to-date information on the artist (much published in English for the first time) and uses her deep understanding of Spanish institutions and Goya's contemporaries to illuminate the trajectory of his career.' *(The Art Book)*

General
Non-Fiction

Art
Art & Ideas

Photography

Collector's
Editions

Film

Architecture

220 × 160 mm
8³⁄₄ × 6¹⁄₄ inches
448 pp
216 col, 36 b&w illus.

Paperback
0 7148 3368 1

£ **14.95** UK
$ **24.95** US
€ **24.95** EUR
$ **35.00** CAN
$ **39.95** AUS

Greek Art

Nigel Spivey

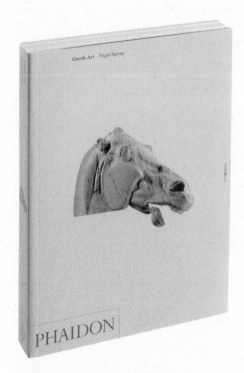

- Considers how Greek art was inextricably bound up with the political, religious, philosophical and social circumstances of the period
- Draws on the author's first-hand experience of Greek archaeological sites
- Covers the full range of Greek art – sculpture, pottery, architecture, metalwork and wall-paintings – from the 8th to the 2nd century BC

Nigel Spivey lectures in classical archaeology at Cambridge University, where he is a fellow of Emmanuel College. He is the author of *Understanding Greek Sculpture* and *Etruscan Art*

'Spivey is a fine writer, knowledgeable [and] independent in his views … he has interesting things to say about Greek myth and Greek history, the relations among art, drama and visual imagery, and about the influential Greek artistic legacy.' (Richard Brilliant, Columbia University, *Choice*)

'An intelligent, well-written account of Greek culture.' (John Boardman, *Anglo-Hellenic Review*)

220 × 160 mm
8³⁴ × 6¹⁴ inches
352 pp
104 col, 117 b&w illus.

Paperback
0 7148 3818 7

£ **12.95** UK
$ **19.95** US
€ **22.95** EUR
$ **29.95** CAN
$ **35.00** AUS

Hogarth

Mark Hallett

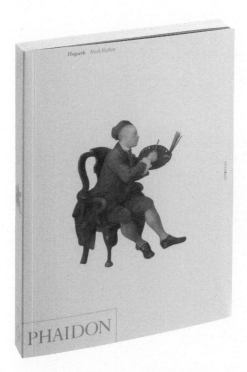

- A uniquely versatile artist, William Hogarth (1697–1764) commented brilliantly on society by simultaneously identifying the benefits of commerce and corruption
- Argues that his art and career can only be properly understood in relation to the particular environment of 18th-century London
- Demonstrates the versatility of Hogarth's repertoire, which ranged from society portraits to nightmare visions of London's lowest classes

Mark Hallett is a lecturer in art history at the University of York and the author of *The Spectacle of Difference: Graphic Satire in the Age of Hogarth*

'Sets Hogarth's art and career firmly in the political and social context of his period, and carefully explores the contradictions between his subversive eye for society's underbelly and his calculating eye for the commercial opportunities offered by its overbelly ... The descriptions of individual paintings ... unravel complexities which are key to understanding this often over-simplified and underrated master.' (John Spurling, *RA*, the magazine of the Royal Academy of Arts)

General Non-Fiction

Art Art & Ideas

Photography

Collector's Editions

Film

Architecture

220 × 160 mm
8³⁴ × 6¹⁴ inches
448 pp
239 col, 31 b&w illus.

Paperback
0 7148 3826 8

£ **14.95** UK
$ **24.95** US
€ **24.95** EUR
$ **35.00** CAN
$ **39.95** AUS

Impressionism

James H Rubin

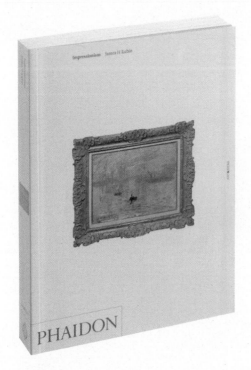

- Brings together the most recent research on the most popular and accessible of all art movements
- Strikes a balance between a chronological narrative and the exploration of the work of individual artists
- Makes accessible the philosophical, political and social background to Impressionism
- As well as the acknowledged masters, includes lesser-known but important Impressionists such as Berthe Morisot, Mary Cassatt and Gustave Caillebotte

James Rubin is Professor of Art History at Stony Brook, State University of New York, and also teaches at The Cooper Union in New York City. His books include *Impressionism*, *Realism and Social Vision in Courbet and Proudhon* and *Manet's Silence and the Poetics of Bouquets*, and, in the Art & Ideas series, *Courbet*

'There is nothing like James Rubin's *Impressionism*… no other existing book covers all its aspects from so many diverse angles, in such a readable fashion… as a potential college course textbook, this one beats the rest.' (Carol Armstrong, Department of Art History, Princeton University)
'A superbly insightful book that provides an original and much needed synthesis of years of Impressionist scholarship.' (Nina Kallmyer, Professor of Art History, University of Delaware)

Design

Fashion &
Contemporary
Culture

Decorative Arts

Music &
Performing Arts

Video

Index

220 × 160 mm
8³⁄₄ × 6¹⁄₄ inches
448 pp
250 col, 27 b&w illus.

Paperback
0 7148 3496 3

£ **14.95** UK
$ **24.95** US
€ **24.95** EUR
$ **35.00** CAN
$ **39.95** AUS

Indian Art

Vidya Dehejia

- The only full and up-to-date history of the subcontinent's artistic heritage
- Covers the whole range of Indian art across 4,500 years, from the great cities of the early Indus civilization to the art of the British Raj and of the late 20th century
- Considers the meaning of the word 'art' in the Indian cultural milieu, the relationship between art and the subcontinent's religious traditions, the status of artists and the impact of trade and travel on artistic development
- Written by a leading authority on the subject

Vidya Dehejia is Barbara Stoler Miller Professor of Indian Art at Columbia University in New York. Her publications include *Discourse in Early Buddhist Art: Visual Narratives of India*

'This is certainly the best book covering the full history of Indian Art. It is accessible but at the same time raises important issues and has the distinct advantage of comprehensive coverage.' (Frederick Asher, Department of Art History, University of Minnesota)
'Beautifully illustrated, delightfully written and well suited to those approaching Indian art for the first time.' *(Times Higher Education Supplement)*
'Surely the most evenly balanced survey of Indian art yet to appear.' (George Michell, *South Asian Studies)*

General Non-Fiction

Art Art & Ideas

Photography

Collector's Editions

Film

Architecture

220 × 160 mm
8³⁄₄ × 6¹⁄₄ inches
448 pp
193 col, 35 b&w illus.

Paperback
0 7148 3176 X

£ **14.95** UK
$ **24.95** US
€ **24.95** EUR
$ **35.00** CAN
$ **39.95** AUS

Islamic Arts

Jonathan Bloom and Sheila Blair

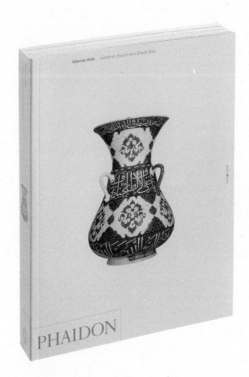

- A comprehensive survey covering the period 600–1800 and countries as far apart as Spain and India
- Highlights the characteristics that connect the various arts of all the Islamic lands without minimizing the differences
- Captures the essence of Islamic culture as expressed in its buildings, books and applied arts
- Written by two of the world's leading experts in the field

Jonathan Bloom and **Sheila Blair**, a husband-and-wife team of scholars, hold the Calderwood University Professorship in Islamic and Asian Art at Boston College. They are joint authors of *The Art and Architecture of Islam: 1250–1800*

'Will revive the wanderlust, even of those who have "been everywhere, seen everything".'
(New York Times Book Review)
'This is a wonderful new contribution – it reflects current scholarship in a way easy to read and demystifies Islamic art.' (Catherine Asher, Department of Art History, University of Minnesota)
'Islamic Arts is a visual as well as an intellectual treat, a successful collaboration of the best contemporary authors and the best contemporary design.' (Walter B Denny, Department of Art History, University of Massachusetts at Amherst)

Design

Fashion & Contemporary Culture

Decorative Arts

Music & Performing Arts

Video

Index

220 × 160 mm
8³⁄₄ × 6¹⁄₄ inches
352 pp
185 col, 20 b&w illus.

Paperback
0 7148 3483 1

£ **12.95** UK
$ **19.95** US
€ **22.95** EUR
$ **29.95** CAN
$ **35.00** AUS

Michelangelo

Anthony Hughes

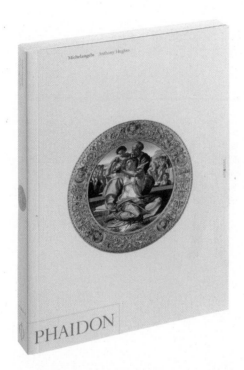

- Covers all the artistic output of Michelangelo (1475–1564), one of the greatest masters of the Renaissance and a legend in his own lifetime
- Interprets the works not only as the expressions of an individual sensibility but also as the results of often difficult transactions between artist and clients
- Employs the latest evidence from research and restoration projects
- Explores the artist's relations with family and friends, his sexuality and his position in the 16th-century world

Anthony Hughes was formerly Senior Lecturer in the History of Art at the University of Leeds

'It would be difficult to imagine a better introduction to the man and his work than this.' (Bruce Boucher, Department of the History of Art, University College London)
'An excellent, single volume introduction to Michelangelo that successfully integrates history and social context with sensitive analysis of the master's art.' (William E Wallace, Professor of Art History, Washington University, St Louis)

General
Non-Fiction

Art
Art & Ideas

Photography

Collector's
Editions

Film

Architecture

220 × 160 mm
8³⁄₄ × 6¹⁄₄ inches
352 pp
160 col, 50 b&w illus.

Paperback
0 7148 3500 5

£ 12.95 UK
$ 19.95 US
€ 22.95 EUR
$ 29.95 CAN
$ 35.00 AUS

Monet

Carla Rachman

- An accessible and engaging introduction to the life and work of Claude Monet (1840–1926), a leading member of the Impressionist movement
- Analyses the development of the artist's work in the light of both a changing art world and market, and the social and political context of his time
- Traces critical reaction to Monet's work from the early years to the present

Carla Rachman has lectured on 19th-century art at both the University of London and Boston University's London campus

'The painter is portrayed against the background of his own times; he is shown to be an entrepreneurial figure armed with a marketing strategy and a shrewd notion of the value of his own work … Rachman presents a fresh overview of the artist and his works for contemporary readers.' *(The Art Book)*

Design

Fashion &
Contemporary
Culture

Decorative Arts

Music &
Performing Arts

Video

Index

220 × 160 mm
8³⁄₄ × 6¹⁄₄ inches
448 pp
160 col, 84 b&w illus.

Paperback
0 7148 3369 X

£ **14.95** UK
$ **24.95** US
€ **24.95** EUR
$ **35.00** CAN
$ **39.95** AUS

Neoclassicism

David Irwin

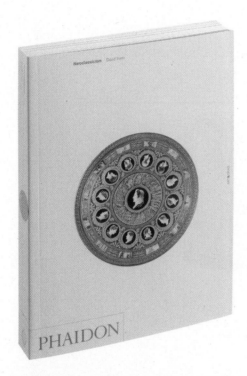

- The favourite style of Napoleon and Thomas Jefferson, Neoclassicism was the most pervasive style in the history of European art
- The first book to embrace all manifestations of the style, not only its broad territorial scope, but also its versatility in every branch of art
- Provides an insight into the richness and variety of one of the most fertile and dynamic styles in the history of art
- Covers the years 1750–1830 when the style was at its height but also shows how it has exerted an influence to the present day

David Irwin is Professor Emeritus of Art History at the University of Aberdeen

'A most elegant and sophisticated summary of a complex subject, based on the most recent research.' (David Watkin, Department of the History of Architecture, Cambridge University)
'The text is splendidly written, with enthusiasm as well as finely honed judgement …
the examples are well chosen and liable to provoke curiosity and further enquiry by students.
It is a great book.' (Michael McCarthy, University College, Dublin)

General
Non-Fiction

Art
Art & Ideas

Photography

Collector's
Editions

Film

Architecture

220 × 160 mm
8³⁄₄ × 6¹⁄₄ inches
352 pp
191 col, 6 b&w illus.

Paperback
0 7148 3852 7

£ **12.95** UK
$ **19.95** US
€ **22.95** EUR
$ **29.95** CAN
$ **35.00** AUS

Piero della Francesca

Marilyn Aronberg Lavin

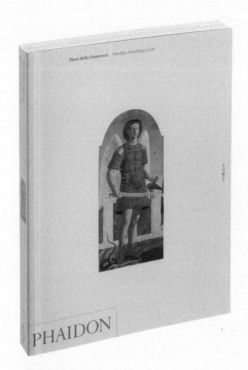

- The artist's artist Piero della Francesca (c.1413–92) is admired for the timeless, geometrical balance of his compositions
- A comprehensive survey that maps his achievement in the 15th century and his timeless appeal
- Sets the work within the political structures and religious beliefs and practices of the time as well as looking at Piero's patrons and the purposes of their commissions
- Detailed analyses of all of Piero's surviving works and consideration of his achievements as a mathematician
- Includes superlative new photography of recently cleaned frescos

Marilyn Aronberg Lavin, an outstanding authority on painting of the early Italian Renaissance, has taught at Princeton and Yale, and is a director of the Piero Project, a computer database on the artist

Design

Fashion &
Contemporary
Culture

Decorative Arts

Music &
Performing Arts

Video

Index

220 × 160 mm
8³⁄₄ × 6¹⁄₄ inches
352 pp
198 col, 9 b&w illus.

Paperback
0 7148 3857 8

£ **12.95** UK
$ **19.95** US
€ **22.95** EUR
$ **29.95** CAN
$ **35.00** AUS

Rembrandt

Mariët Westermann

- The most poignant and honest portrait painter of all time, Rembrandt van Rijn (1606–69) was Holland's most celebrated painter by the age of 26
- Reveals how he understood the artistic potential of Amsterdam, the leading city of the newly independent Dutch Republic and the centre of a global trade empire
- Based on the latest Rembrandt research, by one of the leading scholars of Netherlandish art
- Demonstrates how a contextual study can stimulate the reader's delight in the art itself
- Analyses why the artist has enduring appeal

Mariët Westermann is Director of the Institute of Fine Arts at New York University. She is the author of *The Art of the Dutch Republic 1585–1718* and *The Amusements of Jan Steen: Comic Painting in the Seventeenth Century*

'There is an engaging freshness in [Westermann's] approach to the subject. She is very well-informed about the general culture of the period and up-to-date in her scholarship … The book will appeal to a wide range of reader … And it is not excluded that a Rembrandt specialist might learn a thing or two. I did.' (Christopher White, *Historians of Netherlandish Art Newsletter*)
'Westermann's book has been widely anticipated as a text that could fulfil many roles – an assigned textbook …, an accessible introduction to the artist for lay people, and a quick refresher for art historians. The book … satisfies all these roles admirably.' (Catherine Scallen, Case Western Reserve University, *CAA Reviews Online*)

General Non-Fiction

Art Art & Ideas

Photography

Collector's Editions

Film

Architecture

220 × 160 mm
8³⁄₄ × 6¹⁄₄ inches
448 pp
248 col, 4 b&w illus.

Paperback
0 7148 3443 2

£ **14.95** UK
$ **24.95** US
€ **24.95** EUR
$ **35.00** CAN
$ **39.95** AUS

Romanticism

David Blayney Brown

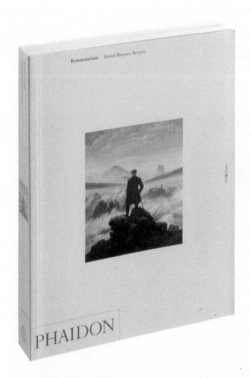

- Provides a clear understanding of a complex movement that in the period c.1775–1830 produced some of the greatest European art, literature and music
- Discusses how artists as diverse as Goya, Delacroix, Friedrich and Turner responded to landscapes or depicted historical events
- Examines artists such as David and Ingres who are not usually considered Romantics
- Takes a thematic approach to Romanticism, relating it to the concurrent more stylistic movements of Neoclassicism and the Gothic Revival

David Blayney Brown is a Senior Curator at Tate Britain, responsible for the Turner Bequest. He has written monographs on numerous artists of the Romantic era and is a frequent contributor to *Burlington Magazine* and *Master Drawings*

'A blessing to students approaching the subject for the first time … For those already familiar with the period, it will be a welcome addition to the critical literature.' (James Williams, Trinity College, Cambridge, *Art Newspaper)*
'By approaching this huge roaring beast of a subject thematically … [Brown] succeeds in partly taming it; though not to the extent of exhausting the mystery or cooling the passion which continues to energize it.' (John Spurling, *RA*, the magazine of the Royal Academy of Arts)
'One of the best studies of its kind at any price.' (Frank Whitford, *The Sunday Times*)

Design

Fashion & Contemporary Culture

Decorative Arts

Music & Performing Arts

Video

Index

220 × 160 mm
8¾ × 6¼ inches
352 pp
194 col, 24 b&w illus.

Paperback
0 7148 3412 2

£ **12.95** UK
$ **19.95** US
€ **22.95** EUR
$ **29.95** CAN
$ **35.00** AUS

Rubens

Kristin Lohse Belkin

- **Covers the whole career of Peter Paul Rubens (1577–1640), famous not only as an artist but also as a respected diplomat**
- **Pays particular attention to Rubens' relationship with and representation of women, and his preoccupation with peace, as diplomat and painter**
- **Explores Rubens' working methods and studio practices**
- **Draws on the artist's extensive correspondence**

Kristin Lohse Belkin has contributed to the *Corpus Rubinianum Ludwig Burchard*, a multi-volume catalogue of Rubens' complete works, and has written and lectured widely on Rubens and Flemish and German art

'Truly a wonderful, engaging and learned account, beautifully produced.' (Celeste Brusati, Department of Art History, University of Michigan)
'One of those rare texts that works splendidly for both the specialist and the novice. Belkin's logical, lucid presentation of information is exemplary.' (Susan Koslow, Department of Art History, City University of New York)
'Does a marvellous job of tracking the progress of Rubens' artistic, allegorical and iconographic content.' *(Art Libraries Journal)*

General Non-Fiction

Art Art & Ideas

Photography

Collector's Editions

Film

Architecture

220 × 160 mm
8¾ × 6¼ inches
352 pp
190 col, 8 b&w illus.

Paperback
0 7148 3988 4

£ **12.95** UK
$ **19.95** US
€ **22.95** EUR
$ **29.95** CAN
$ **35.00** AUS

Turner

Barry Venning

- Covers all aspects of the prolific career of J M W Turner (1775–1851), one of the most popular and influential British artists
- Features well-known works as well as those rarely reproduced
- Argues that only by looking at the work against the background of early 19th-century Britain can the painter's creative decisions be understood

Barry Venning is Associate Lecturer in Art History at the Open University. He has written and lectured extensively on Turner, and his articles have appeared in *Burlington Magazine*, *Art History* and *Turner Studies*

Design

Fashion & Contemporary Culture

Decorative Arts

Music & Performing Arts

Video

Index

220 × 160 mm
8³⁄₄ × 6¹⁄₄ inches
352 pp
185 col, 18 b&w illus.

Paperback
0 7148 4084 X

£ **12.95** UK
$ **19.95** US
€ **22.95** EUR
$ **29.95** CAN
$ **35.00** AUS

Van Gogh

Judy Sund

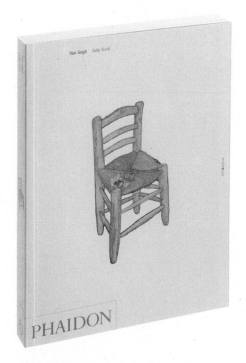

- **Spans the early work of Vincent van Gogh (1853–90) in the Netherlands, the formative years in and around Paris, and ends with the intense, vibrant studies of peasants and the countryside he produced in the South of France**
- **Makes extensive use of Van Gogh's own correspondence to illuminate his artistic development and the personal vision that lies behind his work**
- **Reveals the art as the product of a reflective and idea-driven man who was profoundly interested in and inspired by all manner of literary, musical and artistic sources**

Judy Sund teaches art history at Queens College and the Graduate Center, City University of New York. Her publications include *True to Temperament: Van Gogh and French Naturalist Literature* (1992)

General
Non-Fiction

Art
Gombrich

Photography

Collector's
Editions

Film

Architecture

E H Gombrich

'Gombrich has done more than any other human being to draw people towards an enlightened understanding of art … Wearing his immense learning lightly, tackling abstract ideas without losing his readers in jargon, he has attracted a devoted following.' *The Sunday Times*

'The great gift he gave us was to make the living process of art understandable to us all. Rather than a dry cultural history, he made looking at art – that perceptual experience – an adventure.'
Anthony Gormley, artist

'…did more than any other writer in the last 100 years to introduce a wider public to a love of art. Successive generations of students have been drawn to The Story of Art, his erudite survey of Western art, and his Big Idea:"There is no such thing as art – there are only artists." An academic who stayed firmly outside his profession's charmed circle, his book was intended as a rallying cry against snobbery and elitism, and has remained a classic.' *Antique Dealer and Collector's Guide*

'Ernst Gombrich was the most famous art historian in the world. His reputation was based less on a particular approach to the subject, or the master of a single period, than on the breadth of his interests and his skill at making the history of art interesting to a non-specialist public.' Charles Hope,
The Independent

Sir Ernst Gombrich was one of the greatest and least conventional art historians of his age, achieving fame and distinction in three separate spheres: as a scholar, as a popularizer of art and as a pioneer of the application of the psychology of perception to the study of art. His best-known book, *The Story of Art*, first published 50 years ago and now in its 16th edition, is one of the most influential books ever written about art.

Gombrich was born in Vienna in 1909 and died in London in November 2001. He came to London in 1936 to work at the Warburg Institute, where he eventually became Director from 1959 until his retirement in 1976. He won numerous international honours, including a knighthood, the Order of Merit and the Goethe, Hegel and Erasmus prizes. Gifted with a powerful mind and a prodigious memory, he was also an outstanding communicator, with a clear and forceful prose style. His works are models of good art-historical writing, and reflect his humanism and his deep and abiding concern with the standards and values of our cultural heritage.

Design

Fashion & Contemporary Culture

Decorative Arts

Music & Performing Arts

Video

Index

245 × 172 mm
9⅝ × 6¾ inches
688 pp
376 col, 64 b&w illus.
6 fold-outs

Paperback
0 7148 3247 2

£ **19.95** UK
$ **29.95** US
€ **35.00** EUR
$ **45.00** CAN
$ **59.95** AUS

Hardback
0 7148 3355 X

£ **29.95** UK
$ **49.95** US
€ **49.95** EUR
$ **75.00** CAN
$ **89.95** AUS

Point of Sale
Book tower available

The Story of Art

16th edition
E H Gombrich

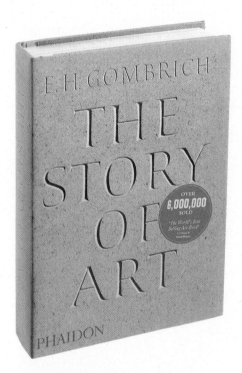

- One of the most famous and popular books on art ever written; has been a world bestseller for over five decades, translated into 34 languages
- Presents the history of art as a single unfolding narrative, 'a living chain that still links our own time with the Pyramid age'
- Owes its lasting popularity to the directness and simplicity of the writing, and to the author's skill in presenting a clear outline
- Combines profound knowledge and wisdom with a unique gift for communication

'Like every art historian of my generation, my way of thinking about pictures has been in large measure shaped by Ernst Gombrich.' (Neil MacGregor, former Director of the National Gallery, London, 1995)
'Almost as well known as the Mona Lisa, Sir Ernst Gombrich's *The Story of Art* unites learning and pleasure.' (Pierre Rosenberg, Président-Directeur, Musée du Louvre, Paris, 1995)
'More people … have been introduced to the world of fine art, in the last 45 years, through Ernst Gombrich's *The Story of Art* than through any other single book.' (Christopher Frayling, Professor of Cultural History, Royal College of Art, London, 1995)

General
Non-Fiction

Art
Gombrich

Photography

Collector's
Editions

Film

Architecture

245 × 172 mm
9⅝ × 6¾ inches
402 pp
7 col, 315 b&w illus.

Paperback
0 7148 4208 7

£ **14.95** UK
€ **24.95** EUR
$ **45.00** AUS

Not available
in the USA and Canada

Art and Illusion

A Study in the Psychology of Pictorial Representation
6th edition
E H Gombrich

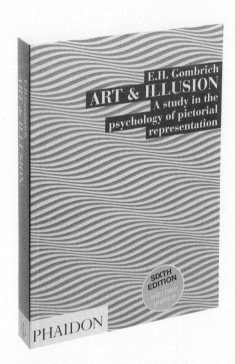

- **Ground-breaking and wide-ranging exploration of the history and psychology of pictorial representation, revealing that pictorial representation is far from being a straightforward matter**
- **Applies the findings of experimental science to the understanding of art, yet retains a sense of wonder at the subtle relationships involved in seeing the world and in making and seeing art**
- **The problems of representation are fundamental to the history of art, and *Art and Illusion* is a crucial text for anyone interested in understanding art**
- **One of the most influential books on art ever published**

'One of the most brilliant books of art criticism that I have ever read.' (Kenneth Clark)
'A classic synthesis of aesthetics, psychology and art history, which leads us on a fascinating intellectual enquiry.' *(Daily Telegraph)*
'This was a seminal book and remains an enjoyable unfolding of the mysteries of art.' *(The Times)*

Design

Fashion & Contemporary Culture

Decorative Arts

Music & Performing Arts

Video

Index

245 × 172 mm
9⅝ × 6¾ inches
624 pp
477 b&w illus.

Paperback
0 7148 3487 4

£ **19.95** UK
$ **29.95** US
€ **35.00** EUR
$ **45.00** CAN
$ **55.00** AUS

Hardback
0 7148 3009 7

£ **29.95** UK
$ **49.95** US
€ **49.95** EUR
$ **75.00** CAN
$ **85.00** AUS

The Essential Gombrich

Edited by Richard Woodfield

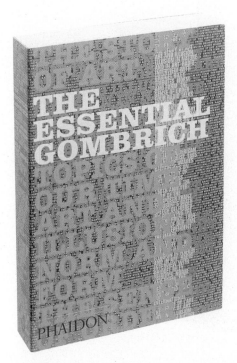

- Presents an accessible selection of Professor Gombrich's best and most characteristic writing, and introduces his ideas and arguments on many fundamental questions
- Includes selections from *The Story of Art, Art and Illusion* and *The Sense of Order,* plus key essays and reviews
- Makes an ideal introduction to the extraordinary range and depth of Gombrich's contribution to the study of art and culture

Richard Woodfield is Professor of Aesthetics and Art Theory at Nottingham Trent University, and the editor of *Reflections on the History of Art,* a collection of E H Gombrich's book reviews

'To read these essays is to feel in close touch with a rare and crucial thing, a large mind at full tilt, curious, ambitious and civilized.' *(New York Times)*

General
Non-Fiction

Art
Gombrich

Photography

Collector's
Editions

Film

Architecture

245 × 172 mm
9⅝ × 6¾ inches
264 pp
c.12 col, 230 b&w illus.

Hardback
0 7148 4154 4

£ **35.00** UK
$ **59.95** US
€ **59.95** EUR
$ **89.95** CAN
$ **120.00** AUS

The Preference for the Primitive

Episodes in the History of Western Taste and Art
E H Gombrich

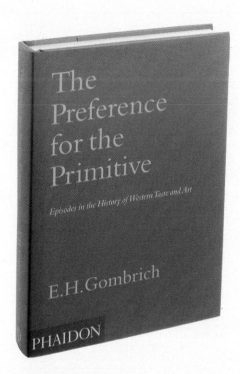

- Professor Gombrich's last book and first narrative book in over twenty years
- Studies the feeling that older and less sophisticated (i.e. 'primitive') works are somehow morally and aesthetically superior to later works that have become soft and decadent
- Takes a long view of the subject, finding the theme expressed in key documents in Classical Antiquity, resuming the debate in the 18th century, and culminating in an examination of the radical expressions of primitivism in modern times
- Summing up more than 40 years of study and reflection on this theme, the book presents a closely argued narrative supported by extensive quotations that document with precision the role of authors, critics and artists in shaping and changing opinion
- Important both as a personal testament and as a documentary anthology, this long-awaited book fittingly provides a deep and revealing insight into the history and psychology of taste

Design

Fashion &
Contemporary
Culture

Decorative Arts

Music &
Performing Arts

Video

Index

265 × 203 mm
10³⁄₈ × 8 inches
412 pp
11 col, 444 b&w illus.

Paperback
0 7148 2259 0

£ **19.95** UK
$ **29.95** US
€ **35.00** EUR
$ **45.00** CAN
$ **59.95** AUS

The Sense of Order

A Study in the Psychology of Decorative Art
E H Gombrich

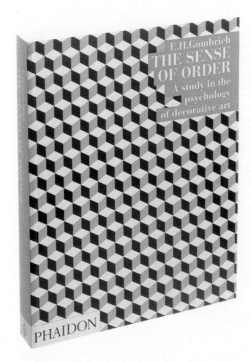

- A magisterial examination of the role of decoration in life and art, regarded by the author himself as his most original work
- Provides a comprehensive survey of the history and theory of decorative art
- Examines the universal human impulse to seek order and rhythm in space and time, as can be seen in children's play and in poetry, dance, music and architecture as well as art
- Frames an explanation of the impulse to order in terms of our biological heritage

'It would be hard to imagine a more intelligent discussion of the natural history of decoration and ornament.' (Jonathan Miller, *The Sunday Times*)

General Non-Fiction

Art Gombrich

Photography

Collector's Editions

Film

Architecture

245 × 172 mm
9⁵⁸ × 6³⁴ inches
256 pp
140 b&w illus.

Paperback
0 7148 3245 6

£ **14.95** UK
$ **24.95** US
€ **24.95** EUR
$ **39.95** CAN
$ **45.00** AUS

Meditations on a Hobby Horse

And Other Essays on the Theory of Art
E H Gombrich

- The first and most famous of Professor Gombrich's enormously influential volumes of collected essays, first published in 1963
- Contains 14 essays focusing on issues raised by 20th-century art and theory, and presenting many of Gombrich's most important statements on theory and method
- Taking abstraction and expression as their main themes, these essays encompass the whole of the history of art, including major articles on the social history of art, visual metaphor, tradition and expression, and psychoanalysis

'A worthy successor to the earlier books, exhibiting to a high degree their author's supreme merit as a theorist of art.' *(New Statesman)*

Design

Fashion & Contemporary Culture

Decorative Arts

Music & Performing Arts

Video

Index

245 × 172 mm
9⁵⁸ × 6³⁴ inches
224 pp
165 b&w illus.

Paperback
0 7148 2791 6

£ **14.95** UK
$ **24.95** US
€ **24.95** EUR
$ **39.95** CAN
$ **45.00** AUS

Topics of Our Time

20th-Century Issues in Learning and in Art
E H Gombrich

- A collection of hard-hitting, highly readable essays reflects Professor Gombrich's preoccupation with the central questions of value and tradition in our culture, and confronts some of the most urgent issues facing modern civilization
- Topics include radical proposals for the reform of higher education, an attack on relativism and a plea for the conservation of our cities, alongside thought-provoking studies of the work of Oskar Kokoschka, Abram Games, Saul Steinberg and Henri Cartier-Bresson

'The most stimulating series of essays published in many a year.' *(The Sunday Times)*

General
Non-Fiction

Art
Gombrich

Photography

Collector's
Editions

Film

Architecture

245 × 172 mm
9⅝ × 6¾ inches
304 pp
354 b&w illus.

Paperback
0 7148 3969 8

£ **14.95** UK
$ **24.95** US
€ **24.95** EUR
$ **35.00** CAN
$ **45.00** AUS

Hardback
0 7148 3655 9

£ **24.95** UK
$ **39.95** US
€ **39.95** EUR
$ **59.95** CAN
$ **69.95** AUS

The Uses of Images

Studies in the Social Function of Art and Visual Communication
E H Gombrich

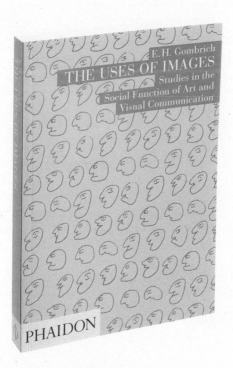

- This volume reflects Professor Gombrich's lifelong interest in the social dynamics that help to determine the course art takes
- It discusses the role of supply and demand, the 'ecology' of images, the idea of 'feedback' as developing skills in turn stimulate new demands, and the use (or misuse) of images as historical evidence
- These themes are exemplified in wide-ranging studies of both 'high' and 'low' art, from fresco painting, altar painting, the International Gothic Style and outdoor sculpture to doodles, pictorial instructions, caricature and political propaganda

Design
Fashion & Contemporary Culture
Decorative Arts
Music & Performing Arts
Video
Index

245 × 172 mm
9⅝ × 6¾ inches
320 pp
253 b&w illus.

Paperback
0 7148 3243 X

£ **14.95** UK
$ **24.95** US
€ **24.95** EUR
$ **39.95** CAN
$ **45.00** AUS

The Image and the Eye

Further Studies in the Psychology of Pictorial Representation
E H Gombrich

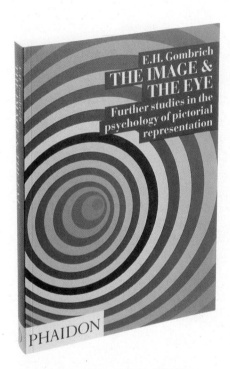

- A companion volume to *Art and Illusion*
- Provides an intriguing overview of art and our perception of it
- Discusses subjects as diverse as photography's tricks with perspective, the problems of expressing emotion through art and how pictorial representation affects the way in which we see the world

'A generous clarity of style and a quite breathtaking amplitude of reference. Gombrich's unique combination of wisdom and curiosity is exhilarating.' *(The Sunday Times)*

General Non-Fiction

Art Gombrich

Photography

Collector's Editions

Film

Architecture

245 × 172 mm
9⅝ × 6¾ inches
308 pp
186 b&w illus.

Paperback
0 7148 2380 5

£ **14.95** UK
$ **24.95** US
€ **24.95** EUR
$ **39.95** CAN
$ **45.00** AUS

Gombrich on the Renaissance Volume I

Norm and Form
E H Gombrich

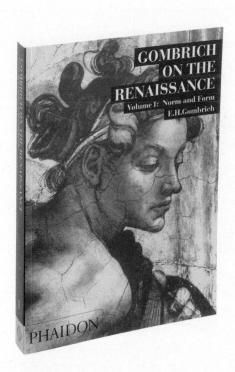

- The first in Gombrich's famous and highly influential series of essays on the Renaissance
- Essential reading for all students of Renaissance art
- Deals with fundamental questions of style, patronage, taste, working methods and theories of art
- Written with the author's customary learning and clarity of thought

'Professor Gombrich sees art history as illuminating our understanding of the world man has created for himself. In *Norm and Form* great learning is not disguised, but is made enthralling by good writing.' (Terence Mullaly, *Daily Telegraph*)

Design

Fashion & Contemporary Culture

Decorative Arts

Music & Performing Arts

Video

Index

245 × 172 mm
9⅝ × 6¾ inches
340 pp
170 b&w illus.

Paperback
0 7148 2381 3

£ **14.95** UK
$ **24.95** US
€ **24.95** EUR
$ **39.95** CAN
$ **45.00** AUS

Gombrich on the Renaissance Volume II

Symbolic Images
E H Gombrich

- Classic volume of essays on visual symbolism in the Renaissance
- Pioneering and influential critique of art-historical method that has helped to shape the evolving discipline of art history
- Combines rigorous analysis of theoretical issues with detailed studies of the great masters

'Perhaps it is Professor Gombrich's wealth of wit, brilliance, and common sense which so commends his writings.' *(Yale Review)*

General
Non-Fiction

Art
Gombrich

Photography

Collector's
Editions

Film

Architecture

245 × 172 mm
9⅝ × 6¾ inches
250 pp
4 col, 250 b&w illus.

Paperback
0 7148 2011 3

£ **14.95** UK
$ **24.95** US
€ **24.95** EUR
$ **39.95** CAN
$ **45.00** AUS

Gombrich on the Renaissance Volume III

The Heritage of Apelles
E H Gombrich

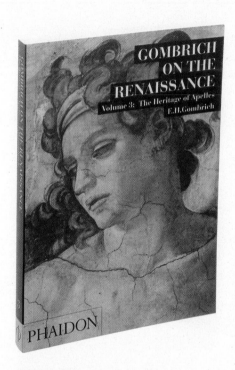

- The third volume in the series focuses on the classical tradition and the twin ideals of perfect beauty and the perfect imitation of nature
- Contains important and influential analyses of the survival and revival of classical techniques and ideas in the Renaissance
- Raises fundamental questions about the validity of standard, and values hat are still highly relevant

'Great learning is made enthralling by good writing.' *(Daily Telegraph)*

Design

Fashion & Contemporary Culture

Decorative Arts

Music & Performing Arts

Video

Index

245 × 172 mm
9⅝ × 6¾ inches
192 pp
6 col, 157 b&w illus.

Paperback
0 7148 2989 7

£ **14.95** UK
$ **24.95** US
€ **24.95** EUR
$ **39.95** CAN
$ **45.00** AUS

Gombrich on the Renaissance Volume IV

New Light on Old Masters
E H Gombrich

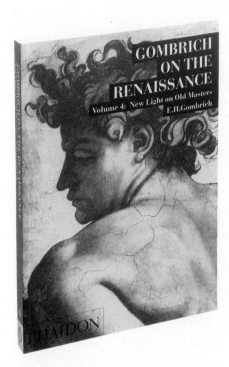

- The concluding volume of the series looks afresh at some of the greatest masters, including Giotto, Leonardo, Raphael and Michelangelo
- Original, lucid and undogmatic in their approach to methods, these essays are models of good art-historical writing
- As a series, *Gombrich on the Renaissance* represents a vitally important humanistic tradition in scholarship and criticism

General
Non-Fiction

Art
Gombrich

Photography

Collector's
Editions

Film

Architecture

245 × 172 mm
9⁵⁄₈ × 6³⁄₄ inches
224 pp
10 b&w illus.

Paperback
0 7148 3127 1

£ 14.95 UK
$ 24.95 US
€ 24.95 EUR
$ 39.95 CAN
$ 45.00 AUS

Ideals and Idols

Essays on Values in History and in Art
E H Gombrich

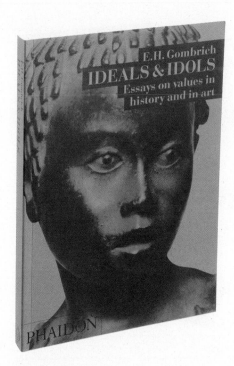

- An important collection of essays containing some of Professor Gombrich's most famous contributions to the discussion of values and their place in the humanities
- Ranges in subject from the philosophy of Hegel to wartime propaganda broadcasts, the future of museums and the role of reason and feeling in the study of art
- Includes one of Gombrich's most influential essays, 'In Search of Cultural History'
- In this volume Gombrich consistently argues for the ideals of tolerance and pluralism and against the idols of determinism and relativism that would threaten all culture

Design

Fashion & Contemporary Culture

Decorative Arts

Music & Performing Arts

Video

Index

245 × 172 mm
9⅝ × 6¾ inches
270 pp
75 b&w illus.

Hardback
0 7148 2338 4

£ **19.95** UK
$ **29.95** US
€ **35.00** EUR
$ **45.00** CAN
$ **59.95** AUS

Tributes

Interpreters of our Cultural Tradition
E H Gombrich

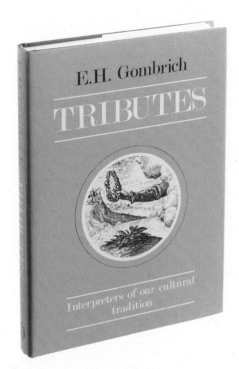

- **In this volume of essays, Professor Gombrich pays tribute to a variety of illustrious figures to whom we owe the ideas and values which are woven into the fabric of our intellectual life**
- **Includes studies of Lessing, Hegel and Freud, among others, in an attempt to exemplify the nature and value of branches of learning that are in danger of being squeezed out of higher education**

General Non-Fiction

Art Gombrich

Photography

Collector's Editions

Film

Architecture

245 × 172 mm
9⅝ × 6¾ inches
420 pp
28 col, 157 b&w illus.

Hardback
0 7148 2971 4

£ **39.95** UK
$ **59.95** US
€ **65.00** EUR
$ **89.95** CAN
$ **99.95** AUS

Sight and Insight

Essays on Art and Culture in Honour of E H Gombrich
Edited by John Onians

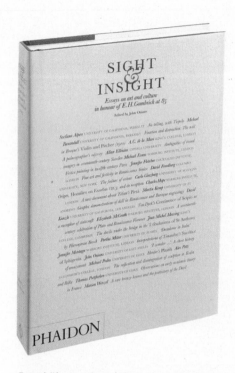

- *Festschrift* presented to Professor Gombrich to celebrate his 85th birthday in 1994
- Contributors to this collection of essays by former pupils of Gombrich include Svetlana Alpers, Michael Baxandall, David Freedberg, Martin Kemp and Michael Podro
- The essays, written in affectionate tribute to the master, reflect his influence in their wide range of subject matter and their robust individualism

John Onians is Professor and Director of the European Art Research Programme in the School of World Art Studies, University of East Anglia

'It would be hard to exaggerate the knowledge I have gained or the pleasure and stimulation I have received from studying this book.' *(Literary Review)*

Design

Fashion & Contemporary Culture

Decorative Arts

Music & Performing Arts

Video

Index

245 × 172 mm
9⁵⁄₈ × 6³⁄₄ inches
128 pp

Hardback
0 7148 3981 7

£ **25.00** UK
$ **40.00** US
€ **40.00** EUR
$ **60.00** CAN
$ **65.00** AUS

E H Gombrich: A Bibliography

J B Trapp

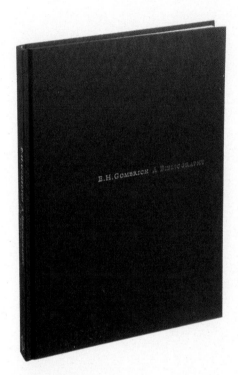

- A scholarly bibliography of all Professor Gombrich's writings, including full listings of translations and reprints
- Documents the remarkable range of Gombrich's publications over 70 years, from 1930 to 2000
- An invaluable tool for scholars, libraries and bibliophiles, and a tribute to one of the greatest scholars of the age

Professor **J B Trapp** succeeded Professor Gombrich as Director of the Warburg Institute and Professor of the History of the Classical Tradition in the University of London

245 × 210 mm
9⅝ × 8¼ inches
704 pp
343 b&w illus.

Hardback
0 7148 4244 3

£ **49.95** UK
$ **75.00** US
€ **75.00** EUR
$ **120.00** CAN
$ **150.00** AUS

Real Spaces

World Art History and the Rise of Western Modernism
David Summers

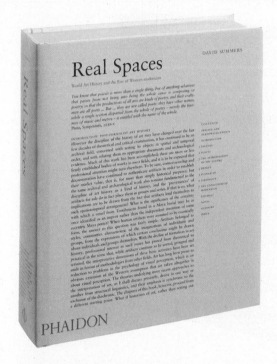

- Major new theoretical work that presents a fresh approach to thinking about art and its history
- Replaces the notion of the 'visual arts' with that of the 'spatial arts,' comprising two fundamental categories: 'real space' and 'virtual space'
- Traces the development of human skill from the first hominid tools to the sophisticated universal three-dimensional grid of modern technology, and presents new insights into the making of three-dimensional images and the development of 'virtual' images on plane surfaces
- Proposes an innovative, flexible conceptual framework for the analysis and understanding of all art – enabling us to treat all traditions on an equal footing and to understand opposition and conflict both within and between cultures

David Summers is the William R. Kenan Jr Professor of the History of Art at the University of Virginia. He is the author of two major studies, *Michelangelo and the Language of Art* (1981) and *The Judgment of Sense: Renaissance Naturalism and the Rise of Aesthetics* (1987)

Design

Fashion &
Contemporary
Culture

Decorative Arts

Music &
Performing Arts

Video

Index

David Summers is internationally recognized as one of the most distinguished historians of art and ideas of his generation, noted for his learning, originality and clear thinking. His book *The Judgment of Sense* won the Forkasch Prize from the *Journal of the History of Ideas* for the best book in intellectual history published in 1987. In 1996 he was elected to the American Academy of Arts and Sciences. Throughout his career Professor Summers has been preoccupied with what he sees as deep conceptual problems at the heart of Western thinking about art, and he argues that current approaches cannot provide the basis for a truly global and intercultural art history. He has devoted the years since 1987 to the research and thinking to provide an alternative, more inclusive framework within which all art can be approached on an equal footing. *Real Spaces* is the culmination of this ambitious project, and has long been eagerly anticipated in the scholarly community.

245 × 172 mm
9⅝ × 6⅞ inches
294 pp
15 col, 194 b&w illus.

Paperback
0 7148 2974 9

£ **14.95** UK
$ **19.95** US
€ **24.95** EUR
$ **29.95** CAN
$ **39.95** AUS

Classic Art

An Introduction to the Italian Renaissance
5th edition
Heinrich Wölfflin

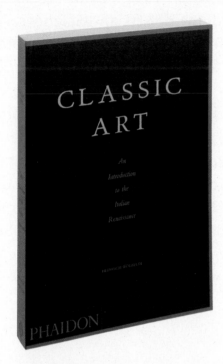

- First published in 1899, *Classic Art* is itself a classic introduction to the study of art
- It pioneered new and rigorous methods of formal analysis that are still relevant today
- Remains an excellent appraisal of the great Renaissance artists, among them da Vinci, Michelangelo, Raphael and del Sarto
- This Phaidon edition is reissued in its original elegant format with key works illustrated throughout

Heinrich **Wölfflin** was a Swiss art historian who developed new methods of interpreting art works that profoundly influenced generations of art scholars and critics. He succeeded his teacher Jacob Burckhardt in the Chair of Art History at the University of Basel and wrote extensively on Renaissance and Baroque art

'Wölfflin's *Classic Art* has done more than any other volume to promote an understanding of High Renaissance art.' (John Pope-Hennessy)

Design

Fashion & Contemporary Culture

Decorative Arts

Music & Performing Arts

Video

Index

234 × 156 mm
9¹⁄₈ × 6¹⁄₈ inches
384 pp
68 b&w illus.

Paperback
0 7148 2991 9

£ **14.95** UK
$ **19.95** US
€ **24.95** EUR
$ **29.95** CAN
$ **39.95** AUS

Art History and its Methods: A Critical Anthology

An Open University set book
Selection and commentary by Eric Fernie

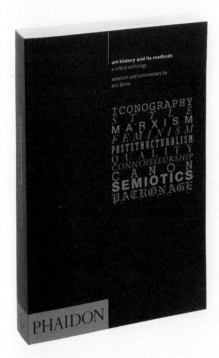

- A collection of critical essays on method in art history, culled from the works of significant art historians and writers
- Writings range from Renaissance-era Giorgio Vasari's biographical approach and Goethe's praise of Gothic style, to Erwin Panofsky's discussion of humanism and Griselda Pollock's present-day feminist analysis
- Author's introductory overview of approaches to art history, his comments preceding each essay and a glossary provide a substantial framework for the erudite writings
- An Open University set book

Eric Fernie was formerly Director of the Courtauld Institute, London

General
Non-Fiction

Art
Art History

Photography

Collector's
Editions

Film

Architecture

245 × 172 mm
9²₃ × 6⁷₈ inches
400 pp
110 col, 198 b&w illus.

Paperback
0 7148 2422 4

£ **14.95** UK
$ **19.95** US
€ **24.95** EUR
$ **29.95** CAN
$ **39.95** AUS

The Story of Modern Art

2nd edition
Norbert Lynton

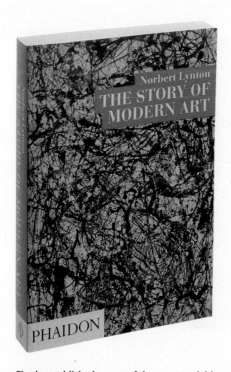

- Firmly established as one of the most readable and intelligent introductions to modern art
- Explores artwork of the 20th century, and examines the motives behind the main developments of the last 100 years
- Provides information and biographical details about some 200 artists, along with a wealth of illustrations
- Aims to help the reader form a relaxed and sympathetic relationship to art

Norbert Lynton is a distinguished art historian, lecturer, teacher and critic. From 1975 to 1989 he was Professor of the History of Art at the University of Sussex. He is the author of *Ben Nicholson*, also published by Phaidon

'Likely to stand as the best account of its period.' *(Art Review)*

Design

Fashion &
Contemporary
Culture

Decorative Arts

Music &
Performing Arts

Video

Index

234 × 156 mm
9¹⁄₈ × 6¹⁄₈ inches
352 pp
56 b&w illus.

Paperback
0 7148 2840 8

£ **14.95** UK
$ **19.95** US
€ **24.95** EUR
$ **29.95** CAN
$ **39.95** AUS

Art in Modern Culture

An Anthology of Critical Texts
Edited by Francis Frascina and Jonathan Harris

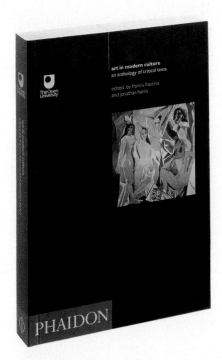

- An essential anthology of key texts reflecting contemporary debates on the status of art and its role in culture and history
- Selected writings span the 20th century, including classics from the 1930s to the 1960s alongside more current works
- Authors include such key critical and creative forces as Berthold Brecht, Clement Greenberg, Noam Chomsky, Edward Said and Richard Shiff
- An Open University set book, co-published with the Open University

Francis Frascina is John Raven Professor of Visual Arts at Keele University
Jonathan Harris is Reader in the History of Art, School of Architecture, Liverpool University

General Non-Fiction

Art Arts & Letters

Photography

Collector's Editions

Film

Architecture

Arts & Letters

Each volume
186 × 110 mm
7¹3 × 4¹3 inches

Paperback

£ 6.95 UK
$ 9.95 US
€ 9.95 EUR
$ 14.95 CAN
$ 19.95 AUS

'Mini-triumphs of contemporary design … the words contained within these gem-like covers are lapidary as well.' *Times Literary Supplement*

- A collection of some of the best-known writings of renowned artists, critics and interpreters of our cultural traditions
- Revival of a famous Phaidon series
- Each volume is an acknowledged classic
- Each contains an introduction and notes by a distinguished editor and a wide range of specially chosen illustrations

Design

Fashion &
Contemporary
Culture

Decorative Arts

Music &
Performing Arts

Video

Index

The Civilization of the Renaissance in Italy
Jacob Burckhardt
Translated by S G C Middlemore
506 pp, 101 b&w illus.
0 7148 3363 0

- A classic introduction to the study of the Renaissance, and one that remains a source of inspiration
- Enjoyable as a great work of literature as well as history

The Journal of Eugène Delacroix
Selection edited with an introduction by Hubert Wellington, translated by Lucy Norton
570 pp, 82 b&w illus.
0 7148 3359 2

- The journal of the French 19th-century Romantic painter Eugène Delacroix is one of art history's most important documents
- Expressive and unselfconsciously spontaneous, it offers a compelling insight into the painter's life and times

The Lamp of Beauty
Writings on Art by John Ruskin
Selected and edited by Joan Evans
476 pp, 78 b&w illus.
0 7148 3358 4

- John Ruskin was arguably the most important art critic of the 19th century
- This book makes available a generous selection of his finest writings on painting, sculpture and architecture

The Life of Benvenuto Cellini
Translated by
John Addington Symonds
Introduction by
John Pope-Hennessy
582 pp, 97 b&w illus.
0 7148 3364 9

- In this masterful autobiography Cellini describes court life, his career as a Renaissance sculptor and goldsmith, and his views of his contemporaries, including Michelangelo

Memoirs of the Life of John Constable
C R Leslie
Edited by Jonathan Mayne
424 pp, 72 b&w illus.
0 7148 3360 6

- This memoir of the great British 19th-century landscape painter is chiefly compiled from Constable's own correspondence and conversation
- Combining the merits of classic biography and intimate self-portrait, this is an invaluable sourcebook

The Painter of Modern Life and Other Essays
Charles Baudelaire
Translated and edited by Jonathan Mayne
264 pp, 58 b&w illus.
0 7148 3365 7

- Charles Baudelaire, the 19th-century French poet and writer, has also been called 'the father of modern criticism'
- This stimulating volume gathers together some of his most celebrated critical writings

General Non-Fiction

Art Colour Library

Photography

Collector's Editions

Film

Architecture

Each volume
305 × 225 mm
12 × 8⅞ inches
128 pp
c.50 col, 36 b&w illus.

Paperback

£ **5.95** UK
$ **9.95** US
€ **9.95** EUR
$ **14.95** CAN
$ **16.95** AUS

Colour Library

'Ideal introductions for students and museum-goers.' *The Independent*

- Series of introductory books on the great masters and movements in art
- Each volume contains an extensive essay, 48 full-page colour plates, accompanied by extensive notes and comparative illustrations
- Provides incomparable value
- Highly regarded for its insight and authority

Design

Fashion & Contemporary Culture

Decorative Arts

Music & Performing Arts

Video

Index

Fra Angelico
Christopher Lloyd
0 7148 2785 1

Bonnard
Julian Bell
0 7148 3052 6

Bruegel
Keith Roberts
0 7148 2239 6

Canaletto
Christopher Baker
0 7148 3249 9

Caravaggio
Timothy Wilson-Smith
0 7148 3485 8

Cézanne
Catherine Dean
0 7148 2682 0

Chagall
Gill Polonsky
0 7148 3403 3

Chardin
Gabriel Naughton
0 7148 3336 3

Constable
John Sunderland
0 7148 2754 1

Cubism
Philip Cooper
0 7148 3250 2

Dalí
Christopher Masters
0 7148 3338 X

Degas
Keith Roberts
0 7148 2757 6

Dürer
Martin Bailey
0 7148 3334 7

Dutch Painting
Christopher Brown
0 7148 2865 3

Ernst
Ian Turpin
0 7148 2866 1

Gainsborough
Nicola Kalinsky
0 7148 3178 6

Gauguin
Alan Bowness
0 7148 2683 9

Goya
Enriqueta Harris
0 7148 2975 7

General
Non-Fiction

Art
Colour Library

Photography

Collector's
Editions

Film

Architecture

Holbein
Helen Langdon
0 7148 2867 X

Impressionism
Mark Powell-Jones
0 7148 3053 4

**Italian
Renaissance
Painting**
Sara Elliott
0 7148 2868 8

**Japanese
Colour Prints**
J Hillier
0 7148 2721 5

Klee
Douglas Hall
0 7148 2730 4

Klimt
Catherine Dean
0 7148 3377 0

Magritte
*Richard
Calvocoressi*
0 7148 2760 6

Manet
John Richardson
0 7148 2755 X

Matisse
Nicholas Watkins
0 7148 2709 6

Modigliani
Douglas Hall
0 7148 2758 4

Monet
John House
0 7148 2723 1

Munch
*John
Boulton Smith*
0 7148 2732 0

Picasso
Roland Penrose
0 7148 2708 8

Pissarro
Christopher Lloyd
0 7148 2729 0

Pop Art
Jamie James
0 7148 3332 0

**The Pre-
Raphaelites**
Andrea Rose
0 7148 2907 2

Rembrandt
Michael Kitson
0 7148 2743 6

Renoir
William Gaunt
0 7148 2756 8

Design

Fashion & Contemporary Culture

Decorative Arts

Music & Performing Arts

Video

Index

Rossetti
David Rodgers
0 7148 3341 X

Schiele
Christopher Short
0 7148 3393 2

Sisley
Richard Shone
0 7148 3051 8

**Surrealist
Painting**
Simon Wilson
0 7148 2722 3

Toulouse-Lautrec
*Edward
Lucie-Smith*
0 7148 2761 4

Turner
William Gaunt
0 7148 2759 2

Van Gogh
Wilhelm Uhde
0 7148 2724 X

Vermeer
Martin Bailey
0 7148 3463 7

Whistler
Frances Spalding
0 7148 3186 7

Photography

General
Non-Fiction

Art

Photography
NEW TITLE

Collector's
Editions

Film

Architecture

300 × 230 mm
11⁷⁸ × 9¹⁴ inches
448 pp
c.20 col, 450
duotone illus.

Hardback
0 7148 4315 6

£   **59.95** UK
$ **95.00** US
€   **95.00** EUR
$ **139.95** CAN
$ **175.00** AUS

Related exhibitions
Major retrospective at
Maison Européenne de la
Photographie, Paris, opening
in February 2004. Exhibition
will tour internationally

Published October

René Burri Photographs

Hans-Michael Koetzle

- René Burri (b.1933) is one of the giants of photography of the 20th century
- The first retrospective of his entire career
- Known the world over for his iconic images of Che Guevara and Brasília
- A pioneering body of work that covers many of the major political events and key politicians of the last 50 years
- Covers Burri's unique relationships with some of the major cultural figures of the 20th century, including Picasso, Le Corbusier, Giacometti and Barragán

Hans-Michael Koetzle is Editor-in-Chief of *Leica World* magazine and a regular contributor to numerous photography books and magazines. *René Burri Photographs* is the culmination of many years of scholarly research by the author

Design

Fashion &
Contemporary
Culture

Decorative Arts

Music &
Performing Arts

Video

Index

spreads from René
Burri Photographs
showing (from top)
Che Guevara, 1963;
scenes from South
Africa in 1968; Picasso
with Jaqueline Roque
and in his studio, 1957

300 × 225 mm
11⁷⁄₈ × 8⁷⁄₈ inches
448 pp
c.460 col illus.

Hardback
0 7148 4223 0

£ **45.00** UK
$ **75.00** US
€ **75.00** EUR
$ **99.95** CAN
$ **140.00** AUS

Marketing information
Major publicity and
serialization campaigns

Published September

The Devil's Playground

*Photographs by Nan Goldin, texts by writers and critics including Guido Costa, Enrique Juncosa,
Catherine Lampert, Christine Macel and Giorgio Verzotti*

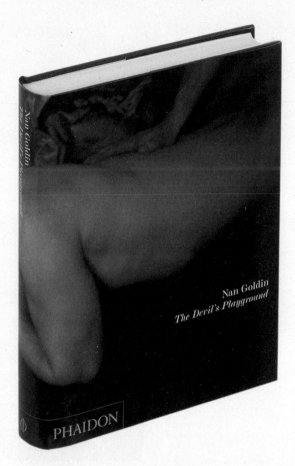

- A major collection of work by Nan Goldin, one of the leading chroniclers of our time
- An intimate and compelling photographic portrait which tells personal stories of relationships, friendships and identity, but also chronicles different eras and the passage of time
- Includes new work from Goldin's series of photographs such as *Elements*, *Heartbeat, Still on Earth* and *Maternity*
- Features previously unpublished works by Goldin, alongside earlier classics
- Photographic sequences are interspersed with a series of short essays which discuss different aspects and themes in Goldin's work, such as narrative, love, the family and gender politics
- The most comprehensive book published on Nan Goldin to date

Guido Costa is an internationally renowned curator and writer and has worked closely with Goldin for many years
Enrique Juncosa is Director of the Irish Museum of Modern Art, Dublin
Catherine Lampert was previously Director of London's Whitechapel Gallery; she currently works as a freelance writer and curator
Christine Macel is a curator for contemporary art at the Centre Pompidou, Paris
Giorgio Verzotti is a freelance curator

Design

Fashion &
Contemporary
Culture

Decorative Arts

Music &
Performing Arts

Video

Index

The Blue Grotto, Capri, 1997

241

Gigi in the blue grotto with light, Capri, 1997

Bruno's hand on Valerie's shoulder, Paris, 2001

Valerie in bright light, Paris, 2001

541

Bruno smiling out of shadow, Paris, 2001

Jacket image: Jens'
hand on Clemens'
back, Paris, 2001;
spreads showing (from
top, left to right) The
Blue Grotto, Capri,
1997; Gigi in the blue
grotto with light,
Capri, 1997; Bruno
smiling out of shadow,
Paris, 2001; Valerie in
bright light, Paris,
2001; Bruno's hand on
Valerie's shoulder,
Paris, 2001

General
Non-Fiction

Art

Photography
NEW TITLE

Collector's
Editions

Film

Architecture

185 × 123 mm
7¹⁄₄ × 4⁷⁄₈ inches
408 pp
c.200 col illus.

Hardback
0 7148 4301 6

£ **12.95** UK
$ **19.95** US
€ **19.95** EUR
$ **29.95** CAN
$ **39.95** AUS

Point of Sale
10-copy counter
display pack available

Published September

Fish Face

Portraits
Photographs and text by David Doubilet

- A collection of 200 fish portraits by underwater photographer David Doubilet
- First book of fish portraits ever published
- Features full-page pictures of an astounding variety of fish species, which take us from the beautiful to the ugly, from the spiky to the rotund
- Will appeal to photography lovers, naturalists, *National Geographic* readers, divers and anyone interested in marine life
- Compact format at an affordable price
- Captures the colourful, fun and bizarre fish that David Doubilet has encountered in his 25-year career as an underwater photographer

David Doubilet (b.1946), arguably the world's leading underwater photographer, has shot more than 60 stories for *National Geographic*. He began diving when he was 12 and has since captured ground-breaking images of great white sharks, creatures of the undersea desert, fluorescent coral and shipwrecks. He was awarded the prestigious Lennart Nilsson prize in 2001

Design

Fashion &
Contemporary
Culture

Decorative Arts

Music &
Performing Arts

Video

Index

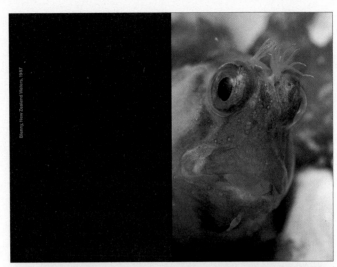

Cover image: Cow fish,
Tasmania, 1995;
spreads showing (from
top) Blenny, New
Zealand waters, 1987;
Black Cod guards
shipwreck, Middleton
Reef, Australia, 1984;
Surgeon fish,
Seychelles, 1994

General Non-Fiction

Art

Photography NEW TITLE

Collector's Editions

Film

Architecture

250 × 250 mm
9⁷⁄₈ × 9⁷⁄₈ inches
144 pp
c.100 col illus.

Hardback
0 7148 4346 6

£ **24.95** UK
$ **39.95** US
€ **39.95** EUR
$ **59.95** CAN
$ **69.95** AUS

Related exhibitions
Major exhibition starting
at National Geographic
Museum, Washington
D.C., opening October
2003. Exhibition will tour
internationally

Marketing information
Extensive photographer
tour

Published October

The Path to Buddha

Photographs by Steve McCurry

- An intimate photographic portrait of Tibetans and Buddhism by Steve McCurry
- Divided into five parts, the two main chapters are devoted to the religious and lay Buddhists on their pilgrimages to holy sites, interspersed with three sections of portraits
- McCurry's images capture fleeting and intimate moments of monks in animated discussion, meditation and prayer, and follow the devout believers on their arduous journeys to prayer
- Explores subjects as diverse as landscapes, portraits, religious rituals and everyday life
- Rich and stunning photography offers a rare insight into a unique and dignified culture

Steve McCurry (b.1950) launched his career as a photojournalist when, disguised in native garb, he crossed the Pakistan border into Afghanistan before the Russian invasion. His coverage won him the Robert Capa Gold Medal given to photographers exhibiting exceptional courage and enterprise. Famous also for his work in South East Asia, his photographs are beautiful, uplifting and powerful. McCurry has worked for *National Geographic* magazine for many years and is a member of the prestigious Magnum agency

Design

Fashion &
Contemporary
Culture

Decorative Arts

Music &
Performing Arts

Video

Index

Jacket image: Boy in
the Academy of
Larung Gar, Kham,
1999; spreads
showing (from top,
left to right) Devotee
at Tibetan prayer
festival, Bodhgaya,
2000; Devotees travel
to Lhasa, Kham, 1999;
Young Rinpoche in Tea
shop, Bodhgaya, 2000;
Monks debate, Sarya,
Bylakuppe, 2001;
Monks debate,
Amdo, 2001

General
Non-Fiction

Art

Photography
NEW TITLE

Collector's
Editions

Film

Architecture

245 × 210 mm
9⁵⁸ × 8¹⁴ inches
256 pp
c.150 duotone illus.
including magazine
spreads in colour

Hardback
0 7148 4283 4

£ **29.95** UK
$ **49.95** US
€ **49.95** EUR
$ **75.00** CAN
$ **89.95** AUS

Related exhibitions
Major retrospective at
Bibiothèque Nationale,
Paris, until July 2003.
Exhibition will tour
internationally

Marketing information
Extensive review and
media coverage

Published October

Compelled to Witness

The photographic reportage of Henri Cartier-Bresson
Claude Cookman

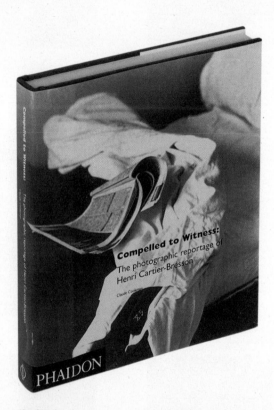

- **The first book to analyse Cartier-Bresson's early work as a photojournalist**
- **Analyses how his working methods when he was on assignment for newspapers and magazines played an important role in the making of his most famous images**
- Features important works as well as little-known images shown here in their historical context
- **Features fascinating stories about Cartier-Bresson's political consciousness and his hunger for life and adventure**
- **An academic and extremely accessible text**

Claude Cookman shared in the 1975 Pulitzer Prize for Photography and received a PhD in the History of Photography from Princeton University. He currently teaches at Indiana University. Cookman offers a highly original analysis of Cartier-Bresson's photojournalism based on years of archive research

Design

Fashion & Contemporary Culture

Decorative Arts

Music & Performing Arts

Video

Index

spreads from Compelled to Witness (from top) Sunday Afternoon on the Banks of the Marne, 1936; Coronation Day, London, 1936

General
Non-Fiction

Art

Photography
55
NEW TITLE

Collector's
Editions

Film

Architecture

156 × 136 mm
6¹₄ × 5¾ inches
128 pp
25 col, 31 b&w illus.

Paperback
0 7148 4193 5

£ **5.95** UK
$ **9.95** US
€ **9.95** EUR
$ **14.95** CAN
$ **16.95** AUS

Related exhibitions
Solo exhibition at
Centre for Photography,
Lectoure, France, to open
February 2004.
Curated by author
Michel Metayer

Published September

Erwin Blumenfeld

Michel Metayer

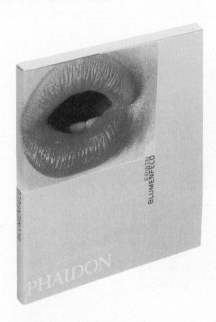

- **Erwin Blumenfeld (1897–1969) created some of the most memorable fashion imagery of the 1930s, 1940s and 1950s**
- **Contains photographs that were seen by millions in *Vogue*, *Harper's Bazaar* and *Cosmopolitan***
- **Seminal innovator of colour photography when the medium was just developing**
- **Photographs are rich in hybrid imagery, imbuing images of celebrities and black-and-white graphical shapes with saturated colour and eroticism**
- **Offers new interpretation to key works and features little-known surrealist images**

Michel Metayer is the Director of the prestigious Toulouse School for Fine Art. Trained as a Germanist, Metayer has lectured widely on art and literature and has curated numerous exhibitions both in France and abroad, including two exhibitions on Blumenfeld in Prague and Fribourg, Switzerland

Design

Fashion &
Contemporary
Culture

Decorative Arts

Music &
Performing Arts

Video

Index

The Eiffel Tower, French Vogue portfolio, Paris, May 1939. In October 1938 French Vogue devoted twenty pages of the magazine to a portfolio of Blumenfeld's fashion photographs. Others appeared in February, then again in March 1939. The May issue is devoted to the 50th anniversary of the Eiffel Tower, and this image here was the principle photograph in the series. Despite bringing to life such innovative motifs for his employers such as this, Blumenfeld's year-long contract with Vogue was not renewed, prompting him to leave for New York the same year.

16.17

Blue Veil, New York, 1951. Blumenfeld originally produced 'Blue Veil' for a commission, but it was rejected. It was published for the first time on the cover of the book by William A. Ewing & Marina Schinz: Blumenfeld: A Fetish for Beauty (1996). Veils, as seen here covering the face of the model Leslie Redgate, is a recurring motif in Blumenfeld's work. As a child, he was drawn to the fine veils in the paintings of Botticelli and Cranach, and at the beginning of the 1930's took a photograph inspired by eccentric photographer Rogier van der Weyden prefiguring this one.

18.19

spreads from
Erwin Blumenfeld 55
showing (from top)
The Eiffel Tower, Paris,
1939; Blue Veil, New
York, 1951; Dayton's
Oval Room, New York,
c.1960

Dayton's Oval Room (Minneapolis), New York, c.1960. During the 1950's Blumenfeld established an excellent working relationship with Stuart Wells, vice-president of the well-known Dayton's Department Store in Minneapolis. His good relationship with Wells afforded him complete artistic freedom in his work for store. Blumenfeld chose the subjects, the clothes, the models, the decor and the composition. Benefiting from all of this, we see here how he enhanced the contrast and framed the image to appear as if spread across a double page.

20.21

General
Non-Fiction

Art

Photography
55
NEW TITLE

Collector's
Editions

Film

Architecture

156 × 136 mm
6¹⁄₄ × 5³⁄₄ inches
128 pp
56 b&w illus.

Paperback
0 7148 4022 X

£ **5.95** UK
$ **9.95** US
€ **9.95** EUR
$ **14.95** CAN
$ **16.95** AUS

Related exhibitions
Solo exhibition at
Woodmere Art Museum,
Philadelphia, Fall 2003.
Group show 'Architecture
of Homelessness'
, Pinakothek der Moderne,
Munich, September 2003

Published August

Larry Fink

Laurie Dahlberg

- American photographer Larry Fink (b.1941) is famous for capturing intimate exchanges between people in ordinary circumstances
- Whether he portrays the poorest in society or the most privileged his images are imbued with a warmth and sensitivity towards his subjects
- Fink is the recipient of some of the most important awards and fellowships in photography and has had solo exhibitions devoted to his work at the Museum of Modern Art, New York, The Whitney Museum of American Art, New York, The San Francisco Museum of Art and the Kunstmuseum Düsseldorf
- Having studied under Lisette Model and Alexey Brodovitch, Fink is now a highly influential teacher himself

Laurie Dahlberg is Assistant Professor of the History of Photography at Bard College, New York. A writer and curator, Dahlberg has been on the faculty of the Photography Department at Bard for seven years. Fink also teaches there

Design

Fashion & Contemporary Culture

Decorative Arts

Music & Performing Arts

Video

Index

New York City, 1967. This early picture, made when Fink was still regularly using the 35mm format, recalls his teacher Lisette Model's interest in the expressivity of those most pedestrian of body parts: legs and feet. Fink manages to draw a telling portrait of a woman without showing her face. Centring her in the vertical photographic frame to maximize the presence and stability of her physical frame, Fink studies her sturdy legs, back and formidable body language – feet spread, hand on hip – and constructs the image of a strident, no-nonsense woman, a real New Yorker.

26.27

Boxing, Champs Gym, Philadelphia, Pennsylvania, January 1993. With its union of physicality and psychology, boxing became a natural photographic obsession for Fink. Part of his interest in the sport lies in its being a traditional medium of black aspiration for success and recognition, hence his preference for small, inner-city gyms and the regional boxing culture. What he found there was an 'amazing combination of innocence and power, both in body and mind.'

76.77

spreads from Larry Fink 55 showing (from top) New York City, 1967; Boxing, Champs Gym, Pennsylvania, 1993; Joyce and Antoine's Wedding, New York, 1998

Joyce and Antoine's Wedding, New York, September 1998. Photographed from below, with the soaring trees behind her, this formidable woman becomes a nature goddess, a Diana figure: powerful, beautiful and unobtainable. The video camera has replaced her bow and arrow, but she is on the hunt nonetheless.

118.119

156 × 136 mm
6¹₄ × 5³₄ inches
128 pp
56 b&w illus.

Paperback
0 7148 4224 9

£ **5.95** UK
$ **9.95** US
€ **9.95** EUR
$ **14.95** CAN
$ **16.95** AUS

Published September

Weegee

Kerry William Purcell

- Weegee (1899–1968) was the supreme news photographer who captured car crashes, gangland murders and tenement infernos of 1930s and 1940s New York
- Born Arthur Fellig, he borrowed his name from the ouija board to advertise his uncanny ability for turning up on the scene of the crime before the police
- Revered for elevating the sordid side of human life to high art, he is also credited with ushering in the age of tabloid culture
- His images both shock and entertain and together amount to an extraordinary portrait of the dark side of New York City

Kerry William Purcell is an independent writer based in the UK. A former archivist at The Photographers Gallery, his previous publications include Phaidon's *Alexey Brodovitch* (2002)

Design

Fashion &
Contemporary
Culture

Decorative Arts

Music &
Performing Arts

Video

Index

On the Spot, c.1940. Once again, Weegee utilises a street sign to produce a ready-made caption for this murder. Possibly at Weegee's request, the white blanket covering the corpse has been pulled back to reveal the man's bloody head. While the fresh corpse lies bleeding into the gutter, the police officers line up on the sidewalk, seemingly posing for Weegee's camera.

16,17

The Critic, December 6, 1943. This is Weegee's most famous image. Reproduced more times than any other of his photos, he personally believed it marked a turning point in his career. Covering the opening night of the Metropolitan Opera, New York, Weegee noted in Naked City that he saw a Rolls Royce pull up, and when the two figures climbed out he just snapped them. The lady on the left is Mrs George Washington Kavanaugh, and her friend on the right is Lady Decies. It is hard to believe that, as Weegee repeatedly stated, he only saw the dishevelled woman casting her critical eye when he began to print the photograph in his darkroom. Originally produced for PM, the newspaper decided against its publication on the basis that such opulent evening dress was incongruous with the austerity of wartime America. It eventually appeared in Life magazine.

20,21

spreads from
Weegee 55 showing
(from top) On the
Spot, c.1940; The
Critic, 1943; Sudden
Death for One …
Sudden Shock for
the Other, 1944

Sudden Death for One...Sudden Shock for the Other, September 7, 1944. Documenting the unfolding events of an automobile accident, Weegee once again employs a car window to frame the scene. This is a photograph of Mrs Dorothy Reportella. She has just hit a bread truck, killing the driver. Dressed as if returning from a night out on the town, it appears that the horrific consequences of the accident have just been recounted to her by the cop. Clearly doubting the reality of the situation, as if the incident was just a bad dream, she reaches out to touch his hand. According to the PM story, suffering from shock and hysteria, Mrs Reportella was eventually taken to Bellevue Hospital.

24,25

General Non-Fiction

Art

Photography
Stationery
NEW CARDBOX

Collector's Editions

Film

Architecture

Martin Parr Postcards

Photographs by Martin Parr

Box dimensions
142 × 202 mm
5⁵⁸ × 8 inches .

Postcard box (45 cards)
0 7148 4345 8

incl. VAT £ **14.95** UK
$ **19.95** US
€ **24.95** EUR
$ **29.95** CAN
$ **39.95** AUS

Marketing information
Major retrospective at
the Museo Nacional
Centro de Arte Reina,
Madrid, Spain
(16 September–
8 December 2003) and at
the Maison Européenne
de la Photographie, Paris,
France (8 April–
10 June 2004

Published September

- A selection of 45 postcards from Martin Parr's highly successful retrospective book published by Phaidon
- A major photographer who bridges the gap between art and photojournalism, Parr's provocative work is widely known throughout Europe and the United States
- A range of colour and black-and-white photographs
- Includes some of the most amusing and ironic images from Parr's entire career
- Box created to look like a mini version of the book

The work of **Martin Parr** (b.1952) bridges the divide between art and documentary photography. His studies of the idiosyncrasies of mass culture and consumerism around the world, his innovative imagery and his prolific output have placed him firmly at the forefront of contemporary art. A world authority on photography books and, more recently, a film-maker, Parr joined Magnum in 1994

Design

Fashion &
Contemporary
Culture

Decorative Arts

Music &
Performing Arts

Video

Index

45 postcards contained
in card box

General
Non-Fiction

Art

Photography
NEW IN PAPERBACK

Collector's
Editions

Film

Architecture

338 × 263 mm
13¼ × 10⅜ inches
208 pp
196 tritone illus.

Paperback
0 7148 4331 8

£ **24.95** UK
$ **39.95** US
€ **39.95** EUR
$ **59.95** CAN
$ **69.95** AUS

Hardback
0 7148 4123 4

£ **50.00** UK
$ **75.00** US
€ **79.95** EUR
$ **110.00** CAN
$ **140.00** AUS

**Paperback published
July**

The Sound I Saw

Photographs and text by Roy DeCarava

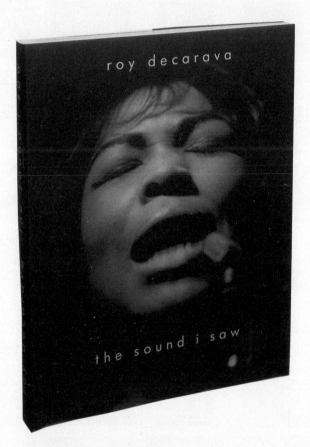

- Originally conceived, designed, written and made by hand as a prototype by master photographer DeCarava (b.1919) in the early 1960s
- For many years, *The Sound I Saw* existed largely as a legend among the cognoscenti of the photography world
- A portrait of Harlem and the key figures of jazz of the late 1950s and early 1960s
- Presented as a stream of 196 soulful images interspersed with DeCarava's own evocative poetry

Roy DeCarava, a life-long New Yorker, is a legend in the photography world. He was first recognized for his images of daily life in Harlem, as in *The Sweet Flypaper of Life*, his 1955 collaboration with Harlem Renaissance poet Langston Hughes, and for portraits of musicians like Duke Ellington and Billie Holiday

Design

Fashion &
Contemporary
Culture

Decorative Arts

Music &
Performing Arts

Video

Index

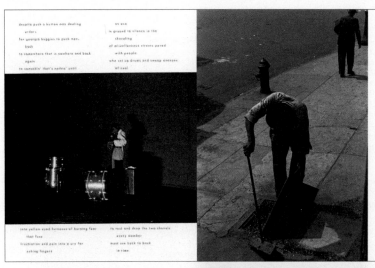

The book's layout is an exact reproduction of Roy DeCarava's original hand-made prototype. DeCarava's poetry is interspersed between the photographs, which are specially printed to emphasize their deep, dark tones. DeCarava's pages are an ode to Harlem and jazz

250 × 250 mm
9⁷/₈ × 9⁷/₈ inches
536 pp
175 col, 345 b&w illus.

Paperback
0 7148 4356 3
See also p.268 for hardback

£ **24.95** UK
$ **39.95** US
€ **39.95** EUR
$ **59.95** CAN
$ **69.95** AUS

Published October

Awards

Winner of a Distinctive Merit
Award from the New York Art
Directors' Club, 2000

Winner of Kodak
Fotobuchpreis, 2000

I.D.
Winner of an award
from I.D. magazine's
Annual Design Review, 2000

Exhibited at the 19th
International Biennale
of Graphic Design
BRNO 2000

magnum°

With an introduction by Michael Ignatieff

- A vision of the world through the eyes of the photographers of Magnum at the beginning of the new millennium
- Fifty years since the legendary group began its documentary mission, here the photographers address the world following the fall of the Berlin Wall in 1989
- A major book that identifies the political, human, social and cultural themes that permeate our world today
- Includes work by Henri Cartier-Bresson, James Nachtwey, Elliott Erwitt and Steve McCurry as well as work by Magnum's newest recruits

Michael Ignatieff is currently the Director of the Carr Center of Human Rights Policy at Harvard University

'Beautifully designed and printed, it will arrest the imagination long after other books of photographs have become sterile and dead.' *(Sunday Times)*

Design

Fashion &
Contemporary
Culture

Decorative Arts

Music &
Performing Arts

Video

Index

Spreads from
Magnum° showing
(from top, left to righ)
Henri Cartier-Bresson,
portraits of Elisabeth
Chojnacka (above
left), Louis Pons
(below left), Louis-
René des Forêts
(above right), Balthus
(below left); Bruno
Barbey, photographs
taken in Morocco,
1985–97; Guy le
Querrec, African
Journeys: the Lobi,
Burkina Faso, 1998

General Non-Fiction

Art

Photography

Collector's Editions

Film

Architecture

Hardback
290 × 250 mm
11³⁄₈ × 9⁷⁄₈ inches
512 pp
144 col, 356 b&w photos

0 7148 3634 6

£ **29.95** UK
$ **45.00** US
€ **49.95** EUR
$ **69.95** CAN
$ **79.95** AUS

Paperback mini format
163 × 123 mm
6³⁄₈ × 4⁷⁄₈ inches
520 pp
116 col & 384 duotone photos

0 7148 3937 X

£ **6.95** UK
$ **9.95** US
€ **11.95** EUR
$ **14.95** CAN
$ **16.95** AUS

Point of Sale
10-copy counterpack available

The Photography Book

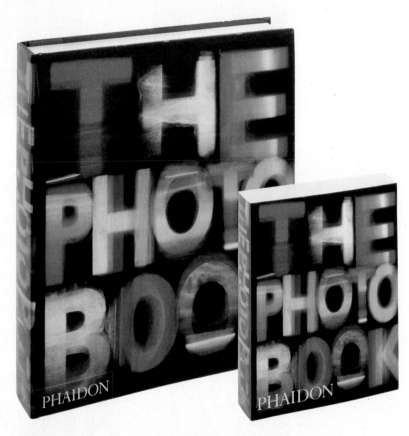

- Widely acclaimed as the most important reference book ever on its subject
- Five hundred superb images that represent the world's best photographers
- Encompasses fashion, sport, natural history, reportage and society portraiture, documentary and art
- Arranged alphabetically by photographer
- Illuminating text provides useful insight into each work and its creator
- With extensive cross-references, glossaries of technical terms and movements and a directory of museums and galleries

Ian Jeffrey is a photography writer, lecturer and curator. His other books include *Magnum Landscape* (Phaidon, 1997), *Portraits of Artists* (2000) and *Revisions: An Alternative History of Photography* (1999)

'Possibly the best reference book of the year. No photographer should be without this on their bookshelf' *(Amateur Photographer)*
'Phaidon has published a miracle of clarity, surprise and information in this collection. Comprehensive and witty, beautifully produced and impeccably organized – if you can afford only one book on the subject, this has to be it.' *(The Times)*

Design

Fashion &
Contemporary
Culture

Decorative Arts

Music &
Performing Arts

Video

Index

'The most important photography book, ever.'

Practical Photography

General Non-Fiction

Art

Photography

Collector's Editions

Film

Architecture

220 × 195 mm
8²₃ × 7¹₃ inches
208 pp
100 photos

Hardback
0 7148 4278 8

£ **29.95** UK
$ **49.95** US
€ **49.95** EUR
$ **75.00** CAN
$ **89.95** AUS

One Hundred Photographs

A Collection by Bruce Bernard
Text by Bruce Bernard and Mark Haworth-Booth

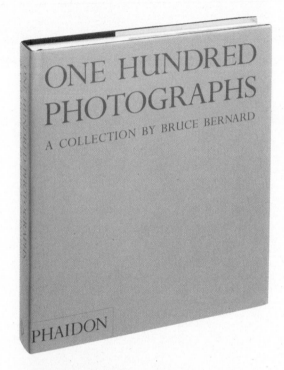

- A unique collection of works spanning the whole history of photography, that captures the magic of the medium
- Curated by Bruce Bernard, the leading picture editor of his generation
- Many of the most famous names in the history of photography are included

Bruce Bernard (1929–2000) was Picture Editor of *The Sunday Times Magazine* and in 1980 he produced *Photodiscovery* – a highly respected account of the revolution in attitudes to photography. Bernard was Visual Arts Editor of the *Saturday Independent Magazine* for its first four years. He curated the exhibition 'All Human Life' at London's Barbican Centre in 1996, and was the curator of a private collection of photographs. *Century* is the culmination of his extensive knowledge and the experience he gained during 30 years of looking at pictures. **Mark Haworth-Booth** is a curator and writer on photography and is Acting Head of Research at the Victoria and Albert Museum, London. His other books include *British Photography* (1989) and *Photography: An Independent Art* (1997)

'An extraordinary collection of images, drawn from virtually every photographic genre since 1840... The best, most aesthetically pleasing, but not necessarily the best-known images ever captures on film, salt prints and calotypes. If *Century* was Bruce Bernard's most expansive work, 100 Photographs is his most personal.' (*The Sunday Times, Magazine*, September 1st 2002)

225 × 337 mm
8⁷⁄₈ × 13¹⁄₄ inches
448 pp
480 col, 320 b&w photos

Hardback
0 7148 4199 4

£ **39.95** UK
$ **69.95** US
€ **69.95** EUR
$ **95.00** CAN
$ **120.00** AUS

BLINK.

100 photographers, 10 curators, 10 writers
Curated by Shahidul Alam, Marcelo Brodsky, Joan Fontcuberta, Alasdair Foster, Dennis Freedman, Christine Frisinghelli, Shino Kuraishi, Simon Njami, Wendy Watriss and Paul Wombell

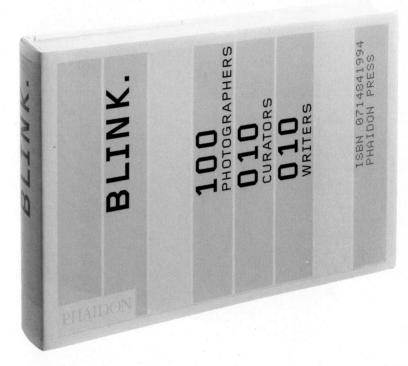

- A global up-to-the-minute overview of contemporary photography, including all types of work, from art to photojournalism, fashion to digital photography
- Following on from Cream and 10x10, BLINK. presents the work of 100 rising stars of photography, who have emerged and broken new ground in the last five years, chosen by 10 world class curators
- Each of the photographers (arranged A–Z) is featured over two double-page spreads, which show numerous examples of their work alongside an explanatory text by the selecting curator
- The curators have also chosen texts by 10 writers, ranging from fiction to journalism, which they feel illustrate the cultural context surrounding the photography

'Blink is a wonderful book ... a photographic roller-coaster ride on a global scale ... adventurous ... This is what Blink is all about, going from on genre to another, from one unexpected discovery to another: a photographic surprise party.' *(Free-Eye)*
'Beautifully structured, cool and calm in its appearance ... a discreetly paced book full of rigour.' *(Design Week)*
'A truly international mix which makes an interesting and useful compendium of work.' *(Creative Review)*

General Non-Fiction

Art

Photography

Collector's Editions

Film

Architecture

290 × 250 mm
11³⁄₈ × 9⁷⁄₈ inches
352 pp
128 col, 222 b&w photos

Hardback
0 7148 3954 X

£ 29.95 UK
$ 49.95 US
€ 49.95 EUR
$ 75.00 CAN
$ 85.00 AUS

Sportscape

The evolution of sports photography
Photographs from Allsport and Hulton/Archive, selected and presented by Paul Wombell, with an introduction by Simon Barnes

- Tells the story of how sport has been shown by photographers over a period of 100 years
- With an introduction by Sports columnist for *The Times* and Sports feature writer of the Year, 1999, Simon Barnes
- Photographs selected from the collection of Allsport, the world's leading sports photographic agency, and the historic Hulton Getty Archive
- A fascinating story of social, political and technological development over time

Paul Wombell is the Director of the Photographers' Gallery in London. He has had a lifetime interest in sport and is the author of *Photovideo* (1991) as well as many exhibition catalogues for the Photographers' Gallery
Simon Barnes has been the sports columnist for *The Times* (London) for over 20 years and was awarded the 1999 Sportswriter of the Year

'You don't have to be a jock to fall for *Sportscape* a massive slab of sports images... the images have been chosen with an eye trained on art as well as action.' *(The Village Voice,* New York)
'Faster! Stronger! Higher! This quirky but ambitious history of sports attempts to illuminate various aspects of competition....There's enough variety and off-beat material here to surprise the most well-schooled of aficionados.' *(Biography Magazine* (A&E))
'An intimate insight into the life of one of the twentieth century's great figures.' *(Sunday Times Magazine)*

245 × 210 mm
9⁵⁄₈ × 8¹⁄₄ inches
208 pp
128 col, 79 b&w photos

Hardback
0 7148 4014 9

£ **29.95** UK
$ **45.00** US
€ **49.95** EUR
$ **69.95** CAN
$ **89.95** AUS

Different

Photographs edited by Stuart Hall and Mark Sealy, text by Stuart Hall

- Explores ways in which contemporary Black and Asian artists examine questions of identity in photography
- Excellent resource for courses in sociology, cultural studies and photography
- A visual feast with over 180 powerful images

Mark Sealy is a producer and curator of photography, and since 1991 Director of Autograph (Association of Black Photographers)
Stuart Hall is Emeritus Professor of Sociology at Britain's Open University and Chairman of both inIVA (Institute of International Visual Arts) and Autograph

'A comprehensive selection.' *(Black Issues Book Review Magazine)*
'An unmissable look at a part of photographic history that has been neglected for too long.' *(British Journal of Photography)*

General Non-Fiction

Art

Photography

Collector's Editions

Film

Architecture

150 × 210 mm
6 × 8¼ inches
184 pp
32 col, 101 duotone photos

Hardback
0 7148 3642 7

£ **14.95** UK
$ **19.95** US
€ **24.95** EUR
$ **29.95** CAN
$ **39.95** AUS

Magnum Landscape

Foreword by Ian Jeffrey

- A grouping of landscape photographs by Magnum photographers from the past fifty years
- Reveals an awareness that the land itself has been shaped by man, and that the very notion of a landscape depends on a human viewpoint
- Presents endless variations on the theme – landscapes of war, agriculture, industry, cities and motorways, desolation, celebration and tranquillity

Ian Jeffrey is a photography writer, lecturer and curator. His other books include *The Photography Book* (Phaidon, 2000), *Portraits of Artists* (2000) and *Revisions: An Alternative History of Photography* (1999)

'A collection of cracking landscapes from members of the world renowned picture agency.' *(Practical Photography)*
'An inspiring and diverse collection.' *(Amateur Photographer)*
'One of the most successful photography books of this year. To shamelessly pilfer the joke of the great Dorothy Parker: me Leica.' *(Wallpaper*)*

Design

Fashion &
Contemporary
Culture

Decorative Arts

Music &
Performing Arts

Video

Index

150 × 210 mm
6 × 8¼ inches
184 pp
9 col, 79 duotone photos

Hardback
0 7148 4236 2

£ **14.95** UK
$ **24.95** US
€ **24.95** EUR
$ **39.95** CAN
$ **45.00** AUS

Magnum Football

Magnum Soccer
Introduction by Simon Kuper

- **An uplifting array of images by outstanding Magnum photographers working across the globe to document football**
- **Features photographers Henri Cartier-Bresson, James Nachtwey, Steve McCurry, Martin Parr, Abbas, Luc Delahaye and many more**
- **Celebrates football's ability to cut across all geographic and social divides**

Simon Kuper writes a regular sports column for the *Observer* and is the author of *Football Against the Enemy*, which won the William Hill Sports Book of the Year award in 1994

'Striking football images from across the world, by an array of outstanding photographers from Cartier-Bresson in Italy to Steve McCurry in Burma.'
(*The Bookseller*)
'Demonstrates the universal appeal of the game.' (*Creative Review*)
'You don't have to be a fan of the game to enjoy the wonderful images that have been put together by the world's leading photographers of our time…an absolute gem.'
(*Time Out*)

General
Non-Fiction

Art

Photography

Collector's
Editions

Film

Architecture

250 × 250 mm
10 × 10 inches
175 col, 345 b&w photos

Hardback
0 7148 3821 7
See also p.258 for paperback

£ **39.95** UK
$ **69.95** US
€ **69.95** EUR
$ **98.00** CAN
$ **99.95** AUS

Awards

Winner of a Distinctive Merit
Award from the New York Art
Directors' Club, 2000

25. KODAK
FOTOBUCHPREIS
2000
Winner of Kodak
Fotobuchpreis, 2000

I.D.
Winner of an award
from I.D. magazine's
Annual Design Review, 2000

Exhibited at the 19th
International Biennale
of Graphic Design
BRNO 2000

magnum°

Photographs by Magnum photographers, with an introduction by Michael Ignatieff

- A vision of the world through the eyes of the photographers of Magnum at the beginning of the new millennium
- Fifty years since the legendary group began its documentary mission, here the photographers address the world following the fall of the Berlin Wall in 1989
- A major book that identifies the political, human, social and cultural themes that permeate our world today
- Includes work by Henri Cartier-Bresson, James Nachtwey, Elliott Erwitt and Steve McCurry as well as work by Magnum's newest recruits

Michael Ignatieff is currently the Director of the Carr Center of Human Rights Policy at Harvard University

'Beautifully designed and printed, it will arrest the imagination long after other books of photographs have become sterile and dead.' *(Sunday Times)*

Design

Fashion &
Contemporary
Culture

Decorative Arts

Music &
Performing Arts

Video

Index

Box dimensions
161 × 161 mm
6⁵₁₆ × 6⁵₁₆ inches

Postcard box (50 cards)
0 7148 4008 4

incl. VAT £ **14.95** UK
$ **19.95** US
€ **24.95** EUR
$ **29.95** CAN
$ **39.95** AUS

magnum° postcards

Photographs by Magnum photographers

- **Specially designed tin box of 50 postcards from best-selling book *Magnum°***
- **A unique gift and souvenir collection of outstanding images by Magnum's best-known photographers**
- **Includes postcards by Henri Cartier-Bresson, René Burri, Steve McCurry, James Nachtwey and Martin Parr**
- **A richly varied collection of images that make strong and exciting statements about the reality of the world, while others are playful, delighting in colour and form**
- **Box contains 50 postcards, each a different image**

General Non-Fiction

Art

Photography

Collector's Editions

Film

Architecture

280 × 230 mm
11 × 9 inches
360 pp
2 col, 450 duotone photographs

Paperback
0 7148 3772 5

£ 24.95 UK
$ 39.95 US
€ 39.95 EUR
$ 59.95 CAN
$ 69.95 AUS

magnum cinema

Photographs from 50 years of movie-making
Alain Bergala

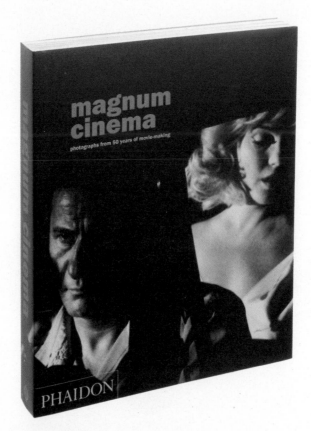

- 50 years of the movie industry covered by photographers from the world's most prestigious picture agency
- An intimate and enjoyable glimpse behind the scenes of cinema history
- Includes stars, such as Ingrid Bergman, Humphrey Bogart, James Dean, Marilyn Monroe, Clint Eastwood and directors, such as Billy Wilder, John Houston, Alfred Hitchcock, François Truffaut and Andrei Tarkovsky
- On- and off-set photographs are gathered together for the first time
- Photographs by Eve Arnold, Henri Cartier-Bresson, Josef Koudelka, Eugene Smith and Dennis Stock

Alain Bergala is a writer and film-maker and former editor of the French magazine *Cahiers du Cinéma*

'These are the photographs of the great, taken by the great … history in the making on both sides of the camera.' (*The Guardian*)
'Most movie books are ephemeral by nature; this is one to savor.' (*Los Angeles Times*)

Design

Fashion &
Contemporary
Culture

Decorative Arts

Music &
Performing Arts

Video

Index

133 × 180 mm
5¹⁴ × 7 inches
112 pp
80 duotone photos

Hardback
0 7148 3472 6

£ **14.95** UK
$ **19.95** US
€ **24.95** EUR
$ **29.95** CAN
$ **39.95** AUS

Zoo

Photographs by Britta Jaschinski

- **A collection of atmospheric and enigmatic portraits of animals by Britta Jaschinski**
- **Hauntingly beautiful photographs of dolphins, polar bears and zebras that owe their inspiration to portraiture rather than documentation**
- **Masterful photographs imbue the animals with a shadowy and melancholy dignity**

Britta Jaschinski (b.1965) was born in Bremen and has lived and worked in England since 1990. Her body of work on animals won her instant recognition which resulted in exhibitions throughout the world, including a solo show at London's Photographers Gallery

General
Non-Fiction

Art

Photography

Collector's
Editions

Film

Architecture

250 × 189 mm
9⁷₈ × 7³₈ inches
144 pages
81 tritone photos

Hardback
0 7148 4253 2

£ **35.00** UK
$ **59.95** US
€ **59.95** EUR
$ **89.95** CAN
$ **99.95** AUS

Grafters

Photographs by Colin Jones, text by Mark Haworth-Booth

- A timeless and sympathetic tale of industrial post-war Britain by Colin Jones
- Known for his iconic photographs of sixties rock stars, this is the first time that Jones's highly respected, personal body of work has been brought to light
- A moving portrait of poverty and physical hardship endured with dignity
- A fascinating social record of a time gone by

Colin Jones (b.1936), formerly a dancer with the Royal Ballet began to take photographs of mining communities while on tour in the north of England. His career as a photographer started at the *Observer* in the 1960s and he became known for his portraits of rock icons of the period **Mark Haworth-Booth** is a curator and writer on photography, and is Acting Head of Research at the Victoria & Albert Museum, London. His other books include *British Photography* (1989) and *Photography: An Independent Art* (1997)

'A wonderful evocation of ways of life that will never be the same again.' *(Amateur Photography)*
'An exceptional record of the old industrial world.' *(Independent on Sunday)*

Design

Fashion & Contemporary Culture

Decorative Arts

Music & Performing Arts

Video

Index

290 × 250 mm
11³⁸ × 9⁷⁸ inches
448 pp
684 duotone photos

Hardback
0 7148 4159 5

£ **45.00** UK
$ **69.95** US
€ **75.00** EUR
$ **99.95** CAN
$ **130.00** AUS

Mario Giacomelli

With an introduction by Alistair Crawford

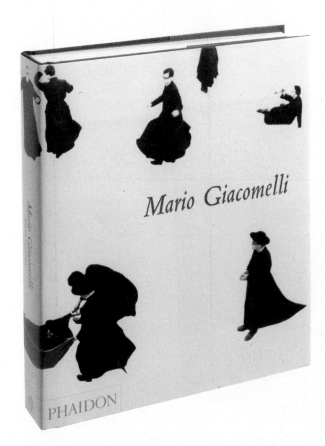

- **The first comprehensive monograph on the work of the great, poetic, Italian photographer Mario Giacomelli (1925–2000)**
- **Arranged in themes, each section is a testament to his highly personal, striking and artistically atmospheric visual style**
- **Demonstrates his life-long preoccupation with landscapes, rural townscapes, street scenes, still life and portraits of everyday Italian life**
- **Includes exclusive interview with Giacomelli by Alessandra Mauro**

Alistair Crawford has contributed widely to photography books, catalogues and journals in Britain, France, Italy, New Zealand and the US. He has also curated several major touring photographic exhibitions including 'Mario Giacomelli'

'This monograph skilfully rehearses one of the most extraordinary, original and engaging careers in photography.' *(Times Literary Supplement)*

General
Non-Fiction

Art

Photography

Collector's
Editions

Film

Architecture

178 × 131 mm
7 × 5¼ inches
132 pp
39 duotone photos

Hardback
0 7148 3840 3

£ 12.95 UK
$ 19.95 US
€ 22.95 EUR
$ 29.95 CAN
$ 35.00 AUS

Village of the Nubas

Photographs and text by George Rodger

- Taken in 1949, George Rodger's photographs of the Nuba tribe in the Sudan are a unique and highly influential documentation of African life
- After experiencing the atrocities of Belsen, Rodger became determined to find a world in which universal values prevailed and went in search of a society that had not been tainted by Western 'civilization'
- A compelling, diary-sized book that documents the Nubas' rituals and way of life; it deeply influenced other photographers, including Leni Reifenstahl
- The first English language version of one of the classics of photographic literature, *Village of the Nubas* was originally published in France in 1955

Co-founder of the prestigious Magnum agency, **George Rodger** (1908–95) was a war correspondent with *Life* from 1939 to 1945. Traumatized by the experience of war, he embarked on a 28,000-mile journey to Africa and the Middle East, concentrating on rituals and ways of life in close relationship with nature

'One of the classics of photographic literature…a remarkable anthropological study cum travel book, small in format, yet perfectly formed.' *(Art Newspaper)*

Humanity and Inhumanity

The Photographic Journey of George Rodger

Photographs by George Rodger, text by Bruce Bernard, picture research by Peter Marlow, foreword by Henri Cartier-Bresson

290 × 250 mm
11⅜ × 9⅞ inches
320 pp
230 duotone photos

Paperback
0 7148 3901 9

£ 24.95   UK
$ 39.95   US
€ 39.95   EUR
$ 59.95   CAN
$ 69.95   AUS

Hardback
0 7148 3165 4

£ 45.00   UK
$ 69.95   US
€ 75.00   EUR
$ 98.00   CAN
$ 125.00   AUS

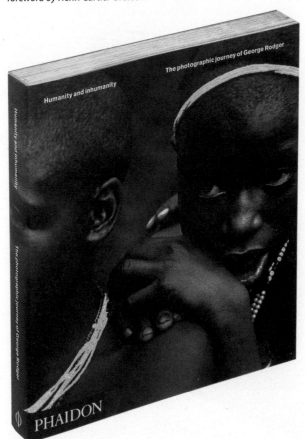

- The first and only monograph of the complete career of George Rodger, co-founder of the Magnum photo agency
- Covers his work from *Life* magazine, the 1940 London Blitz and assignments in Africa, Asia and the Middle East
- A gentle man and determined chronicler of his times, this book presents the pictures that define George Rodger's long career, together with reflections by Bruce Bernard on each phase of his extraordinary life's journey
- A foreword by Henri Cartier-Bresson complements 230 powerful images in a fitting tribute to Rodger's oeuvre

Bruce Bernard was a picture editor for some of Britain's leading newspapers and magazines. He was the author of the award-winning *Century* published by Phaidon
Peter Marlow was President of Magnum from 1989 to 1993. He started his photographic career in 1977, working on news and features with Sygma. His work has been published internationally and his latest publication is *Liverpool: Looking out to Sea* (1993)
Henri Cartier-Bresson, born in 1908, is a world-renowned pioneer of photojournalism and documentary photography and was one of the founding members of Magnum Photos in 1947

'The outstanding photographic book of the year.' *(British Journal of Photography)*

General Non-Fiction

Art

Photography

Collector's Editions

Film

Architecture

380 × 275 mm
15 × 10¾ inches
480 pp
382 tritone photos

Hardback
0 7148 3815 2

£ **75.00** UK
$ **125.00** US
€ **125.00** EUR
$ **180.00** CAN
$ **215.00** AUS

Award
Winner of National Press Photographers Association and the Missouri School of Journalism 'Pictures of the Year Competition'

Inferno

Photographs and afterword by James Nachtwey, with an introduction by Luc Sante

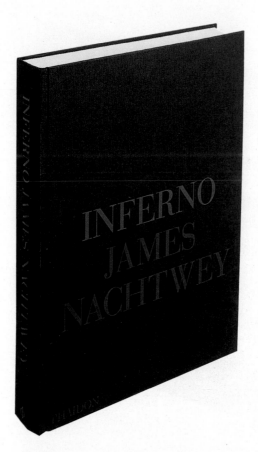

- Inspired by an overwhelming belief in the human possibility of change, this is the first major monograph of humanitarian and photojournalist James Nachtwey
- Aims to communicate the horrors that we often choose to ignore, addressing victims' suffering and powerlessness with an unflinching gaze
- Guides us through issues from Somalia's famine to genocide in Rwanda, from Romania's abandoned orphans and 'irrecoverables' to the lives of India's 'untouchables', from war in Bosnia to conflict in Chechnya
- With text by award-winning writer Luc Sante, author of *Low Life, The Factory of Facts* and *Evidence*

James Nachtwey is one of the world's most highly respected photo-journalists. His photographs have appeared regularly in *Time, Life, Newsweek, National Geographic* and many others.
Luc Sante is the author of *Low Life, Evidence* and *The Factory of Facts*, and, most recently, *Walker Evans*. He is currently Visiting Professor at Bard College

'Brilliant and often shocking images by the world's greatest photojournalist.' *(Publishing News)*
'Not just a moral triumph but an aesthetic one.' (David Reiff, *Los Angeles Times Book Review*)
'These pictures, unrelenting in the exposure of inhumanity, do not spare us and are not meant to, yet Nachtwey's belief in their necessity and power put them among the most hopeful pictures produced in the century.' (Vicki Goldberg, *American Photo*)

Design

Fashion & Contemporary Culture

Decorative Arts

Music & Performing Arts

Video

Index

250 × 250 mm
9⅞ × 9⅞ inches
572 pp
»tone and 24 biographical photos

Hardback
0 7148 4067 X

£   **45.00**   UK
$ **69.95**   US
€   **75.00**   EUR
$ **99.95**   CAN
$ **130.00**   AUS

Robert Capa

The Definitive Collection
Photographs by Robert Capa, with text by Richard Whelan

- **The only definitive collection of the entire career of Robert Capa, perhaps the most influential war photographer the world has ever known**
- **Includes all the iconic stories, including his coverage of the Spanish Civil War, the landing of American troops on Omaha beach and the Liberation of Paris, as well as his world famous images of, among others, Picasso and Hemingway**
- **Sequenced in chronological order, the book covers many of the major events and people that shaped the 20th century**

Robert Capa (1913–54) died while on assignment in Indochina, after stepping on a landmine. Known for his extreme bravery, amazing eye and irresistible charm, his life and work were inextricably interlinked and both have had a marked influence on generations of photographers. He was a co-founder of the Magnum co-operative.
Richard Whelan is an outstanding authority on Capa's life and work. He is a New York-based independent cultural historian and the author of several books including acclaimed biographies of Robert Capa and Alfred Stieglitz

'Provides the images, depth and context to reinforce his reputation as the greatest war photographer.' *(Columbus Dispatch)*
'[A] deeply humane quality is … detectable in all of his pictures, which is why they are so moving.' *(Times Literary Supplement)*

330 × 248 mm
400 pp incl 16 fold-outs
24-page caption booklet
Over 350 duotone photos

Paperback
0 7148 3718 0

£ **45.00** UK
€ **75.00** EUR
$ **125.00** AUS

Not available in the
USA and Canada

Workers

An Archaeology of the Industrial Age

Photographs and text by Sebastião Salgado, with essays by Eric Nepomuceno, Maria Thereza and José Solano Bastos

- A global epic by acclaimed photographer Sebastião Salgado that affirms the enduring spirit of working women and men
- Through sequences of extraordinary photographs Salgado unearths layers of visual information to reveal that ceaseless human activity at the core of modern civilization
- An elegy to the passing of traditional methods of labour and production
- With extended captions by the photographer, the book is divided into six chapters: Agriculture, Food, Mining, Industry, Oil and Construction
- Includes workers from all corners of the globe, including brick layers in India and builders on the Channel Tunnel

Sebastião Salgado (b.1944) is one of the leading photojournalists working today. Born in Brazil and trained as an economist, his lively political activities led to his exile in the late 1960s. He has received many of photojournalism's most prestigious awards, including the W Eugene Smith Grant in Humanistic Photography, and his many books have been published to great acclaim. He is currently based in Paris

'A vast and beautiful anthology of the condition of labour.' *(Guardian)*

330 × 245 mm
13 × 9²⁄₃ inches
144 pp
109 duotone photos

Paperback
0 7148 3700 8

£ **24.95** UK
$ **39.95** US
€ **39.95** EUR
$ **59.95** CAN
$ **69.95** AUS

Terra

Struggle of the Landless

Photographs by Sebastião Salgado, with an introduction by José Saramango

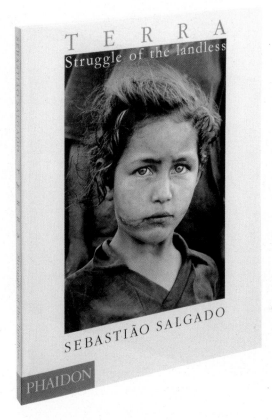

- A story in photographs by Sebastião Salgado of the forced migration of Brazilian peasants and their struggle to survive in the face of joblessness and extreme poverty
- Documents the efforts of the peasants to reclaim the arable land they see as their natural heritage
- Recounts how the fight has often ended in bloodshed
- Accompanied by poems by the Brazilian composer and popular singer Chico Buarque de Hollanda

Sebastião Salgado (b.1944) is one of the leading photojournalists working today. Born in Brazil and trained as an economist, his lively political activities led to his exile in the late 1960s. He has received many of photojournalism's most prestigious awards, including the W Eugene Smith Grant in Humanistic Photography, and his many books have been published to great acclaim. He is currently based in Paris

José Saramango is a Portuguese writer, whose work combines myths, the history of his own country and a surrealistic imagination. He was awarded the Nobel Prize for Literature in 1998

'Buy this book for a collection of outstanding documentary photography and you've got your money's worth. But you will soon realize it is worth more than just that.' *(The Photographic Journal)*

General
Non-Fiction

Art

Photography

Collector's
Editions

Film

Architecture

295 × 420 mm
11⁵⁸ × 16¹₂ inches
112 pp
108 duotone photos

Hardback
0 7148 3900 0

£ **39.95** UK
$ **69.95** US
€ **69.95** EUR
$ **98.00** CAN
$ **99.95** AUS

Chaos

*Photographs by Josef Koudelka with a foreword by Robert Delpire and an introduction
by Bernard Noël*

- A collection of powerful urban and environmental panoramic landscapes by Josef Koudelka
- An outstanding body of work by one of the most critically acclaimed documentary
  photographers of our time, these photographs span a 12-year period
- One of the leading members of Magnum, this is Koudelka's first major monograph since his
  acclaimed *Exiles*

Robert Delpire is an editor, art director and curator. From 1982 to 1996 he was Director of the
Centre National de la Photographie, Paris, where he curated over 150 exhibitions. He has played
a seminal role in promoting the understanding and appreciation of photography worldwide

'Only the greatest of photographers, such as Koudelka, can reconcile such diametrically
opposed elements as documentary and aesthetic truth into one seamless image so that [it] is
at once highly significant and utterly compelling. *Chaos* ... destined to be a classic, succeeds
in doing so time and again.' (Richard Pinsent, *Art Newspaper*)
'A book of complex, and very often beautiful, images…a wonderful monograph ... Koudelka
confirms his standing at the top of any hierarchy of 20th century image-makers with this book'
(British Journal of Photography)
'*Chaos* confirms Josef Koudelka as one of the world's greatest living photographers ... This is
not just a landmark photographic book but a landmark book per se.' *(Scotland on Sunday)*

Design

Fashion & Contemporary Culture

Decorative Arts

Music & Performing Arts

Video

Index

280 × 202 mm
11 × 8 inches
224 pp
266 duotone photos

Hardback
0 7148 4152 8

£ **24.95** UK
$ **39.95** US
€ **39.95** EUR
$ **59.95** CAN
$ **69.95** AUS

Vietnam Inc.

Photographs and text by Philip Jones Griffiths, with a foreword by Noam Chomsky

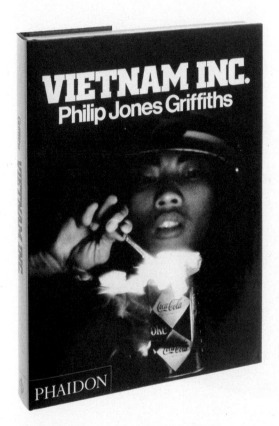

- **A groundbreaking, classic book, originally published in 1971, that was essential in turning the tide of opinion in the US and ultimately helping to put an end to the Vietnam War**
- **The outcome of three years' work on the ground in Vietnam resulting in one of the most detailed surveys of any conflict**
- **This new edition was recreated with the photographer and includes his same personal layouts and commentaries**
- **New foreword discusses the book's impact on American public opinion**

Highly influential, master photojournalist, **Philip Jones Griffiths** (b. 1936) is also a writer and film-maker. His photographs have appeared in every major magazine in the world and his assignments have led him to all five continents. He became a member of Magnum in 1971 **Noam Chomsky** is one of the most prominent political dissidents. A renowned professor of linguistics at the Massachusetts Institute of Technology, he has written over 30 political books

'Few photo books can claim the social and historic importance of *Vietnam Inc.*' *(Bookforum)* '"The greatest description of war since Goya," raved Henri Cartier-Bresson ... Thirty years on, *Vietnam Inc.* is still a classic ... essential to anyone interested in Vietnam's history, America, photography or war. ... Like many photojournalists, however, Griffiths retains his faith in both the ultimate goodness of humanity and the power of the photographic image. *Vietnam Inc.* is a testament to the latter.' *(Far Eastern Economic Review)*

281

General
Non-Fiction

Art

Photography

Collector's
Editions

Film

Architecture

303 × 219 mm
12 × 8⅞ inches
108 pp
103 duotone photos

Hardback
0 7148 4001 7

£ **24.95** UK
€ **39.95** EUR
$ **39.95** US
$ **59.95** CAN
$ **65.00** AUS

Dorchester Days

Photographs and text by Eugene Richards

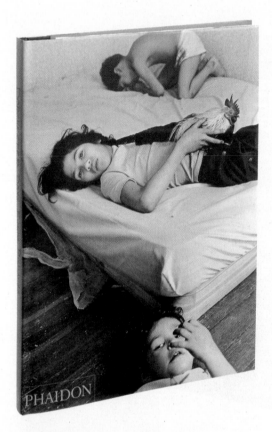

- A photographic portrait of the blue collar Boston neighbourhood where the documentary photographer Eugene Richards came of age
- A personal portrayal of a town and nation in a state of transition and decline
- Tackles subjects such as racial tension, violence, poverty and crime head-on
- A respected classic that has been reordered and expanded in this new edition to include many previously unpublished photographs

Originally a social worker, **Eugene Richards** (b.1944) is best known for his books and photo essays on cancer, drug addiction, poverty, emergency medicine and paediatric HIV. His intense vision and unswerving commitment have led him to become arguably America's greatest living social documentary photographer

'I can go places in the world, but the lessons you learn at home stay with you.'
(Bill Forry, *The Dorchester Reporter*)

Design

Fashion & Contemporary Culture

Decorative Arts

Music & Performing Arts

Video

Index

250 × 189 mm
9⁷⁸ × 7³⁸ inches
292 pp
119 duotone photos

Hardback
0 7148 3961 2

£ 35.00 UK
$ 59.95 US
€ 59.95 EUR
$ 89.95 CAN
$ 95.00 AUS

The Mennonites

Photographs and text by Larry Towell

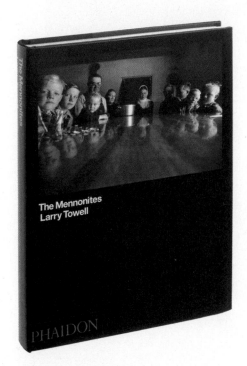

- The culmination of a ten-year project exploring the way of life of Mennonite communities in Canada and Mexico
- The definitive collection of Larry Towell's most important work to date
- A unique documentary record of a culture where photography is normally not permitted
- An important survey of a way of life that may soon change beyond recognition
- Accompanied by Towell's own text written in the tradition of Steinbeck, making the book an unusually successful and complete portrait of a way of life

The work of **Larry Towell** (b.1953) is based on intimacy. His photographs of the Nicaraguan contra war, the 'Disappeared' of Guatemala, US Vietnam veterans and Palestine, as well as those of his own family, all demonstrate an acutely personal relationship with his subjects which is underpinned by his beautiful prose. Poet and folk musician Towell became a member of Magnum in 1988

Citation of Excellence, Best Documentary, Photo-Eye Awards, 2000
'An astonishing collection of photographs whose haunting, grainy beauty takes the ... reader on a most unlikely journey – to another time and another place.' *(Daily Telegraph)*
'Larry Towell offers his reader a considered, intimate and honest insight into the joys and hardships of this invisible nation. Highly recommended.' *(Royal Photographic Society Journal)*

General
Non-Fiction

Art

Photography

Collector's
Editions

Film

Architecture

290 × 250 mm
11³⁄₈ × 9⁷⁄₈ inches
256 pp
218 duotone photos

Hardback
0 7148 3523 4

£ **45.00** UK
$ **69.95** US
€ **75.00** EUR
$ **98.00** CAN
$ **125.00** AUS

Living Apart

South Africa under apartheid
Photographs by Ian Berry, foreword by the Most Reverend Desmond M Tutu

- A unique record of South African apartheid by photographer Ian Berry
- Documents the tragic and disturbing results of institutionalized segregation
- Captures significant moments in South African history, such as the election and its remarkable aftermath

Ian Berry moved to South Africa in 1952. There he worked for several newspapers and journals, among them the magazine *Drum*. The recipient of many awards, including the Arts Council's first major photographic bursary in 1974 and Nikon's Photographer of the Year Award in 1977, Ian Berry is a member of Magnum Photos and has exhibited worldwide

'A compelling history that is beautifully presented.' *(American Photo)*

Archbishop Desmond Tutu, was awarded the Nobel Peace Prize in 1984, in recognition of his non-violent campaign to limit international trade and investment activities in South Africa. After retiring as Archbishop in 1996 he became Chairman of the Truth and Reconciliation Commission in South Africa. He is now a Visiting Professor at the Candler School of Theology at Emory University in the USA

Design

Fashion & Contemporary Culture

Decorative Arts

Music & Performing Arts

Video

Index

290 × 250 mm
11³⁄₈ × 9⁷⁄₈ inches
320 pp
266 duotone photos

Paperback
0 7148 4233 8

£ **24.95** UK
$ **39.95** US
€ **39.95** EUR
$ **59.95** CAN
$ **69.95** AUS

Hardback
0 7148 3162 X

£ **45.00** UK
$ **69.95** US
€ **69.95** EUR
$ **98.00** CAN
$ **125.00** AUS

Allah O Akbar

A Journey Through Militant Islam
Photographs and text by Abbas

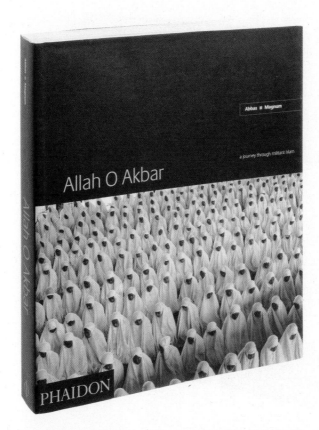

- An in-depth study by Iranian photojournalist Abbas of the Muslim world
- A unique photographic record of a seven-year journey from Sinkiang to Morocco and Paris to Timbuktu
- With a sensitive and enquiring eye, Abbas seeks to reveal the nature of Muslim societies across the globe

Born in Iran, **Abbas** (b.1944) is currently based in Paris. He has covered many of the major political events in Iran, Ulster, Bangladesh, Chile, Cuba, South Africa and the Middle East, and his work is published in magazines worldwide. He is a member of the prestigious photo agency Magnum

'His book fulfils one of the classic roles of great photojournalism, in that it helps both to illuminate an issue and to understand its complexities.' *(British Journal of Photography)*

General Non-Fiction

Art

Photography

Collector's Editions

Film

Architecture

303 × 245 mm
12 × 9⅝ inches
124 pp
83 tritone photos

Hardback
0 7148 3719 9

£ **19.95** UK
$ **29.95** US
€ **35.00** EUR
$ **45.00** CAN
$ **55.00** AUS

To Sleep, Perchance to Dream

Ferdinando Scianna

- A collection of photographs spanning 30 years of work portraying people and animals wrapped in the arms of life's great healer: sleep
- Interspersed with evocative quotations about sleep and dreaming
- Explores a dimension of life that is natural and mysterious, necessary and disturbing, everyday and universal

Ferdinando Scianna (b.1946) became a member of Magnum in 1989. His photographs have been widely exhibited and published internationally, and he has worked on assignments in Europe, Africa and America. *To Sleep, Perchance to Dream* is his first book to be published in English

Design

Fashion & Contemporary Culture

Decorative Arts

Music & Performing Arts

Video

Index

230 × 285 mm
88 pp
60 duotone photos

Paperback
0 7148 3054 2

£ **19.95** UK
€ **35.00** EUR
$ **55.00** AUS

Not available in the
USA and Canada

Sally Mann: Immediate Family

Photographs and introduction by Sally Mann, with an afterword by Reynolds Price

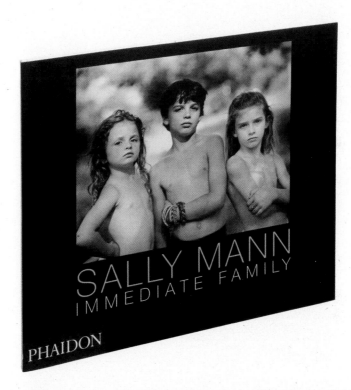

- A collection of extraordinarily intimate photographs of her children by Sally Mann
- A seminal book by an important and influential contemporary photographer
- A remarkable record of the photographer's children as they explore their woodland home in Virginia
- Shows the ambiguities and dramas of family life and hauntingly evokes the mysteries of childhood
- Ethereal, tender and sometimes disquieting

Sally Mann (b.1951) has exhibited her artwork around the world, and her work is in the permanent collections of the Metropolitan Museum of Art, the Museum of Modern Art, the Whitney Museum of American Art and the Corcoran Gallery, among others. Other publications by Sally Mann include *At Twelve: Portraits of Young Women* (1988)
Reynolds Price is an American novelist who was awarded the William Faulkner Award for his first novel. He is a James B Duke Professor of English at Duke University, North Carolina

'A beguiling insight into the enigma of childhood.' *(The Sunday Times)*

General
Non-Fiction

Art

Photography

Collector's
Editions

Film

Architecture

250 × 250 mm
9⁷⁸ × 9⁷⁸ inches
120 pp
61 duotone photos

Hardback
0 7148 4058 0

£ **29.95** UK
$ **49.95** US
€ **49.95** EUR
$ **75.00** CAN
$ **85.00** AUS

Award
Winner of the
Best Photography
Book Prize at
PhotoEspana 2001
Madrid, Spain

Outland

Photographs by Roger Ballen, with an introduction by Peter Weiermair

- A shocking and powerful portrayal of whites on the fringe of South African society
- Combines strong social statements and disturbing psychological studies
- The culmination of almost 20 years of work for artist-photographer Roger Ballen
- One of the most extraordinary photographic documents of the late 20th century

Roger Ballen was born in New York in 1950. On leaving school, he spent several years travelling before settling in Johannesburg, South Africa, in 1982, where he established a practice as a geologist, prospecting mineral deposits across southern Africa. While travelling to outlying regions of South Africa, he also made photographs. He published two books of his photographs: *Dorps: Small Towns of South Africa* in 1986, and *Platteland: Images from Rural South Africa* in 1994
Peter Weiermair is Director of the Rupertinum Museum in Salzburg, Austria

'Compelling, powerful, haunting.' *(Guardian)*
'His photographs breathe new life into the great documentary tradition of August Sanders, Walker Evans and Diane Arbus.' *(Art Newspaper)*

Design

Fashion & Contemporary Culture

Decorative Arts

Music & Performing Arts

Video

Index

270 × 190 mm
10⅝ × 7½ inches
512 pp
508 duotone photos

Paperback
0 7148 4330 X
See also collector's
edition on p.360

£ **29.95** UK
$ **49.95** US
€ **49.95** EUR
$ **75.00** CAN
$ **89.95** AUS

Hardback
0 7148 4150 1

£ **45.00** UK
$ **69.95** US
€ **75.00** EUR
$ **99.95** CAN
$ **130.00** AUS

Elliott Erwitt Snaps

Photographs by Elliott Erwitt, with texts by Murray Sayle and Charles Flowers

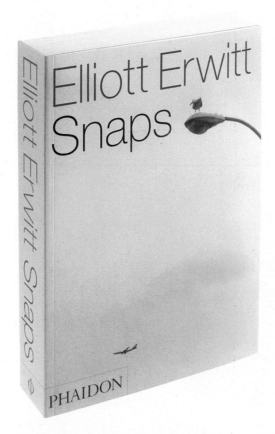

- The first comprehensive monograph covering the complete career of Elliott Erwitt, one of the leading photographers of his generation
- Offers a snapshot of the famous and the ordinary, the strange and the amusing over a period of more than half a century through the lens of one of the period's finest image makers
- Artist and documenter and a Magnum member since 1954, Erwitt's camera has taken him all over the globe
- Includes images of places, things, people and animals, all in Erwitt's unmistakable, often witty, style
- Contains over 200 previously unpublished photographs

Murray Sayle is an Australian writer based in Japan and a regular contributor to *The New Yorker*
Charles Flowers is a freelance writer based in New York, was named Best Columnist by the New York Press Association for his arts and theatre criticism

'Rare among photographers, Erwitt can make you laugh out loud (just turn to pages 86–87), but his scope is Tolstoyan. This 550-page retrospective will absorb you for years.' *(Independent)*
'An essential career-spanning retrospective that reveals Erwitt's unassuming wit, brilliant framing and deep humanity.' *(New York Post)*

General
Non-Fiction

Art

Photography

Collector's
Editions

Film

Architecture

185 × 123 mm
7 × 4³⁄₄ inches
512 pp
500 duotone photos

Paperback
0 7148 3805 5

£ **6.95** UK
$ **9.95** US
€ **11.95** EUR
$ **14.95** CAN
$ **16.95** AUS

DogDogs

Photographs by Elliott Erwitt, text by P G Wodehouse

- A collection of thousands of dogs photographed over 50 years by Magnum photographer Elliott Erwitt
- A fun, must-have item for all dog lovers
- Includes old, new, wild and domestic dogs; Poodles, Airedales and Highland Terriers; dogs at play and rest; on beaches, hearthrugs, riverbanks, sofas and park benches

One of the greatest image makers of his generation, **Elliott Erwitt** (b.1928) describes himself as 'a professional photographer by trade and an amateur photographer by vocation'. A member of Magnum since 1954, his camera has taken him all over the globe and his pictures have been the subject of many books and exhibitions worldwide. Artist and documenter, his work spans many traditions, subjects and approaches to photography
Sir Pelham Grenville Wodehouse (1881–1975) was an English humorist who wrote novels, short stories, plays, lyrics and essays, all with the same light touch of gentle satire. He was a great admirer of Elliott Erwitt's work during his lifetime

'This book is a must for all dog-lovers.' *(Marie Claire)*
'Barking dogs, laughing dogs, big dogs, small dogs, lazy dogs, crazy dogs: they're all here ... will provide hours of delight.' *(Amateur Photographer)*

Design

Fashion &
Contemporary
Culture

Decorative Arts

Music &
Performing Arts

Video

Index

Box dimensions
190 × 125 mm
7¹₂ × 5 inches

Postcard box (50 cards)
0 7148 5057 8

•tings card box (25 cards)
(horizontal)
0 7148 5056 X

tings card box (25 cards)
(vertical)
0 7148 3841 1

incl. VAT £ **9.95** UK
$ **12.95** US
€ **16.95** EUR
$ **18.95** CAN
$ **19.95** AUS

DogDogs Card Boxes

Photographs by Elliott Erwitt

- **Three specially designed card boxes containing a selection of the most popular images from Elliott Erwitt's best-selling book *DogDogs***
- **Includes old, new, wild and domestic dogs: Poodles, Airedales and Highland Terriers; dogs at play and at rest**
- **A perfect gift for all dog lovers**
- **Postcard box contains 50 postcards, each a different image**
- **Two boxes of greeting cards each contain 25 blank greeting cards with envelopes and a selection of 25 different images in each box**

One of the greatest image makers of his generation, **Elliott Erwitt** (b.1928) describes himself as 'a professional photographer by trade and an amateur photographer by vocation'. A member of Magnum since 1954, his camera has taken him all over the globe and his pictures have been the subject of many books and exhibitions worldwide. Artist and documenter, his work spans many traditions, subjects and approaches to photography·

General Non-Fiction

Art

Photography

Collector's Editions

Film

Architecture

245 × 210 mm
9⁵⁸ × 8¹⁴ inches
160 pp
160 duotone photos

Hardback
0 7148 3894 2

£ **19.95** UK
$ **29.95** US
€ **35.00** EUR
$ **45.00** CAN
$ **55.00** AUS

Museum Watching

Photographs and text by Elliott Erwitt

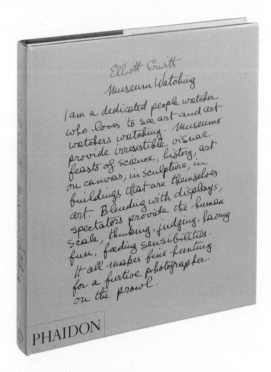

- Entertaining collection of Elliott Erwitt's visual observations on people in museums
- An affectionate, wry album of gentle humour and visual puns, accompanied by the photographer's own text
- Includes work spanning Erwitt's career from the late 1950s to the present

One of the greatest image makers of his generation, **Elliott Erwitt** (b.1928) describes himself as 'a professional photographer by trade and an amateur photographer by vocation'. A member of Magnum since 1954, his camera has taken him all over the globe and his pictures have been the subject of many books and exhibitions worldwide. Artist and documenter, his work spans many traditions, subjects and approaches to photography

'A minor masterpiece.' *(Art Quarterly)*
'Reveals us at our most endearingly human in the hallowed halls of great art.' *(Boston Globe)*

Design

Fashion & Contemporary Culture

Decorative Arts

Music & Performing Arts

Video

Index

283 × 210 mm
11⅛ × 8¼ inches
196 pp
145 duotone photos

Hardback
0 7148 3973 6

£ **29.95** UK
$ **49.95** US
€ **49.95** EUR
$ **75.00** CAN
$ **85.00** AUS

Too Much Time

Women in Prison
Photographs and introduction by Jane Evelyn Atwood

- **A ground-breaking documentary survey of the experience of women in prison by award-winning photojournalist Jane Evelyn Atwood**
- **Raises provocative questions about the relative treatment of men and women in prison and about the links between women's crimes and male violence**
- **Takes the reader into the lives of women in prison as they reflect on personal responsibility and social realities, guilt and reparation, change, loss and survival**

Jean Evelyn Atwood (b.1947) has received many honours including the W Eugene Smith Award and an Alfred Eisenstaedt Award. Her photographs have been exhibited in museums worldwide and published in magazines such as *Life, Stern, Paris Match* and *The New York Times Magazine*

'This is engaged, politically aware photojournalism at its best.' *(New Internationalist)*

General Non-Fiction

Art

Photography

Collector's Editions

Film

Architecture

220 × 167 mm
8⁵⁸ × 6¹₂ inches
192 pp
90 duotone photos

Paperback
0 7148 3842 X

£ **19.95** UK
$ **29.95** US
€ **35.00** EUR
$ **45.00** CAN
$ **55.00** AUS

L'Autre

Photographs by Luc Delahaye, with text by Jean Baudrillard

- Contains 90 photographs that Luc Delahaye took of passengers on the Paris Métro between 1995 and 1997 using a hidden camera
- An exploration of the relationship between the photographer and his subject, and a revealing investigation into the meaning of the human image
- Accompanied by text by major cultural theorist Jean Baudrillard

Luc Delahaye was born in France in 1962. Since 1989 he has photographed many of the conflicts around the world, receiving numerous awards including the Robert Capa Gold Medal and, most recently, the Oskar Barnack Award 2000 for the *Winterreise* photographs. He became a member of the Magnum photo agency in 1994
Jean Baudrillard is a French cultural theorist and philosopher whose writings on Postmodernism, Marxism and contemporary culture have been hugely influential internationally

'If you've ever feigned sleep on the Tube to avoid eye contact with other passengers, you will identify with the subjects of *L'Autre* ... it's a compelling book: the text alone will keep you coming back to it, and the fact that the Metro travellers refuse to look at you just makes you want to stare at them even more.' *(Scene)*

Design

Fashion &
Contemporary
Culture

Decorative Arts

Music &
Performing Arts

Video

Index

178 × 131 mm
7 × 5¼ inches
232 pp
144 col photos

Paperback
0 7148 4339 3

£ **14.95** UK
$ **24.95** US
€ **24.95** EUR
$ **39.95** CAN
$ **45.00** AUS

Hardback
0 7148 3997 3

£ **24.95** UK
$ **39.95** US
€ **39.95** EUR
$ **59.95** CAN
$ **65.00** AUS

Winterreise

Photographs by Luc Delahaye

- **A compelling, sad and beautiful road story across Russia told by photographer Luc Delahaye**
- **A look into the private face of Russia's moral and social crisis**
- **An exceptional body of work that bridges the divide between art and journalism**
- **With poetic photographs that are simultaneously terrifying, exciting, intimate, moving and revealing**

Luc Delahaye was born in France in 1962. Since 1989 he has photographed many of the conflicts around the world, receiving numerous awards including the Robert Capa Gold Medal and, most recently, the Oskar Barnack Award 2000 for the *Winterreise* photographs. He became a member of the Magnum photo agency in 1994

'... photographer Luc Delahaye finds a country's soul ... his sojourn is an epic new book...one of the most compelling photojournalism monographs to emerge in recent years.' *(American Photo)*

297 × 198 mm
11⁵⁸ × 7³⁴ inches
104 pp
46 col photos

Hardback
0 7148 3910 8

£ 24.95 UK
$ 39.95 US
€ 39.95 EUR
$ 59.95 CAN
$ 65.00 AUS

Acta Est

Photogaphs by Lise Sarfati, with an introduction by Olga Medvedkova

- The first book by the emerging photographer-artist Lise Sarfati
- Weaves images of Russia during the 1990s into a visual drama of dysfunction and deterioration, change and beauty
- Documents a world of decaying buildings and neglected factories peopled with lost characters – young transsexuals and teenage runaways interned in 're-education' camps
- With a thought-provoking introduction by the Russian-born art historian Olga Medvedkova

Lise Sarfati (b.1958) studied Russian at the Sorbonne in Paris before taking up photography. During the 1990s she won many major photography awards for her photographs of Russia. She became an associate member of Magnum Photos in 1999
Olga Medvedkova is an art historian based in Paris. Born in Moscow in 1963, she studied history of art in Moscow and Paris. She is the co-author of several books including *L'art russe* (Paris, 1991), *Histoire de Saint Pétersbourg* (Paris, 1996) and *L'architecture française en Russie au XVIIIe siècle (forthcoming)*

'Lise Sarfati's starkly lit photos of a disintegrating Russia are deceptively simple. Look a little longer and you'll see why her work, published for the first time in *Acta Est*, has won every award going.' *(Red)*

Design

Fashion & Contemporary Culture

Decorative Arts

Music & Performing Arts

Video

Index

280 × 295 mm
11 × 11¹₂ inches
40 Chinese-folded pages
25 col photos

Hardback
0 7148 3809 8

£ **35.00** UK
$ **49.95** US
€ **59.95** EUR
$ **69.95** CAN
$ **95.00** AUS

Sightwalk

Photographs by Gueorgui Pinkhassov

- Rich in visual poetry, Japanese-style, this exquisite collection of photographs by Gueorgui Pinkhassov is the first to be published in book form
- A beautiful object and an extraordinary piece of design, a modernist Japanese photo album created from Oriental fabrics and papers, bound by hand
- Explores how singular details such as the play of light and reflections can shape an atmosphere

Gueorgui Pinkhassov (b.1952) is a highly acclaimed photographic artist and innovator who was born and raised in the Soviet Union. In 1979 his pictures were noticed during a group exhibition on Soviet photography in Paris and in 1991 he became a member of Magnum

'Gueorgui Pinkhassov's first book is a visual gem. Immerse yourself for a rush a sensual joy.' *(Elle Decoration)*
'Beguiling, calm and unhurried, it is a beautiful collection of photographs.' *(Independent)*

General Non-Fiction

Art

Photography

Collector's Editions

Film

Architecture

210 × 325 mm
8¼ × 12¾ inches
168 pp
132 col photos

Paperback
0 7148 3996 5

£ **19.95** UK
$ **29.95** US
€ **35.00** EUR
$ **45.00** CAN
$ **59.95** AUS

Award
Winner Best
Retrospective Book,
Photo-Eye Awards
1999

River of Colour

The India of Raghubir Singh
Photographs and text by Raghubir Singh, preface by David Travis

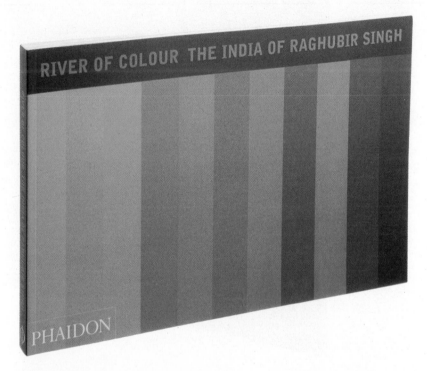

- The only retrospective of Raghubir Singh (1942–99), one of the 20th century's finest colour documentary photographers
- A series of vibrant photographs that capture the exuberant spirit and restless activity of his native India
- Arranged in 11 sections that depict aspects integral to Indian life, including the street, monuments, icons, water and pilgrimages
- With an engaging and informative introduction focusing in particular on the importance of colour in India

David Travis is Curator of Photography at the Art Institute of Chicago. Books include *Taken by Design: Photographs from the Institute of Design, 1937–1971* and *Edward Weston: The Last Years in Carmel*

'*River of Colour* is a sumptuous book, a carefully arranged, beautifully printed documentary of the enormous variety of life and colours of a country that, at times, can almost overwhelm the senses.' *(The Times)*

Design

Fashion & Contemporary Culture

Decorative Arts

Music & Performing Arts

Video

Index

189 × 270 mm
7¹₂ × 10⁵₈ inches
128 pp
108 col photos

Hardback
0 7148 4211 7

£ **24.95** UK
$ **39.95** US
€ **39.95** EUR
$ **59.95** CAN
$ **69.95** AUS

A Way Into India

Photographs and text by Raghubir Singh

- The last great photographic project of one of the 20th century's finest documentary photographers
- A testament to Singh's love affair with the sights, sounds and colours of India, but also with one of its most unexpected icons – the Ambassador car
- Temples and tourists, monsoon rains, paddy fields, tea plantations and elephants are dramatically framed by the Ambassador's distinctive curves
- The old and the new sit side by side, as Singh and the Ambassador show us a way into India

Raghubir Singh (1942–99) is acclaimed as one of the 20th century's finest colour documentary photographers. Born in Rajasthan, he won an international reputation through his books on various aspects of his homeland. His work is currently in the permanent collections of major museums, including the Art Institute of Chicago, the Metropolitan Museum of Art and the Museum of Modern Art in New York, and the Tokyo Metropolitan Museum of Photography

'A pictorial love affair between man, car and country.' *(Amateur Photographer)*

General
Non-Fiction

Art

Photography

Collector's
Editions

Film

Architecture

250 × 290 mm
9⁷⁄₈ × 11³⁄₈ inches
352 pp
441 col, 156 b&w photos

Hardback
0 7148 3990 6
See also collector's
edition on p.362

£ 45.00 UK
$ 75.00 US
€ 75.00 EUR
$ 115.00 CAN
$ 140.00 AUS

Award
PH**E**02

Winner of the
Photo España 2002
Best Photography Book
of the Year Award 2002

Martin Parr

Photographs by Martin Parr, edited and written by Val Williams

- Martin Parr (b.1952) is a highly influential contemporary photographer whose work bridges the divide between art and documentary photography
- The first comprehensive monograph to chart his complete career
- Explores his approach to the documentation of mass culture and consumerism around the world over the last 30 years
- Features early black-and-white photographs and previously unpublished work, in addition to his most famous bodies of work, including *The Last Resort, The Cost of Living* and *Signs of the Times*
- Covers the prolific output that has placed him firmly at the forefront of contemporary art

Val Williams is a well-respected writer and curator, based in London. She is contributing editor of *Creative Camera* magazine and has written for publications including the *Guardian*, the *Independent*, the *Telegraph Magazine* and the *New Statesman*

'... endless hours of pleasure. This is Britain captured in all its bright brash bawdiness, but celebrated with an artistic sensibility that transforms tackiness into art.' *(Guardian)*
'... one of the world's finest documentary photographers.' *(Art Review)*

Design

Fashion & Contemporary Culture

Decorative Arts

Music & Performing Arts

Video

Index

270 × 190 mm
10⁵₈ × 7¹₂ inches
144 pp
133 col photos

Hardback
0 7148 3991 4

£ **24.95** UK
$ **39.95** US
€ **39.95** EUR
$ **59.95** CAN
$ **65.00** AUS

Think of England

Photographs by Martin Parr

- A comic, opinionated, affectionately satirical, colour-saturated photo-essay about the identity of England
- Tours Ascot and the charity shop, seaside resorts, herbaceous borders, cucumber sandwiches and cups of tea, baked beans and bad footwear
- Innovatively shot with a ring flash camera (normally used for medical photographs), Parr's medium of choice for the past four years

The work of **Martin Parr** (b.1952) bridges the divide between art and documentary photography. His studies of the idiosyncrasies of mass culture and consumerism around the world, his innovative imagery and his prolific output have placed him firmly at the forefront of contemporary art. A world authority on photography books and, more recently, a film-maker, Parr joined Magnum in 1994

'An accessible and funny study into the soul-searching debate about the very nature of Englishness.' *(Pride of Britain)*

General
Non-Fiction

Art

Photography

Collector's
Editions

Film

Architecture

150 × 210 mm
6 × 8¼ inches
176 pp
120 col, 35 b&w photos

Hardback
0 7148 3895 0

£ **14.95** UK
$ **24.95** US
€ **24.95** EUR
$ **35.00** CAN
$ **39.95** AUS

Boring Postcards

Edited by Martin Parr

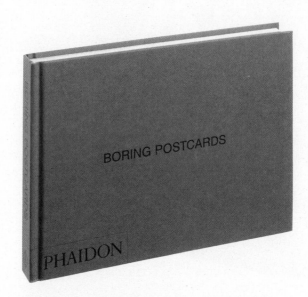

- This is the cream of Martin Parr's fabled postcard collection
- Tackles with wit and irony such subjects as bad taste, food, the tourist, shopping and the foibles of the British
- Functions as commentary on British architecture, social life and identity
- A richly comic photographic entertainment

The work of **Martin Parr** (b.1952) bridges the divide between art and documentary photography. His studies of the idiosyncrasies of mass culture and consumerism around the world, his innovative imagery and his prolific output have placed him firmly at the forefront of contemporary art. A world authority on photography books and, more recently, a film-maker, Parr joined Magnum in 1994

Design

Fashion & Contemporary Culture

Decorative Arts

Music & Performing Arts

Video

Index

'They are, in their boringness, strangely beautiful. They are funny, nostalgic and utterly eccentric. Their banality fascinates. Actually, they're not boring at all.' *Big Issue*

'Far from dull, Parr's book is a strangely compelling commentary on post-war British architecture, social life and identity.'

Independent on Sunday

'Exquisitely tedious visual gems.' *World of Interiors*

'The funniest book [of the year] has been *Boring Postcards* by Martin Parr, which I keep on the kitchen table and chortle over during breakfast. This sends my cornflakes flying.'

Charlotte Cory, *Independent*

General
Non-Fiction

Art

Photography

Collector's
Editions

Film

Architecture

150 × 210 mm
6 × 8¼ inches
176 pp
160 col photos

Hardback
0 7148 4000 9

£ **14.95** UK
$ **19.95** US
€ **24.95** EUR
$ **29.95** CAN
$ **39.95** AUS

Boring Postcards USA

Edited by Martin Parr

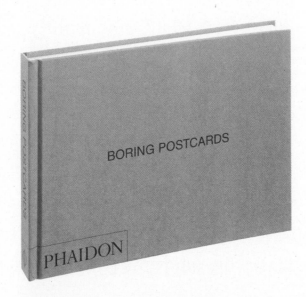

- A companion to Parr's fascinating and extremely funny *Boring Postcards*, which brought together 160 of the dullest postcards of 50s, 60s and 70s Britain
- Now Parr has turned his attention to the USA, recording the non-places and non-events of post-war America
- Though deeply amusing, it also reveals poignant insights into American social, cultural and architectural values

The work of **Martin Parr** (b.1952) bridges the divide between art and documentary photography. His studies of the idiosyncrasies of mass culture and consumerism around the world, his innovative imagery and his prolific output have placed him firmly at the forefront of contemporary art. A world authority on photography books and, more recently, a film-maker, Parr joined Magnum in 1994

'Such American hot spots ... may have been boring then – or, stranger yet, they may not have been – but they're so cheesy now they're delicious.' *(Wall Street Journal)*

Langweilige Postkarten

Edited by Martin Parr

150 × 210 mm
6 × 8¼ inches
176 pp
92 col, 68 b&w photos

Hardback
0 7148 4062 9

£ **14.95** UK
$ **24.95** US
€ **24.95** EUR
$ **35.00** CAN
$ **39.95** AUS

- A collection of hilariously boring postcards made before German reunification
- Provides fascinating insights into German social and architectural values between the 1950s and 1980s
- A companion to Parr's much-discussed *Boring Postcards* of Britain and *Boring Postcards USA*

The work of **Martin Parr** (b.1952) bridges the divide between art and documentary photography. His studies of the idiosyncrasies of mass culture and consumerism around the world, his innovative imagery and his prolific output have placed him firmly at the forefront of contemporary art. A world authority on photography books and, more recently, a film-maker, Parr joined Magnum in 1994

'Not to be missed: 160 views of Germany ... each more dreary than the next – and yet more comical. *Langweilige Postkarten* is not boring at all.' *(Die Tageszeitung)*

General Non-Fiction

Art

Photography

Collector's Editions

Film

Architecture

250 × 315 mm
9⁷⁸ × 12¹² inches
240 pp
175 col, 18 b&w photos

Hardback
0 7148 3828 4

£ **35.00** UK
$ **59.95** US
€ **59.95** EUR
$ **89.95** CAN
$ **99.95** AUS

Award

Pictures of the Year

Winner of an award of excellence in the Best Use of Photography category by National Press Photographers Association and the Missouri School of Journalism 'Pictures of the Year Competition'

Water Light Time

Photographs and text by David Doubilet

- An extraordinary look at the work of David Doubilet, a pioneering artist and diver acclaimed as the world's leading underwater photographer
- A journey beneath the world's waters to landscapes and populations that are as beautiful as those on land but have been explored by few
- Includes over 25 years of Doubilet's work from the Galapagos to the Red Sea, and from the Pacific shores to the fresh waters of North America
- Reveals the mesmerizing beauty of more than 30 bodies of water rich with fascinating life forms

David Doubilet (b.1946), arguably the world's leading underwater photographer, has shot more than 60 stories for *National Geographic*. He began diving when he was 12 and has since captured ground-breaking images of great white sharks, creatures of the undersea desert, fluorescent coral and shipwrecks. He was awarded the prestigious Lennart Nilsson prize in 2001

'A showcase for the work of *National Geographic's* David Doubilet, an heir to Cousteau and Cartier-Bresson, whose underwater photojournalism, with its painterly contortions of colour and geometry, transcends mere reportage.' *(The New Yorker)*
'An inspiring and dramatic book, which takes underwater photography to new levels.' *(Dive)*

Design

Fashion & Contemporary Culture

Decorative Arts

Music & Performing Arts

Video

Index

Box dimensions
137 × 196 mm
5³⁄₈ × 7³⁄₄ inches

Postcard box (45 cards)
0 7148 4227 3

incl. VAT £ **14.95** UK
$ **19.95** US
€ **24.95** EUR
$ **29.95** CAN
$ **39.95** AUS

Water Light Time Postcards

Photographs by David Doubilet

- A specially designed plastic moulded box of 45 postcards with 15 of the best images from David Doubilet's award-winning book *Water Light Time*
- A collection of 15 exquisite photographs, each repeated three times, of the exotic flora and fauna of the deep
- A perfect gift for divers
- Box contains 45 postcards – a selection of 15 images, repeated 3 times

David Doubilet (b.1946), arguably the world's leading underwater photographer, has shot more than 60 stories for *National Geographic*. He began diving when he was 12 and has since captured ground-breaking images of great white sharks, creatures of the undersea desert, fluorescent coral and shipwrecks. He was awarded the prestigious Lennart Nilsson prize in 2001

General Non-Fiction

Art

Photography

Collector's Editions

Film

Architecture

275 × 380 mm
11¹¹⁄₁₆ × 15³⁄₁₆ inches
156 pp
67 col photos

Hardback
0 7148 3938 8

£ 35.00 UK
$ 59.95 US
€ 59.95 EUR
$ 89.95 CAN
$ 95.00 AUS

Award

Pictures of the Year

Awarded First Place
in Best Use of Photography
by National Press
Photographers Association
and the Missouri School
of Journalism

South Southeast

Photographs and text by Steve McCurry

- A portfolio of the best of Steve McCurry's photography: classical, magical and powerful images from South and South East Asia
- Iconic images of the people, places and colours of Afghanistan, India, Sri Lanka, Cambodia, Tibet and Mynanmai (Burma)
- Features sublime images which transcend their original editorial purpose to become classics of photography

Steve McCurry (b.1950) launched his career as a photojournalist when, disguised in native garb, he crossed the Pakistan border into Afghanistan before the Russian invasion. His coverage won him the Robert Capa Gold Medal given to photographers exhibiting exceptional courage and enterprise. Famous also for his work in South East Asia, his photographs are beautiful, uplifting and powerful. McCurry has worked for *National Geographic* magazine for many years and is a member of the prestigious Magnum agency

'... a sublime collection of photographs ... the colours – superbly rendered in this high-quality book – are some of the most exquisite that you are likely to see in a photograph.' *(Sunday Telegraph)*
'This collection paints a vivid picture of the region and confirms McCurry as one of the greatest exponents of colour photography in the world today.' *(Amateur Photography)*
'A celebration of the poetry of photography, of colour, form, chaos and human drama.' *(Traveller)*

Design

Fashion &
Contemporary
Culture

Decorative Arts

Music &
Performing Arts

Video

Index

South Southeast Card Boxes

Photographs by Steve McCurry

Box dimensions
205 × 145 mm
8 × 5⅝ inches

Postcard box (50 cards)
0 7148 4114 5

eting card box (25 cards)
0 7148 4113 7

Each box
incl. VAT £ **14.95** UK
$ **19.95** US
€ **24.95** EUR
$ **29.95** CAN
$ **39.95** AUS

- **Two specially designed tin boxes containing cards of the best images from Steve McCurry's award-winning book *South Southeast***
- **Evocative and timeless images of the cultures and people of South East Asia**
- **Perfect for birthday and thank you cards**
- **Postcard box contains 50 postcards, each a different image**
- **Greeting card box contains 25 blank greeting cards with envelopes and a selection of 25 different images**

Steve McCurry (b.1950) launched his career as a photojournalist when, disguised in native garb, he crossed the Pakistan border into Afghanistan before the Russian invasion. His coverage won him the Robert Capa Gold Medal given to photographers exhibiting exceptional courage and enterprise. Famous also for his work in South East Asia, his photographs are beautiful, uplifting and powerful. McCurry has worked for *National Geographic* magazine for many years and is a member of the prestigious Magnum agency

General
Non-Fiction

Art

Photography

Collector's
Editions

Film

Architecture

189 × 270 mm
7¹⁄₂ × 10⁵⁄₈ inches
144 pp
89 col photos

Hardback
0 7148 4175 7

£ **24.95** UK
$ **39.95** US
€ **39.95** EUR
$ **59.95** CAN
$ **69.95** AUS

Sanctuary

The Temples of Angkor
Photographs by Steve McCurry, with an introduction by John Guy

- Beautiful and evocative photographs of the temples of Angkor in Cambodia, among the world's most impressive monuments
- Documents a magical world of carved gods, weathered masonry, tangled vegetation and orange-robed monks in over 100 photographs
- Accompanied by an informative introduction on the history and meaning of Angkor by John Guy, an authority on the cultural history of South East Asia

Steve McCurry (b.1950) launched his career as a photojournalist when, disguised in native garb, he crossed the Pakistan border into Afghanistan before the Russian invasion. His coverage won him the Robert Capa Gold Medal given to photographers exhibiting exceptional courage and enterprise. Famous also for his work in South East Asia, his photographs are beautiful, uplifting and powerful. McCurry has worked for *National Geographic* magazine for many years and is a member of the prestigious Magnum agency

John Guy is a leading authority on the cultural history of South East Asia. He is Curator of Indian and South East Asian Sculpture at the Victoria & Albert Museum, London, and Consultant to UNESCO on historical monuments in South East Asia

'Steve McCurry captures the beauty and serenity of one of the world's most wonderful sites.' (*Evening Mail*)
'A stunning book documenting this magical world.' (*Traveller*)

Design

Fashion &
Contemporary
Culture

Decorative Arts

Music &
Performing Arts

Video

Index

185 × 123 mm
7¼ × 4⅞ inches
512 pp
255 col photos

Hardback
0 7148 3839 X

£ **12.95** UK
$ **19.95**   US
€ **22.95** EUR
$ **29.95** CAN
$ **35.00** AUS

Point of Sale
Tower and counterpack
available

Portraits

Photographs by Steve McCurry

- **An intriguing collection of unposed and engaging portraits of people from all backgrounds and corners of the globe by award-winning photographer Steve McCurry**
- **A compelling and moving series of unique images of the memorable faces that McCurry has encountered while travelling throughout the world on assignment**
- **Unstylized portraits of children, adolescents and adults from all walks of life that reveal the universality of human emotion**

Steve McCurry (b.1950) launched his career as a photojournalist when, disguised in native garb, he crossed the Pakistan border into Afghanistan before the Russian invasion. His coverage won him the Robert Capa Gold Medal given to photographers exhibiting exceptional courage and enterprise. Famous also for his work in South East Asia, his photographs are beautiful, uplifting and powerful. McCurry has worked for *National Geographic* magazine for many years and is a member of the prestigious Magnum agency

'The global reach of the work, and the knowledge of humanity reflected in it, is breathtaking.'
(The Sunday Times)
'McCurry's talent for catching people with their guard down is on ample display in this ... collection of faces from around the world ... the images speak to the shared humanity of diverse peoples.' *(Life)*

General
Non-Fiction

Art

Photography

Collector's
Editions

Film

Architecture

Box dimensions
182 × 123 mm
7⅛ × 4⅞ inches

Postcard box (50 cards)
0 7148 3885 3

incl. VAT £ **9.95** UK
$ **12.95** US
€ **16.95** EUR
$ **18.95** CAN
$ **19.95** AUS

Point of Sale
10-copy counterpack
available

Portraits Postcards

Photographs by Steve McCurry

- Specially designed card box of 50 images from Steve McCurry's best-selling book *Portraits*
- Ideal to send or pin on the wall for inspiration
- Box contains 50 postcards, each a different image

Steve McCurry (b.1950) launched his career as a photojournalist when, disguised in native garb, he crossed the Pakistan border into Afghanistan before the Russian invasion. His coverage won him the Robert Capa Gold Medal given to photographers exhibiting exceptional courage and enterprise. Famous also for his work in South East Asia, his photographs are beautiful, uplifting and powerful. McCurry has worked for *National Geographic* magazine for many years and is a member of the prestigious Magnum agency

Design

Fashion &
Contemporary
Culture

Decorative Arts

Music &
Performing Arts

Video

Index

Afghan Girl Card Box

Photograph by Steve McCurry

Box dimensions
182 × 123 mm
7¹⁸ × 4⁷⁸ inches

**Postcard and greeting
card box (24 cards)**
0 7148 3975 2

incl. VAT £ **9.95** UK
$ **12.95** US
€ **16.95** EUR
$ **18.95** CAN
$ **19.95** AUS

Point of Sale
10-copy counterpack
available

- Specially designed card box with sliding tray containing 24 cards all bearing the same image of Steve McCurry's world famous and enigmatic Afghan Girl
- Taken in June 1985 in a camp in Pakistan for Afghan refugees, this image is recognized by millions around the world
- 'The girl with the green eyes', Sharbat Gula, was unknown by name until 17 years later when McCurry traced her to a small village in Afghanistan in 2002
- Box contains 12 postcards and 12 blank greeting cards with envelopes

Steve McCurry (b.1950) launched his career as a photojournalist when, disguised in native garb, he crossed the Pakistan border into Afghanistan before the Russian invasion. His coverage won him the Robert Capa Gold Medal given to photographers exhibiting exceptional courage and enterprise. Famous also for his work in South East Asia, his photographs are beautiful, uplifting and powerful. McCurry has worked for *National Geographic* magazine for many years and is a member of the prestigious Magnum agency

General
Non-Fiction

Art

Photography

Collector's
Editions

Film

Architecture

220 × 330 mm
8⅝ × 13 inches
166 pp
c.100 col photos

Hardback
0 7148 4313 X

£ **29.95** UK
$ **49.95** US
€ **49.95** EUR
$ **75.00** CAN
$ **89.95** AUS

Divided Soul

A journey from Iberia
Photographs and text by David Alan Harvey

- An uplifting exploration of the passions and traditions of Hispanic and Portuguese life by David Alan Harvey
- A culmination of 20 years' work in Spain, Portugal and throughout Central and Latin America
- A colourful and lyrical look at the pulsating carnivals and intense religious ceremonies as well as the exuberant street life
- First comprehensive retrospective book of a great colourist photographer

David Alan Harvey (b. 1944) has spent much of the last 20 years exploring the Spanish and Portuguese speaking world. A freelancer for the National Geographic, his lyrical photographs of fleeting moments have been awarded numerous international prizes. He became a member of Magnum in 1996

Design

Fashion & Contemporary Culture

Decorative Arts

Music & Performing Arts

Video

Index

280 × 280 mm
11¹⁄₄ × 11¹⁄₄ inches
120 pp
c.100 col photos

Hardback
0 7184 4307 5

£ **24.95** UK
$ **39.95** US
€ **39.95** EUR
$ **59.95** CAN
$ **69.95** AUS

Bollywood Dreams

An exploration of the motion picture industry and its culture in India
Photographs and text by Jonathan Torgovnik, with an introduction by Nasreen Munni Kabir

- Original photographic essay by award-winning photographer on one of the world's most popular pastimes
- Bollywood and Indian cinema now have an enormous following outside India
- Introductory essay by leading international authority on Indian cinema
- Extended captions explain the people and situations in each photograph
- Shows entire spectrum of movie-making from the sets and stars to the cinemas and fans

Jonathan Torgovnik, who is based in New York, began his career as a combat photographer in the Israeli army. His award-winning photographs have appeared in *Newsweek, Smithsonian, Vanity Fair, Sunday Times Magazine* (London) and *Paris Match,* among others. He was seduced by the spectacular and passionate world of Indian cinema, and *Bollywood Dreams* is the result of a long-term documentary project

Nasreen Munni Kabir is an internationally recognized documentary film-maker and author. She has made several series for television on Hindi cinema and has organized festivals of Indian cinema. In January 2000 she was made a Governor of the British Film Institute

General
Non-Fiction

Art

Photography

Collector's
Editions

Film

Architecture

290 × 224 mm
11³⁄₈ × 8⁷⁄₈ inches
192 pp
112 col photographs

Hardback
0 7148 3967 1

£ **24.95** UK
$ **39.95** US
€ **39.95** EUR
$ **59.95** CAN
$ **65.00** AUS

Impossible Image

Edited by Philip Poynter, with an introduction by Robin Derrick

- A compilation of the best of digitally manipulated imagery from the contemporary fashion world
- Concentrates on the most innovative uses of new technologies and their implementation within the fashion shoot
- Showcases exclusively commissioned work, including the cover by Nick Knight
- Offers a rich sequence of fantastical images that blur the line between fantasy and reality

Philip Poynter is an internationally renowned fashion photographer
Robin Derrick is the Art Director of British *Vogue*

'The best photography book of the past year.' *(Creative Review)*

Design

Fashion &
Contemporary
Culture

Decorative Arts

Music &
Performing Arts

Video

Index

224 × 290 mm
8⁷⁄₈ × 11³⁄₈ inches
192 pp
135 col photographs

Hardback
0 7148 4054 8

£ 29.95 UK
$ 45.00 US
€ 49.95 EUR
$ 69.95 CAN
$ 89.95 AUS

Truth or Consequences

Photographs by Nick Waplington

- An intriguing collection of photographs taken in and around Truth or Consequences, a small town in New Mexico, whose inhabitants voted to change its name to that of a celebrated radio quiz show in 1950
- Records the town behind the extraordinary name, the lives of its people and the landscape in which they live
- Also a personal tribute to American photography and to great pioneers of the genre such as Edward Weston and Walker Evans

Nick Waplington is the recipient of numerous photographic prizes including the British and European Kodak Awards, and the ICP Young Photographer Award, 1993. *Truth or Consequences* is Waplington's sixth book. Previous work has included his celebrated photographic portrait of a family in Leeds, *Living Room*, and a study of the homogenization of youth culture in the West, *Safety in Numbers*

General
Non-Fiction

Art

Photography
55

Collector's
Editions

Film

Architecture

55

'Elegantly designed, beautifully printed … and sensitively laid out … the choice of images is irreproachable … The temptation to keep on collecting the whole set will no doubt afflict many.' *Independent*

'You can afford to … buy a fistful of titles to build up a library of reference works.' *Amateur Photographer*

'Small but surprisingly content rich … these volumes are everyman's photography books – as satisfying on your daily journey as a book of poetry or a great novel – small but mighty.' *Black & White* magazine

'If you have never explored the world of photography, the Phaidon 55 series is the perfect introduction.' *RSA Journal*

- An ongoing programme of accessible titles on the great masters of photography
- Covers all types and approaches to photography from photojournalism to fashion and documentary to scientific
- Each book is devoted to a single photographer
- Contains 55 works that offer an overview of the photographer's career
- Includes the classic and iconic images as well as lesser known works
- Introductory essay discusses the photographer's life and work, placing him or her in the context of their times and placing them within the history of photography
- Extended captions discuss each work in depth
- Affordable and pocket sized

156 × 136 mm
6¹⁄₄ × 5³⁄₄ inches
128 pp
55 b&w photos

Paperback
0 7148 4191 9

£ **5.95** UK
$ **9.95** US
€ **9.95** EUR
$ **14.95** CAN
$ **16.95** AUS

Manuel Alvarez Bravo

Amanda Hopkinson

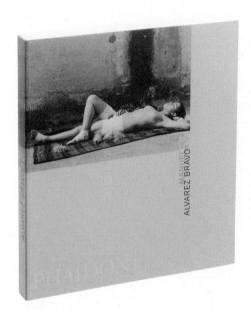

- Manuel Alvarez Bravo is arguably one of the most influential Mexican artists of the 20th century
- His major contribution to photography is made up of eloquent images of dreams, death and transient life
- Reflects a vast career which began in post-revolutionary Mexico City
- Features photography heavily influenced by his native land, its customs and imagination, wit and surreal humour

Amanda Hopkinson is a writer, translator, curator and critic whose area of specialism is Latin America. She is also International Literature Officer for the Arts Council of England and a Senior Research Fellow at Cardiff University

General Non-Fiction

Art

Photography 55

Collector's Editions

Film

Architecture

156 × 136 mm
6¼ × 5¾ inches
128 pp
55 b&w photos

Paperback
0 7148 4049 1

£ **5.95** UK
$ **9.95** US
€ **9.95** EUR
$ **14.95** CAN
$ **16.95** AUS

Eugène Atget

Gerry Badger

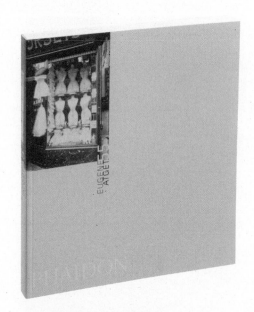

- Considered to be photography's first social documenter, Eugène Atget's (1857–1927) images of Paris are perhaps the most vivid record of a city ever made
- For over 30 years he photographed Parisian street scenes, street traders (from rag-pickers to prostitutes) and the grand parks of Saint-Cloud and Versailles
- A unique portrait of the city of Paris as it became a modern metropolis

Gerry Badger is a photographer and critic. He has published books on Atget and Paul Graham. He has curated a number of exhibitions, including 'The Photographer as Printmaker' for the Arts Council of Great Britain and 'Through the Looking Glass: Postwar British Photography' for the Barbican Arts Centre, London

Design

Fashion & Contemporary Culture

Decorative Arts

Music & Performing Arts

Video

Index

156 × 136 mm
6¹⁄₄ × 5³⁄₄ inches
128 pp
22 col, 33 b&w photos

Paperback
0 7148 4039 4

£ **5.95** UK
$ **9.95** US
€ **9.95** EUR
$ **14.95** CAN
$ **16.95** AUS

Lewis Baltz

Jeff Rian

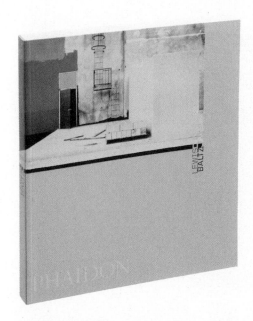

- Lewis Baltz (b.1945) was one of the first to use photography as a means of Conceptual art
- He came to prominence in the mid-1970s as one of a group of artists included in the influential exhibition 'The New Topographics'
- His 'non-judgemental,' matter-of-fact images draw attention to larger social and architectural patterns

Jeff Rian is a writer and professor at the École des Beaux-Arts, Nîmes. He is an editor of *Purple* magazine and the author of *The Buckshot Lexicon* (2000). He regularly contributes to *Art in America* and *Flash Art*

General
Non-Fiction

Art

Photography
55

Collector's
Editions

Film

Architecture

156 × 136 mm
6¼ × 5¾ inches
128 pp
55 b&w photos

Paperback
0 7148 4078 5

£   **5.95**   UK
$ **9.95**   US
€   **9.95**   EUR
$ **14.95**   CAN
$ **16.95**   AUS

Gabriele Basilico

Francesco Bonami

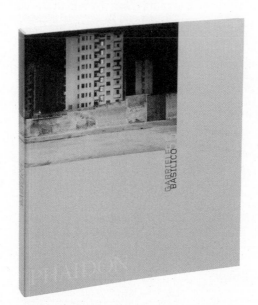

- The work of Gabriele Basilico (b.1944) blurs the boundaries between photography and contemporary art
- Photographs transcend reality and reveal the essence of the metropolis, town or village
- Subjects include cityscapes, residential buildings and factories
- Images explore the relationship between structures and landscapes

Francesco Bonami is currently Manilow Senior Curator at the Chicago Museum of Contemporary Art and Curator of the 1993 Venice Biennale. His books include monographs on Atget and Paul Graham. He currently teaches history of photography at Brighton University

Design

Fashion &
Contemporary
Culture

Decorative Arts

Music &
Performing Arts

Video

Index

156 × 136 mm
6¼ × 5¾ inches
128 pp
55 b&w photos

Paperback
0 7148 4041 6

£ **5.95** UK
$ **9.95** US
€ **9.95** EUR
$ **14.95** CAN
$ **16.95** AUS

Werner Bischof

Claude Cookman

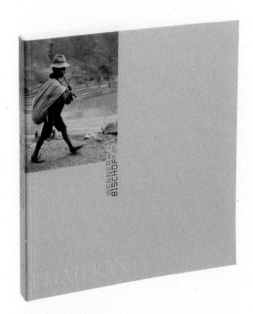

- Swiss born Werner Bischof (1916–54) was compelled to bear witness to the human suffering of the post-war world
- His mission took him to India, Korea, Vietnam, Mexico, the United States and Peru, where he died in a car accident at the age of 38
- The first new photographer to join the original Magnum founders in 1949, Bischof's European work stands as an extraordinary portrait of a continent's slow anguished rebirth

Claude Cookman gained a doctorate in the history of photography from Princeton University before working as a journalist for 18 years. Since 1990 he has taught the history of photography at Indiana University

General
Non-Fiction

Art

Photography
55

Collector's
Editions

Film

Architecture

156 × 136 mm
6¹⁄₄ × 5³⁄₄ inches
128 pp
55 b&w photos

Paperback
0 7148 4065 3

£ **5.95** UK
$ **9.95** US
€ **9.95** EUR
$ **14.95** CAN
$ **16.95** AUS

Mathew Brady

Mary Panzer

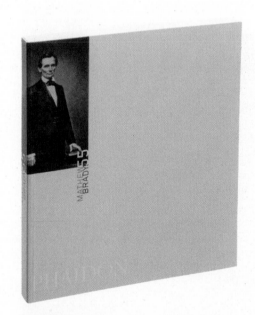

- Mathew Brady (1823–96) was the official portrait photographer of 'illustrious Americans' of the mid-1800s
- An important documenter of the Civil War, his 3,500 pictures offer a unique insight into the actual battles and conditions of the troops
- His work offers a unique insight to the mores of 19th-century America

Mary Panzer is a historian with a special interest in American photographs. She was Curator of Photographs at the National Portrait Gallery, Smithsonian Institution, in Washington DC from 1992–2000

Design

Fashion &
Contemporary
Culture

Decorative Arts

Music &
Performing Arts

Video

Index

156 × 136 mm
6¹⁄₄ × 5³⁄₄ inches
128 pp
4 col, 51 b&w photos

Paperback
0 7148 4029 7

£ **5.95** UK
$ **9.95** US
€ **9.95** EUR
$ **14.95** CAN
$ **16.95** AUS

Wynn Bullock

Chris Johnson and Barbara Bullock-Wilson

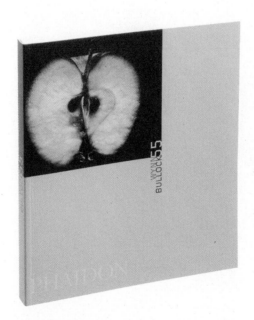

- An important teacher and writer, the magical images of Wynn Bullock (1902–75) have inspired generations of photographers
- Along with Edward Weston and Ansel Adams, Bullock defines the West Coast approach to photography
- Bullock used many of the techniques pioneered in the 1920s in his photography
- Features stunningly beautiful nudes, and images of nature on the West Coast of the United States

Chris Johnson is Professor of Photography at the California College of Arts and Crafts, Chair of the Oakland Cultural Affairs Commission and Director of the Mother Jones International Fund for Documentary Photography
Barbara Bullock-Wilson is a writer and editor. She frequently consults on the photography of her parents, Wynn and Edna Bullock, and has written several books on their work

General Non-Fiction

Art

Photography
55

Collector's Editions

Film

Architecture

156 × 136 mm
6¹⁄₄ × 5³⁄₄ inches
128 pp
55 col photos

Paperback
0 7148 4017 3

£ 5.95 UK
$ 9.95 US
€ 9.95 EUR
$ 14.95 CAN
$ 16.95 AUS

Julia Margaret Cameron

Joanne Lukitsh

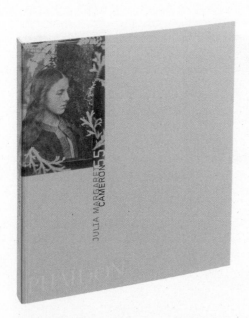

- The 'Pre-Raphaelite' photographer, Julia Margaret Cameron (1815–79) has influenced scores of photographers and painters over the last century
- Discovered by Alfred Stieglitz, she was a self-taught British photographer, who produced some of the most innovative and visually striking portraits of the time
- Highlights her novel use of lighting and focus, which transformed photographic portraiture
- She saw herself as an artist and her photographs reflect her passion for beauty

Joanne Lukitsh is a professor of art history at the Massachusetts College of Art, Boston, USA. She earned her doctorate at the University of Chicago and was the recipient of an award for her research on Cameron by the National Endowment for the Humanities

Design

Fashion &
Contemporary
Culture

Decorative Arts

Music &
Performing Arts

Video

Index

156 × 136 mm
6¹⁄₄ × 5³⁄₄ inches
128 pp
55 b&w photos

Paperback
0 7148 4033 5

£ **5.95** UK
$ **9.95** US
€ **9.95** EUR
$ **14.95** CAN
$ **16.95** AUS

Martin Chambi

Amanda Hopkinson

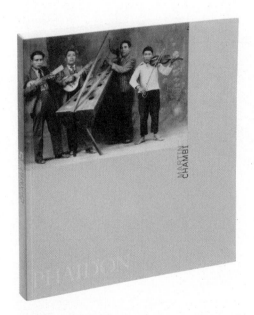

- A campesino of Indian descent, Martin Chambi (1891–1973) was the first Amerindian photographer to receive international acclaim
- His study in Cuzco was favoured by the local élite, whose fiestas, weddings and portraits he imbued with a unique sensibility
- Includes his striking images of Peruvian life, architecture and landscape, which document unique dedication to his people

Amanda Hopkinson is a writer, translator, curator and critic, whose area of specialism is Latin America. She is also International Literature Officer for the Arts Council of England and a Senior Research Fellow at Cardiff University

General Non-Fiction

Art

Photography
55

Collector's Editions

Film

Architecture

156 × 136 mm
6¹₄ × 5³₄ inches
128 pp
5 col, 50 b&w photos

Paperback
0 7148 4047 5

£ **5.95** UK
$ **9.95** US
€ **9.95** EUR
$ **14.95** CAN
$ **16.95** AUS

Walker Evans

Luc Sante

- A major influence on documentary photography, Walker Evans's (1903–75) images of American life in the 1930s are iconic
- Features his famous photographs which document the effects of the Great Depression on the rural population and images which record the everyday details of urban life

Luc Sante is the author of *Low Life*, *Evidence* and *The Factory of Facts*. He is a frequent contributor to the *New York Review of Books* and is a visiting professor in the photography and writing departments of Bard College, New York

Design

Fashion &
Contemporary
Culture

Decorative Arts

Music &
Performing Arts

Video

Index

156 × 136 mm
6¹⁄₄ × 5³⁄₄ inches
128 pp
33 col, 22 b&w photos

Paperback
0 7148 4031 9

£   **5.95** UK
$ **9.95** US
€   **9.95** EUR
$ **14.95** CAN
$ **16.95** AUS

Joan Fontcuberta

Christian Caujolle

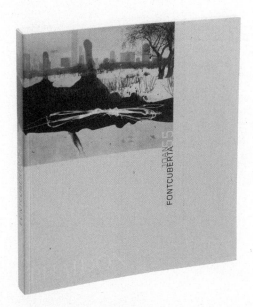

- **Spain's Joan Fontcuberta (b.1955) comes from the tradition of Spanish Surrealism**
- **Documents his photographic world of bizarre plants and creatures of his own manufacture which only on careful scrutiny reveal themselves to be fakes**
- **Fontcuberta's work challenges the old, long-cherished and unquestioning belief that a photograph can be a truthful representation of reality**

Christian Caujolle is a writer and photography critic. He has written several books, including monographs on William Klein, Peter Beard and Sebastião Salgado. He is also Director of the Paris photographic agency VU

General
Non-Fiction

Art

Photography
55

Collector's
Editions

Film

Architecture

156 × 136 mm
6¹⁄₄ × 5³⁄₄ inches
128 pp
5 col, 50 b&w photos

Paperback
0 7148 4051 3

£ **5.95** UK
$ **9.95** US
€ **9.95** EUR
$ **14.95** CAN
$ **16.95** AUS

David Goldblatt

Lesley Lawson

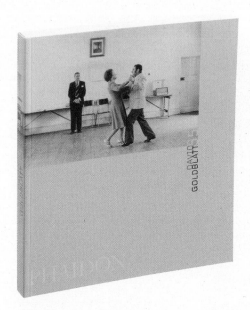

- **The work of David Goldblatt (b.1930) explores South African society with dignity and intelligence**
- **Described as having an 'acute historical and political perception', his images reveal the country's complexities and nuances**
- **His award-winning work has been widely published and exhibited**

Lesley Lawson is a photographer and writer. Since 1990 she has worked in television producing and directing current affairs films and documentaries on environmental issues, South African history, HIV/AIDS and child abuse

Design

Fashion &
Contemporary
Culture

Decorative Arts

Music &
Performing Arts

Video

Index

156 × 136 mm
6¼ × 5¾ inches
128 pp
55 col photos

Paperback
0 7148 4073 4

£ **5.95** UK
$ **9.95** US
€ **9.95** EUR
$ **14.95** CAN
$ **16.95** AUS

Nan Goldin

Guido Costa

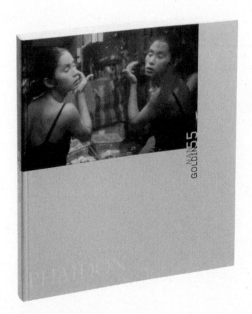

- Nan Goldin (b.1953) is a major figure in the contemporary art world, most famous for the long-term photographic record of the lives of her and her friends, *The Ballad of Sexual Dependency*
- Comments candidly on all aspects of the lives of her immediate circle, the main themes being relationships, sexuality, eroticism and the problems of alcohol and drug addiction
- Her work is by turns disturbing, poignant and celebratory

Guido Costa curates exhibitions worldwide and his writing on art and photography has been widely published. He has worked closely with Goldin for many years and collaborated with her on the book *Ten Years After* (1996)

General
Non-Fiction

Art

Photography
55

Collector's
Editions

Film

Architecture

156 × 136 mm
6¼ × 5¾ inches
128 pp
55 b&w photos

Paperback
0 7148 4197 8

£ **5.95** UK
$ **9.95** US
€ **9.95** EUR
$ **14.95** CAN
$ **16.95** AUS

Lewis Hine

Mary Panzer

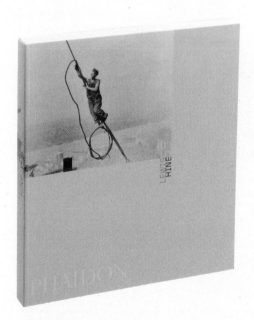

- Photographer, social worker and reformer, Lewis Hine (1874–1940) employed his camera to mobilize public concern and generate corrective legislation
- Achieved considerable fame during his lifetime; he considered his activities as a form of evidence for the present and history for the future
- Established as an embodiment of American values, he celebrated the dignity of working people in the modern world

Mary Panzer is a historian with a special interest in American photography. She was Curator of Photographs at the National Portrait Gallery, Smithsonian Institution, in Washington DC from 1992 to 2000

Design

Fashion & Contemporary Culture

Decorative Arts

Music & Performing Arts

Video

Index

156 × 136 mm
6¼ × 5¾ inches
128 pp
55 b&w photos

Paperback
0 7148 4024 6

£ **5.95** UK
$ **9.95** US
€ **9.95** EUR
$ **14.95** CAN
$ **16.95** AUS

Graciela Iturbide

Cuauhtémoc Medina

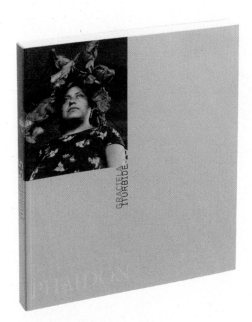

- The work of Graciela Iturbide (b.1942) blends an evocative sense of her native Mexico with her own personal vision
- Her photographs are a mixture of history, lyricism, surrealism and portraiture
- Shows poetic images that have as their themes rite and ceremony, the interaction of nature and culture, and the tensions between tradition, modernity and identity

Cuauhtémoc Medina is a critic and art historian. He was the Curator of Contemporary Art at the Carrillo Gil Museum, Mexico City, from 1989 to 1992. He is also a regular contributor to international art publications

156 × 136 mm
6¹⁄₄ × 5³⁄₄ inches
128 pp
55 b&w photos

Paperback
0 7148 4040 8

£ **5.95** UK
$ **9.95** US
€ **9.95** EUR
$ **14.95** CAN
$ **16.95** AUS

André Kertész

Noël Bourcier

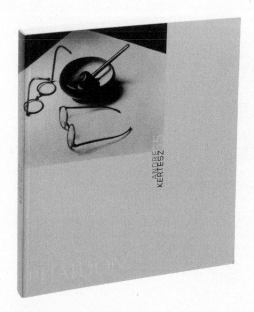

- A leading photographer in the history of the medium, André Kertész (1894–1985) elevated ordinary life to exquisite art and has exercised a profound influence on most photographers since
- A Hungarian who worked in Paris in the 1920s and 30s, he was mentor to photographers like Robert Capa, Brassaï and Cartier-Bresson
- An intuitive artist with an innovative visual language of playful humour and surrealism

Noël Bourcier is Artistic Director of the André Kertèsz Foundation. He has written numerous articles on photography, many of which have appeared in *Art Press*. He has organized numerous exhibitions, including 'Emmanuel Sougez, Éminence Grise' (1993), 'André Kertész, Copy of a Life' (1994) and 'Sovereign England: The Golden Age of British Photography' (1996)

Design

Fashion &
Contemporary
Culture

Decorative Arts

Music &
Performing Arts

Video

Index

156 × 136 mm
6¹⁄₄ × 5³⁄₄ inches
128 pp
55 b&w photos

Paperback
0 7148 4028 9

£ **5.95** UK
$ **9.95** US
€ **9.95** EUR
$ **14.95** CAN
$ **16.95** AUS

Chris Killip

Gerry Badger

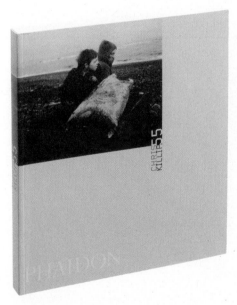

- An influential teacher and curator, Chris Killip (b.1946) is one of Britain's most important social documentary photographers
- He has worked mainly on long-term, historically valuable photographic projects
- Born on the Isle of Man, among his most important work was a series of portraits of his fellow islanders
- His most significant and well-known body of images was made in the northeast of England

Gerry Badger is a photographer, architect and curator. His books include monographs on Atget and Paul Graham. He currently teaches history of photography at Brighton University

General
Non-Fiction

Art

Photography
55

Collector's
Editions

Film

Architecture

156 × 136 mm
6¹⁄₄ × 5³⁄₄ inches
128 pp
55 b&w photos

Paperback
0 7148 4053 X

£ **5.95** UK
$ **9.95** US
€ **9.95** EUR
$ **14.95** CAN
$ **16.95** AUS

Dorothea Lange

Mark Durden

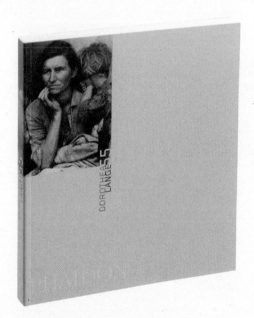

- **Dorothea Lange (1895–1965) is one of the most famous documentary photographers of all time**
- **Her photographs of migrant workers during the Depression are classics and known far beyond the realms of the photography world**
- **Her photographs show her respect for her subjects' dignity in the face of often unbearable circumstances and explicitly condemn those she perceived as their exploiters**

Mark Durden is an artist and writer. He is currently Senior Lecturer in History and Theory of Photography at the University of Derby. He recently curated the exhibition 'Face On' and co-edited the accompanying book

Design

Fashion & Contemporary Culture

Decorative Arts

Music & Performing Arts

Video

Index

156 × 136 mm
6¹₄ × 5³₄ inches
128 pp
55 col photos

Paperback
0 7148 4234 6

£ **5.95** UK
$ **9.95** US
€ **9.95** EUR
$ **14.95** CAN
$ **16.95** AUS

Gustave Le Gray

Sylvie Aubenas

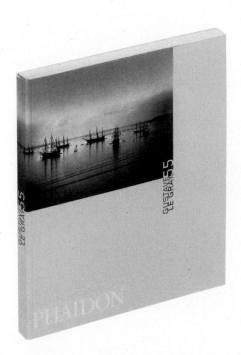

- Gustave le Gray (1820–82) was among the first to claim that photographs should be thought of as artworks
- Originally a painter, Le Gray became the first great teacher in the history of the photographic medium, his students including Charles Nègre and Maxime du Camp
- His interest in experimentation and high technical standards jeopardized his commercial success, however, and he ended his career in Cairo as a teacher of drawing

Sylvie Aubenas is Chief Curator of the 19th-century photographic collections at the Bibliothèque Nationale, Paris. She has curated several exhibitions on the work of such photographers as Nadar, Charles Aubry and Le Gray

General
Non-Fiction

Art

Photography
55

Collector's
Editions

Film

Architecture

156 × 136 mm
6¹₄ × 5³₄ inches
128 pp
5 col, 50 b&w photos

Paperback
0 7148 4046 7

£ **5.95** UK
$ **9.95** US
€ **9.95** EUR
$ **14.95** CAN
$ **16.95** AUS

Mary Ellen Mark

Charles Hagen

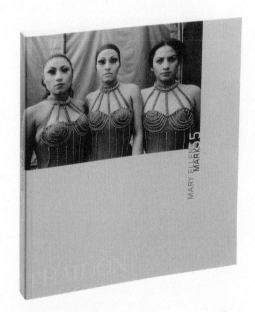

- Highly respected and influential, the images of Mary Ellen Mark (b.1940) have become landmarks in the field of documentary photography
- Her work portrays the world's diverse cultures including Indian circuses, Bombay brothels, Hollywood film stars and runaway children
- Recipient of some of the world's most respected awards, her work has been published and exhibited worldwide

Charles Hagen is a photographer and writer. An art critc for *The New York Times* from 1991 to 1996, he is currently Professor of Photography and Video at the University of Connecticut

Design

Fashion & Contemporary Culture

Decorative Arts

Music & Performing Arts

Video

Index

156 × 136 mm
6¹⁄₄ × 5³⁄₄ inches
128 pp
55 b&w photos

Paperback
0 7148 4112 9

£ **5.95** UK
$ **9.95** US
€ **9.95** EUR
$ **14.95** CAN
$ **16.95** AUS

Ralph Eugene Meatyard

Judith Keller

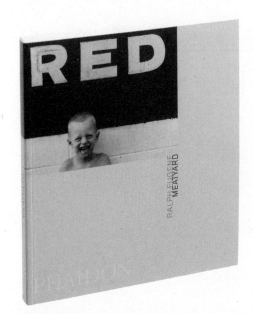

- **Ralph Eugene Meatyard (1925–72) was a visionary photographic artist whose haunting work was heavily influenced by his passion for literature and fascination with the past**
- **Documents his symbolic dramas, set in ordinary, often abandoned places and enacted mostly by his own family, that embody a belief that revelation does not depend on sight**

Judith Keller is Associate Curator of Photographs at the J Paul Getty Museum. She has published books on Walker Evans, Doris Ulmann and Andy Warhol, and has organized exhibitions on the work of Paul Strand, August Sander, Alexander Rodchenko and William Eggleston

General
Non-Fiction

Art

Photography
55

Collector's
Editions

Film

Architecture

156 × 136 mm
6¹⁄₄ × 5³⁄₄ inches
128 pp
27 col, 28 b&w photos

Paperback
0 7148 4021 1

£ **5.95** UK
$ **9.95** US
€ **9.95** EUR
$ **14.95** CAN
$ **16.95** AUS

Joel Meyerowitz

Colin Westerbeck

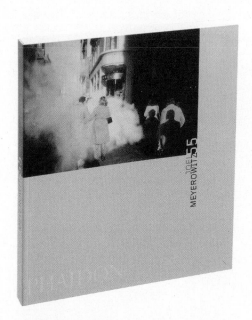

- Joel Meyerowitz (b.1938) is a contemporary street photographer in the tradition of Cartier-Bresson and Gary Windgrand
- An early pioneer of colour photography, he was instrumental in changing the attitude toward the use of colour from one of resistance to revelation
- Best known for his work on the themes of architecture, light and space
- With extremely entertaining personal anecdotes in the commentaries

Colin Westerbeck is Curator of Photography at The Art Institute of Chicago and an award-winning critic and writer. His books include *Bystander, A History of Street Photography*, which he co-authored with Joel Meyerowitz

Design

Fashion &
Contemporary
Culture

Decorative Arts

Music &
Performing Arts

Video

Index

156 × 136 mm
6¼ × 5¾ inches
128 pp
15 col, 40 b&w photos

Paperback
0 7148 4066 1

£   5.95   UK
$ 9.95   US
€   9.95   EUR
$ 14.95   CAN
$ 16.95   AUS

Boris Mikhailov

Gilda Williams

- **Boris Mikhailov (b.1938) is the former Soviet Union's most influential living photographer**
- **His work contains many uses of photography – as conceptual project; as historical record; as the means to produce a work of art; as political commentary; as self-portraiture**
- **Documents his work that questions how an artist can position himself in a defeated, dying world**

Gilda Williams is a critic and curator of contemporary art and photography. Formerly Managing Editor of *Flash Art International* she is currently Commissioning Editor for contemporary art at Phaidon Press

General
Non-Fiction

Art

Photography
55

Collector's
Editions

Film

Architecture

156 × 136 mm
6¹⁄₄ × 5³⁄₄ inches
128 pp
55 b&w photos

Paperback
0 7148 4061 0

£ **5.95** UK
$ **9.95** US
€ **9.95** EUR
$ **14.95** CAN
$ **16.95** AUS

Lisette Model

Elisabeth Sussman

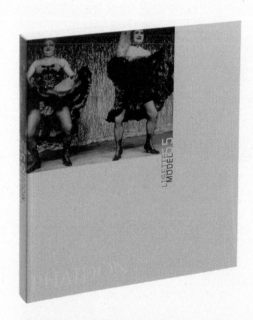

- Influential teacher and photographer Lisette Model (1906–83) began her career in Europe but her lifelong project was 'to photograph America's self-portrait a million times'
- Her photographs of 1940s New York focus with warmth and compassion on the seamier side of life
- Features her striking portraits of jazz artists, such as Ella Fitzgerald and Billie Holiday
- Her most famous pupils were Diane Arbus, Robert Mapplethorpe and Larry Fink

Elisabeth Sussmann was a curator at the Whitney Museum of American Art in New York, the Institute of Contemporary Art in Boston and the Biennale of Sydney, Australia. She was a contributor to *Nan Goldin: I'll be Your Mirror* (1996) and *Keith Haring* (1997)

Design

Fashion &
Contemporary
Culture

Decorative Arts

Music &
Performing Arts

Video

Index

156 × 136 mm
6¼ × 5¾ inches
128 pp
55 b&w photos

Paperback
0 7148 4156 0

£ **5.95** UK
$ **9.95** US
€ **9.95** EUR
$ **14.95** CAN
$ **16.95** AUS

Tina Modotti

Margaret Hooks

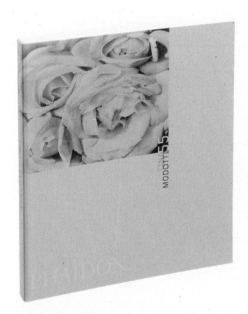

- **Mexican photographer Tina Modotti (1896–1942) was a pioneer among the few women photographers of the 1920s**
- **Her portraits, still lifes and abstract compositions combine a sophisticated sense of design with socially and politically orientated subject matter**
- **Modotti was also a significant influence on future Mexican photographers, including Manuel Alvarez Bravo and Graciela Iturbide**

Margaret Hooks writes on fine art and photography for numerous journals, including *ARTnews* and *Afterimage*. Her most recent publication is the award-winning biography *Tina Modotti: Radical Photographer* (1998)

General Non-Fiction

Art

Photography
55

Collector's Editions

Film

Architecture

156 × 136 mm
6¹⁄₄ × 5³⁄₄ inches
128 pp
21 col, 34 b&w photos

Paperback
0 7148 4018 1

£ **5.95** UK
$ **9.95** US
€ **9.95** EUR
$ **14.95** CAN
$ **16.95** AUS

László Moholy-Nagy

Jeannine Fiedler

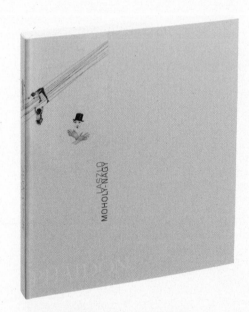

- László Moholy-Nagy (1895–1946) was a major innovator of the avant-garde and one of the 20th century's most important and influential art theoreticians
- Documents his experiments with new ways of seeing – using photomontages, photograms, film and kinetic sculpture
- Believed in the camera as a way of complementing and perfecting the human eye

Jeannine Fiedler is an art historian and critic. She was guest curator at the Bauhaus-Archiv Berlin from 1986 to 1990, and has written and edited a number of books, including *Paul Outerbridge Jr* (1993) and *Bauhaus* (1999)

Design

Fashion & Contemporary Culture

Decorative Arts

Music & Performing Arts

Video

Index

156 × 136 mm
6¹⁄₄ × 5³⁄₄ inches
128 pp
55 b&w photos

Paperback
0 7148 4023 8

£ **5.95** UK
$ **9.95** US
€ **9.95** EUR
$ **14.95** CAN
$ **16.95** AUS

Daido Moriyama

Kazuo Nishi

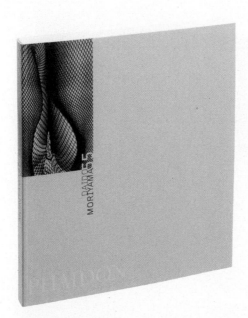

- Contemporary Japanese photographer Daido Moriyama (b.1938) has made a radical impact on the photographic world in both Japan and in the West
- His snapshot aesthetic and no-viewfinder style have succeeded in challenging the medium's prevailing orthodoxies
- Moriyama was a founder member of the famous *PROVOKE* magazine, and a lecturer and theorist, influencing the new generation of Japanese photographers

Kazuo Nishi is a film and photography critic. He was Editor-in-Chief of the Japanese photography magazine *Camera Mainichi* from 1983 to 1985, and has written several books, including *Why Still 'Provoke' Now?* (1996)

General
Non-Fiction

Art

Photography
55

Collector's
Editions

Film

Architecture

156 × 136 mm
6¹⁄₄ × 5³⁄₄ inches
128 pp
55 b&w photos

Paperback
0 7148 4042 4

£ **5.95** UK
$ **9.95** US
€ **9.95** EUR
$ **14.95** CAN
$ **16.95** AUS

Eadweard Muybridge

Paul Hill

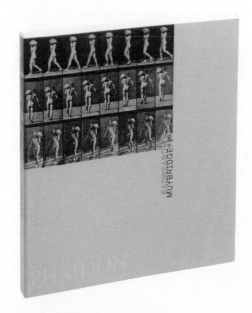

- **Eadweard Muybridge (1830–1904) was the most significant contributor to the early study of human and animal locomotion**
- **His pioneering studies of the 1870s and 1880s, which produced over 20,000 photographs, radically changed the way in which people understood animal and human movement**
- **Documents his less well-known, but beautiful landscape work**

Paul Hill was responsible for the Eadweard Muybridge Collections at Kingston Upon Thames Museum, UK from 1993 to 2000. As well as writing for photography journals and worldwide web publications, he also lectures on the life and work of Eadweard Muybridge

Design

Fashion & Contemporary Culture

Decorative Arts

Music & Performing Arts

Video

Index

156 × 136 mm
6¼ × 5¾ inches
128 pp
55 b&w photos

Paperback
0 7148 4059 9

£ **5.95** UK
$ **9.95** US
€ **9.95** EUR
$ **14.95** CAN
$ **16.95** AUS

Nadar

James H. Rubin

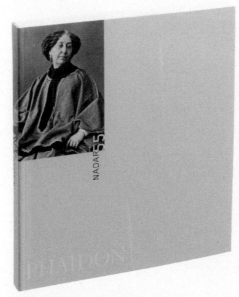

- Caricaturist, journalist, novelist, balloonist, propagandist Nadar (Gaspard-Félix Tournachon, 1820–1910) was the most influential photographer of his generation
- A paragon of enthusiasm, energy and productivity, Nadar is often cited as the first to raise the medium to the level of art
- Documents his portraits made between the mid-1850s and the 1870s, in which he created a lasting image of the French cultural élite

James H Rubin teaches history of art at the State University of New York, and at the Cooper Union. He is well known for his work on 19th-century French art. His books include *Courbet* and *Impressionism* in the Art and Ideas series, and *Manet's Silence and the Poetics of Bouquets*

General
Non-Fiction

Art

Photography
55

Collector's
Editions

Film

Architecture

156 × 136 mm
6¹⁄₄ × 5³⁄₄ inches
128 pp
55 b&w photos

Paperback
0 7148 4025 4

£ **5.95** UK
$ **9.95** US
€ **9.95** EUR
$ **14.95** CAN
$ **16.95** AUS

Eugene Richards

Charles Bowden

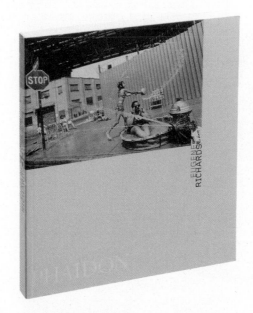

- Eugene Richards (b.1942) has created a body of work that is considered one of the most outstanding of contemporary photojournalism
- Once a social worker, his work unveils the social conditions of his country and confronts the sometimes unpleasant truths of modern life
- A photographer of extreme passion and integrity, he is the author of 12 books and recipient of numerous international awards

Charles Bowden has been a reporter for 20 years and has written 14 books, most recently *Juarez: The Laboratory of Our Future*. He is a contributing editor of *Harper's* and *Esquire*

Design

Fashion &
Contemporary
Culture

Decorative Arts

Music &
Performing Arts

Video

Index

156 × 136 mm
6¹⁄₄ × 5³⁄₄ inches
128 pp
55 b&w photos

Paperback
0 7148 4034 3

£ **5.95** UK
$ **9.95** US
€ **9.95** EUR
$ **14.95** CAN
$ **16.95** AUS

Jacob Riis

Bonnie Yochelson

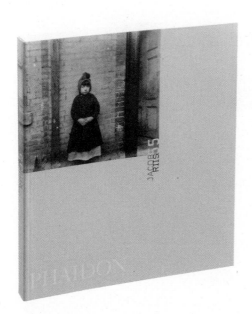

- Known as the 'Emancipator of the Slums', Jacob Riis (1849–1914) is revered first and foremost as a social reformer, who used photography as a powerful support for his campaign to alleviate poverty
- His book *How the Other Half Lives* (1890) was the first of its kind to be illustrated with photographs
- Includes his documentation of sweatshops, disease-ridden tenements and overcrowded schools

Bonni Yochelson is a former curator of prints and photographs at the Museum of the City of New York, where she supervised the cataloguing and printing of the Riis collections. She is completing an interdsiciplinary study on Riis with support from the National Endowment for the Humanities

General Non-Fiction

Art

Photography
55

Collector's Editions

Film

Architecture

156 × 136 mm
6¹⁄₄ × 5³⁄₄ inches
128 pp
55 b&w photos

Paperback
0 7148 4167 6

£ **5.95** UK
$ **9.95** US
€ **9.95** EUR
$ **14.95** CAN
$ **16.95** AUS

Willy Ronis

Paul Ryan

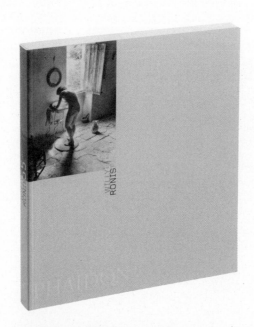

- Known for his unpretentious and honest compositions, Willy Ronis (b.1910) was one of the greatest representatives of French photography of the 1950s
- Unconcerned with the intellectual interpretations of conceptual photography, Ronis's work is accessible and uplifting
- Documents his most important work – a survey of a working-class area of Paris, published as *Belleville-Ménilmontant* (1954)

Paul Ryan has written on the arts for numerous publications and has lectured at the Tate and Hayward galleries in London. In 1996, he was created Chevalier de l'Ordre des Arts et des Lettres by the French government

Design
Fashion & Contemporary Culture
Decorative Arts
Music & Performing Arts
Video
Index

156 × 136 mm
6¹⁄₄ × 5³⁄₄ inches
128 pp
2 col, 53 b&w photos

Paperback
0 7148 4151 X

£ **5.95** UK
$ **9.95** US
€ **9.95** EUR
$ **14.95** CAN
$ **16.95** AUS

Aaron Siskind

James Rhem

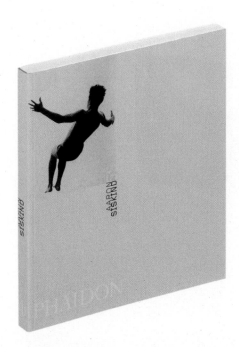

- Aaron Siskind (1903–91) was an acclaimed photographer and teacher who sought to develop a new pictorial language for photography
- Siskind became one of the most important photography teachers in 20th-century America, influencing generations of photographers
- Famous for his beautiful abstract renderings of found objects

James Rhem is Executive Editor and Publisher of The National Teaching and Learning Forum. An independent scholar and curator, Rhem has published extensively on 20th-century photography and art, lectured widely on teaching and is also a practising photographer

General
Non-Fiction

Art

Photography
55

Collector's
Editions

Film

Architecture

156 × 136 mm
6¹⁄₄ × 5³⁄₄ inches
128 pp
55 b&w photos

Paperback
0 7148 4035 1

£ **5.95** UK
$ **9.95** US
€ **9.95** EUR
$ **14.95** CAN
$ **16.95** AUS

W. Eugene Smith

Gary Stephenson

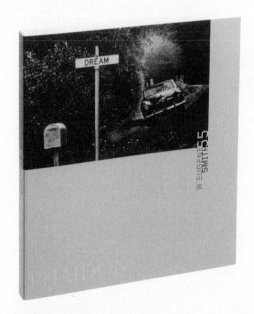

- Both conscientous journalist and poetic artist, W. Eugene Smith (1918–78) is widely acknowledged as the master photo-essayist of his generation
- A staff photographer for *Life* magazine and a member of Magnum, Smith's subjects are wide ranging and include war, family life and architecture
- Includes images from the landmark photo-essays 'Country Doctor', 'Pittsburgh' and 'Minamata' and other work from his huge legacy

Gary Stephenson is a writer and lecturer at the Center for Documentary Studies, Duke University. He prepared an exhibition of Smith's Pittsburgh project of 1955–8 and authored an accompanying book. He is also conducting research on Smith's jazz loft years

Design

Fashion &
Contemporary
Culture

Decorative Arts

Music &
Performing Arts

Video

Index

156 × 136 mm
6¹₄ × 5³₄ inches
128 pp
24 col, 31 b&w photos

Paperback
0 7148 4168 4

£ **5.95** UK
$ **9.95** US
€ **9.95** EUR
$ **14.95** CAN
$ **16.95** AUS

Josef Sudek

Ian Jeffrey

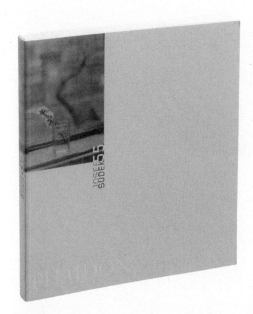

- Enigmatic, surreal and magical, the work of Josef Sudek (1896–1976) has had as much influence on painting as it has on photography
- A founder of the Czech Photographic Society, Sudek's subjects were his immediate surroundings – the streets and buildings of Prague and the objects in his studio
- Best known for the panoramic pictures he took in and around Prague, published in *Praha Panoramatická*

Ian Jeffrey is an art critic, lecturer and photography historian. He has written many books, including *Photography: A Concise History* (1981) and *The Photography Book* (1997), and has curated numerous exhibitions

General
Non-Fiction

Art

Photography
55

Collector's
Editions

Film

Architecture

156 × 136 mm
6¹⁄₄ × 5³⁄₄ inches
128 pp
8 col, 47 b&w photos

Paperback
0 7148 4019 X

£ **5.95** UK
$ **9.95** US
€ **9.95** EUR
$ **14.95** CAN
$ **16.95** AUS

Shomei Tomatsu

Ian Jeffrey

- Shomei Tomatsu (b.1930) is one of the most important photographers of post-war Japan
- Key themes of his work are human contradictions and the Americanization of his homeland
- Documents his own approach to documentary photography – a mix of symbolism and realism – which has greatly influenced subsequent generations of photographers

Ian Jeffrey is an art critic, lecturer and photography historian. He has written many books, including *Photography: A Concise History* (1981) and *The Photography Book* (1997), and has curated numerous exhibitions

Design

Fashion & Contemporary Culture

Decorative Arts

Music & Performing Arts

Video

Index

156 × 136 mm
6¼ × 5¾ inches
128 pp
11 col, 44 b&w photos

Paperback
0 7148 4077 7

£ **5.95** UK
$ **9.95** US
€ **9.95** EUR
$ **14.95** CAN
$ **16.95** AUS

Ed van der Elsken

Hripsime Visser

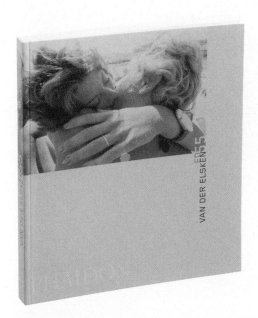

- Ed van der Elsken (1925–90) was one of the most vibrant documentary photographers of the 1950s, 1960s and 1970s
- The subject of his photographs is often the darker side of human existence inspired by Weegee's book *Naked City*
- He created *Love on the Left Bank*, his most celebrated work, which secured his reputation in the early 1950s

Hripsime Visser is a curator at the Stedelijk Museum in Amsterdam. She has organized exhibitions and written widely on the work of contemporary photographers including Lewis Baltz, Gabriele Basilico and Thomas Struth

General
Non-Fiction

Art

Photography
55

Collector's
Editions

Film

Architecture

156 × 136 mm
6¹⁄₄ × 5³⁄₄ inches
128 pp
55 b&w photos

Paperback
0 7148 4169 2

£ **5.95** UK
$ **9.95** US
€ **9.95** EUR
$ **14.95** CAN
$ **16.95** AUS

James Vanderzee

Kobena Mercer

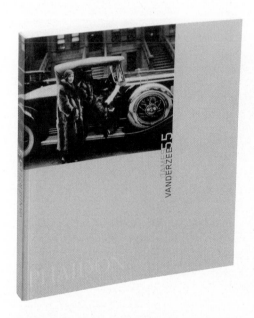

- James Vanderzee (1886–1983) was Harlem's leading photographer from 1916 onwards
- His hybrid style – portraits, weddings and public events – attracted the attention of photographic audiences in the 1990s
- Many of his works were featured in the important 1969 exhibition of African-American art 'Harlem on My Mind' at the Metropolitan Museum of Art, New York

Kobena Mercer writes on the visual arts of the black diaspora and has taught at Cornell, New York University, and the University of California at Santa Cruz. His most recent writings appear in *Art History, Aesthetics, Visual Studies* (2002)

Design

Fashion &
Contemporary
Culture

Decorative Arts

Music &
Performing Arts

Video

Index

156 × 136 mm
6¹⁄₄ × 5³⁄₄ inches
128 pp
55 b&w photos

Paperback
0 7148 4056 4

£ **5.95** UK
$ **9.95** US
€ **9.95** EUR
$ **14.95** CAN
$ **16.95** AUS

Joel-Peter Witkin

Eugenia Parry

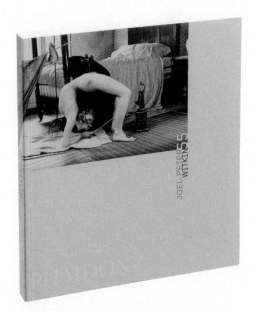

- Joel-Peter Witkin (b.1939) is one of the most well-known and controversial photographic artists working today
- His use of animal and human corpses and his depiction of often horrific acts has led to his photography being called 'Degenerate Art'
- Documents his shocking and provoking images that yet are incredibly beautiful and raise important questions

Eugenia Parry has taught, lectured and written extensively about 19th-century and contemporary art and photography for 30 years. Her other text on Joel-Peter Witkin appeared in *The Bone House* (1998)

Collector's Editions

Elliott Erwitt Snaps

Paris, 1989

Silver gelatin print:
279 × 356 mm, 11 × 14 inches
Printed in 2001 in
an edition of 150
plus 8 artist's proofs
All copies signed
and numbered
by Elliott Erwitt

Box:
380 × 305 × 68.5 mm
15 × 12 × 3⁵⁄₈ inches

0 7148 4238 9

Provence, France, 1955

Silver gelatin print:
254 × 203 mm, 10 × 8 inches
Printed in 2001 in
an edition of 250
plus 12 artist's proofs
All copies signed
and numbered
by Elliott Erwitt

Box:
320 × 245 × 68.5 mm
15 × 12⁵⁄₈ × 3⁵⁄₈ inches

0 7148 4239 7

Marilyn Monroe, New York, 1956

Silver gelatin print:
203 × 254 mm, 8 × 10 inches
Printed in 2001
in an edition of 250
plus 12 artist's proofs
All copies signed
and numbered
by Elliott Erwitt

Box:
320 × 245 × 68.5 mm
15 × 12⁵⁄₈ × 3⁵⁄₈ inches

0 7148 4240 0

Fifth Avenue, New York, 1947

Silver gelatin print:
254 × 203 mm, 10 × 8 inches
Printed in 2001 in
an edition of 100
plus 5 artist's proofs
All copies signed
and numbered
by Elliott Erwitt

Box:
320 × 245 × 68.5 mm
15 × 12⁵⁄₈ × 3⁵⁄₈ inches

0 7148 4243 5

- Commissioned by and created especially for Phaidon Press
- A unique chance to own a limited edition silver gelatin print by Elliott Erwitt
- Six different collector's editions are still available
- Each image shows a different aspect of Erwitt's career
- Each edition (book and print) is individually limited to a run of between 100 and 250 copies
- Each comprises a special edition of the book that is beautifully bound, individually signed and numbered, and presented in a specially bound box together with an original print that is signed and numbered by Elliott Erwitt

One of the finest image makers of his generation, **Elliott Erwitt** describes himself as 'a professional photographer by trade and an amateur photographer by vocation'. A member of Magnum since 1954, his camera has taken him all over the globe and his pictures have been the subject of many books and exhibitions. He sprung to fame through the 'kitchen debate' photograph, taken in 1959 of Khrushchev and Nixon arguing in front of a Westinghouse refrigerator, and has since become one of the best loved observers of life

Artist and documenter, his work spans many traditions, subjects and approaches to photography. *Elliott Erwitt Snaps* is the first book to date to bring together the range and exuberance of his whole career. Iconic images as well as personal photographs of places, things, people and animals, all in Erwitt's unmistakable style, give us a snapshot of the famous and the every day, the strange and the amusing, over a period of more than half a century

Valencia, Spain, 1952

Silver gelatin print:
×203 mm, 10×8 inches
Printed in 2001 in
an edition of 100
plus 5 artist's proofs
All copies signed
and numbered
by Elliott Erwitt

Box:
320×245×68.5 mm
15×12⅝×3⅝ inches

0 7148 4242 7

New York, 1969

Silver gelatin print:
×203 mm, 10×8 inches
Printed in 2001 in
an edition of 100
plus 5 artist's proofs
All copies signed
and numbered
by Elliott Erwitt

Box:
320×245×68.5 mm
15×12⅝×3⅝ inches

0 7148 4241 9

rices available on request
Prices increase as editions
sell out

m top, left to right, Paris,
989; New York, 1969; Fifth
Avenue, New York, 1947;
ncia, Spain, 1952; Marilyn
Monroe, New York, 1956;
Provence, France, 1955

General
Non-Fiction

Art

Photography

**Collector's
Editions**

Film

Architecture

Martin Parr

**Jubilee Street Party
Elland, Yorkshire, 1977**
from 'Bad Weather'

Silver gelatin print:
304 × 406 mm, 12 × 16 inches
Printed in 2002 in an edition
of 100 plus 5 artist's proofs
All copies signed
and numbered by
the photographer

0 7148 4267 2

**Lane Baptist Chapel
Yorkshire, 1978**
from 'The Nonconformists'

Silver gelatin print:
406 × 304 mm, 16 × 12 inches
Printed in 2002 in an edition
of 100 plus 5 artist's proofs
All copies signed
and numbered by
the photographer

0 7148 4266 4

**Badminton Horse Trials
Gloucestershire**
from 'The Cost of Living'

C-type print:
304 × 406 mm, 12 × 16 inches
Printed in 2002 in an edition
of 100 plus 5 artist's proofs
All copies signed
and numbered by
the photographer

0 7148 4268 0

Pink Pig Cakes
from 'Common Sense'

C-type print:
304 × 406 mm, 12 × 16 inches
Printed in 2002 in an edition
of 100 plus 5 artist's proofs
All copies signed
and numbered by
the photographer

0 7148 4269 9

Box:
320 × 245 × 68.5 mm
15 × 12⅝ × 3⅝ inches

Prices available on request
Prices increase as editions
sell out

- A unique chance to own a limited edition print by Martin Parr
- Commissioned by and created especially for Phaidon Press
- Each collector's edition (book and print) is individually limited to 100 copies
- Four different collector's editions are still available
- Each comprises a special edition of the highly acclaimed retrospective book on Martin Parr, beautifully bound, individually signed and numbered and presented in a specially bound box together with an original print also signed and numbered by Martin Parr

The work of **Martin Parr** (b.1952) bridges the divide between art and documentary photography. His studies of the idiosyncrasies of mass culture and consumerism around the world, his innovative imagery and his prolific output have placed him firmly at the forefront of contemporary art. A world authority on photography books and, more recently, a film-maker, Parr joined Magnum in 1994

Design

Fashion &
Contemporary
Culture

Decorative Arts

Music &
Performing Arts

Video

Index

From top, left to right, Jubilee
Street Party, Elland, Yorkshire,
1977; Lane Baptist Chapel,
Yorkshire, 1978; Badminton
Horse Trials, Gloucestershire;
Pink Pig Cakes

General
Non-Fiction

Art

Photography

**Collector's
Editions**

Film

Architecture

The Church of the Light

Wax crayon on
japanese paper
295 × 220 mm
11^6⁄$_8$ × 8^{11}⁄$_{16}$ inches
Drawn in 1996
Edition of 250
All copies signed
by photographer
Richard Pare

Box:
318 × 276 × 51 mm
12^1⁄$_2$ × 10^7⁄$_8$ × 2 inches

0 7148 3541 2

Prices available on request
Prices increase as editions
sell out

Tadao Ando, The Colours of Light

- A special edition of the highly awarded classic Tadao Ando, The Colours of Light, beautifully bound and presented in a specially hand made box
- Each collector's edition includes an original drawing of The Church of the Light by Tadao Ando
- Every book signed by the photographer Richard Pare
- Edition originally of 250 copies, some still available

Design

Fashion &
Contemporary
Culture

Decorative Arts

Music &
Performing Arts

Video

Index

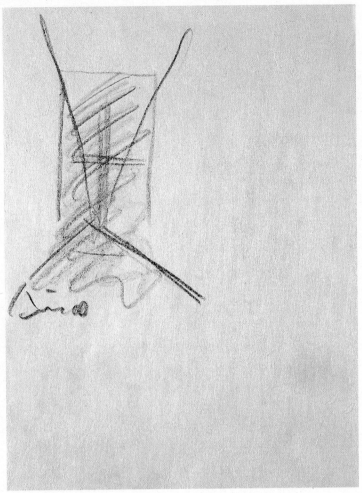

e Church of the Light, wax
on japanese paper, signed

Film

General
Non-Fiction

Art

Photography

Collector's
Editions

Film NEW TITLE

Architecture

290 × 250 mm
11³⁄₈ × 9⁷⁄₈ inches
512 pp
c.675 col, 50 b&w illus.

Hardback
0 7148 4081 5

£ **39.95** UK
$ **69.95** US
€ **69.95** EUR
$ **99.95** CAN
$ **119.95** AUS

Marketing information
Event tie-ins with
international film
and cinema associations

Point of Sale
15-copy display tower
available

Published September

Cinema Today

Edward Buscombe

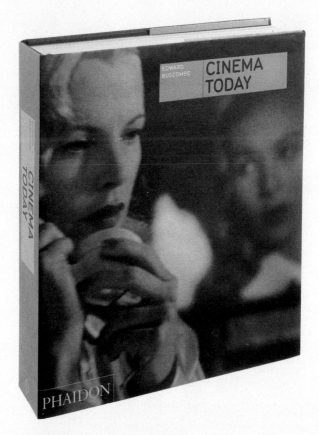

- A comprehensive survey of world cinema since 1970 with an accessible and engaging text which includes over 1,000 film references
- Features in-depth case studies of films such as *Jaws* (Steven Spielberg, 1975), *Talk To Her* (*Hable con ella*, Pedro Almodóvar, 2002) and *Yeelen* (Souleymane Cissé, 1987)
- Films by established directors are featured alongside the work of a new generation of film-makers
- Over 700 images reflecting the visual cinematic medium, including stills, on-set shots, 25 case studies, posters and other visual ephemera
- A comprehensive directors' filmography, bibliography, chronology and index make this book an invaluable reference tool

Edward Buscombe is a leading authority on cinema, having lectured and written on film for over 30 years. Formerly Head of Publishing at the British Film Institute, Buscombe is a regular contributor to film journals and has written several books

Design

Fashion & Contemporary Culture

Decorative Arts

Music & Performing Arts

Video

Index

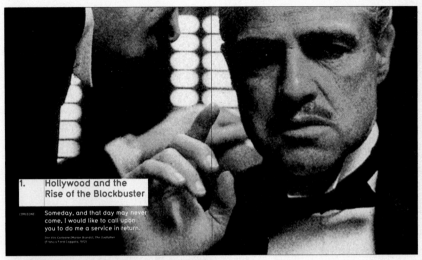

1. Hollywood and the Rise of the Blockbuster

CORLEONE Someday, and that day may never come, I would like to call upon you to do me a service in return.

Don Vito Corleone (Marlon Brando), The Godfather (Francis Ford Coppola, 1972)

Jacket image: *L.A. Confidential* (Curtis Hanson, 1997); spreads showing (from top, left to right) *The Godfather* (Francis Ford Coppola, 1972); *Fitzcaraldo* (Werner Herzog, 1982); *Nosferatu the Vampire* (*Nosferatu: Phantom der Nacht*, Werner Herzog, 1979); *Dil Se* (Mani Rathnam, 1998); *Dilwale Dulhania Le Jayenge* (Aditya Chopra, 1995)

General
Non-Fiction

Art

Photography

Collector's
Editions

Film

Architecture

Hardback
290 × 250 mm
11³⁄₈ × 9⁷⁄₈ inches
512 pp
250 col, 250 b&w illus.

0 7148 3847 0

£ **29.95** UK
$ **45.00** US
€ **49.95** EUR
$ **69.95** CAN
$ **79.95** AUS

Paperback mini format
163 × 123 mm
6³⁄₈ × 4⁷⁄₈ inches
520 pp
250 col, 250 b&w illus.

0 7148 4261 3

£ **6.95** UK
$ **9.95** US
€ **11.95** EUR
$ **14.95** CAN
$ **16.95** AUS

Point of Sale
10-copy counterpack available
0 7148 5251 1

The Movie Book

Original edition

- An A–Z guide to 500 celebrated individuals who have made a landmark contribution to the medium of film
- The entire industry is represented – from actors and directors to costume designers and special-effects wizards; from major movie moguls and pioneers of the silent screen to some of today's most worshipped idols
- Packed with absorbing details and rich with history, all genres of cinema are included
- Each entry is evocatively illustrated with a film still, photograph or cinematic sequence and is accompanied by an authoritative text revealing the significance of each name and including essential biographical information
- Includes a comprehensive cross-referencing system and glossary
- Exclusive to the mini edition is a supplementary index of film titles, actors, actresses and directors

'This encyclopedia-ish tome should provide years of service as both a reference guide and source of reminiscence for movies and the players who made them.' *(Washington Post)*
'The Movie Book is the publishing equivalent of a Hollywood blockbuster.' *(Evening Standard)*
'A deeply pleasurable thing to have around ... a lovely luxury item for all film fans.' *(Heat)*
'A weighty tome in all the right ways ... startling imagery ... brilliant art direction.' *(Arena)*
'Each image is superbly reproduced and neatly captures the essence of its subject ... a volume whose visual pleasures are almost unlimited.' *(Empire Magazine)*

Design

Fashion &
Contemporary
Culture

Decorative Arts

Music &
Performing Arts

Video

Index

'This encyclopedia-ish tome should
provide years of service both
as a reference guide and source
of reminiscence for movies and
the players who made them.'

The Washington Post

'*The Movie Book* is the equivalent
of a Hollywood blockbuster.'

Evening Standard

250 × 184 mm
10¹⁄₈ × 7¹⁄₄ inches
192 pp
200 duotone photographs

Hardback
0 7148 3936 1

£ **22.95** UK
$ **29.95** US
€ **39.95** EUR
$ **45.00** CAN
$ **59.95** AUS

The Misfits

Story of a shoot
Photographs by Magnum photographers, with text by Serge Toubiana and an interview with Arthur Miller

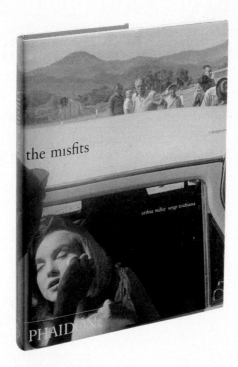

- Documents the making of the legendary film *The Misfits* (1961), directed by John Huston
- An intimate portrait of its stars Marilyn Monroe, Clark Gable and Montgomery Clift – three of the most charismatic actors of all time
- Contains 200 exclusive images by nine of the most famous Magnum photographers, including Henri Cartier-Bresson, Eve Arnold and Elliott Erwitt, who had exclusive access to the shoot
- An essay by Serge Toubiana accompanies a revealing interview between Toubiana and the film's scriptwriter Arthur Miller

Serge Toubiana is Editor-in-Chief of the influential film magazine *Cahiers du cinéma*. He is also the co-author of several books about the cinema, including the biography *Truffant* (1999)

'A must for photography and Monroe fans alike.' *(British Journal of Photography)*
'Even without so many splendid photographs of such photogenic people this would be a fascinating film book.' *(Booklist*, Chicago)
'Even if you're way past sick of Marilyn, you may find yourself surprisingly captivated by *The Misfits*, a look at the making of a classic American rebellion film through unfamiliar images of familiar faces.' *(New York Magazine)*

Design

Fashion &
Contemporary
Culture

Decorative Arts

Music &
Performing Arts

Video

Index

280 × 230 mm
11¹⁴ × 9¹⁴ inches
288 pp
85 col, 200 b&w
photographs
& line drawings

Paperback
0 7148 4333 4

£ **19.95** UK
$ **29.95** US
€ **35.00** EUR
$ **49.95** CAN
$ **59.95** AUS

Hardback
0 7148 3953 1

£ **35.00** UK
$ **59.95** US
€ **59.95** EUR
$ **89.95** CAN
$ **95.00** AUS

Hitchcock at Work

Bill Krohn

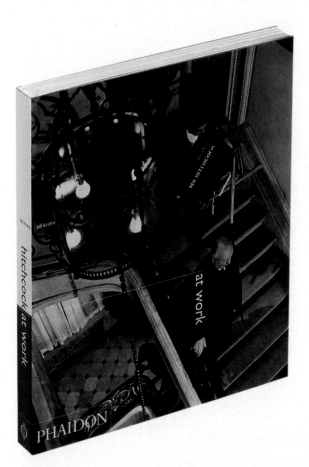

- A comprehensive, behind-the-scenes examination of the work of 'The Master of Suspense,' Alfred Hitchcock (1899–1980)
- Reassesses Hitchcock's working methods, exploding many myths about the director
- Looks beyond the usual anecdotal sources and pays unprecedented attention to film studio archives and Hitchcock's personal papers
- Fully illustrated with film stills, shots taken on set, storyboards and annotated film scripts
- Contains a complete filmography

Bill Krohn has been the Hollywood correspondent of the influential movie magazine *Cahiers du cinéma* for over 20 years. During this time he has interviewed many of Hitchcock's closest collaborators. It was the difference between the man they described and the man he thought he knew that motivated him to write this book

'The most useful book I've read recently about Alfred Hitchcock ... I bought it last year, at first sight mainly for the pictures – rare, unusual and immaculately reproduced in colour and monochrome – and then found it telling me more than I had ever known about the behind-the-scenes Hitch ... a real contribution to primary scholarship.' (Alexander Walker, *Evening Standard*)

'Of all the books on the Master, Bill Krohn's is quite the most splendid and involving. Given the kind of breathtaking visual treatment that is the hallmark of the publisher Phaidon, keen and penetrating text is matched by images that do full justice to the remarkable pictorial qualities of Hitchcock's films. Absolutely essential.' (*News International Genre Hotline*)

General
Non-Fiction

Art

Photography

Collector's
Editions

Film

Architecture
NEW TITLE

290 × 250 mm
11³⁄₈ × 9⁷⁄₈ inches
240 pp
c.200 col, 85 b&w illus.
150 line drawings

Hardback
0 7148 4194 3

£ **45.00** UK
$ **75.00** US
€ **75.00** EUR
$ **99.95** CAN
$ **129.95** AUS

Published October

Shigeru Ban

Matilda McQuaid, with a foreword by Frei Otto

- Shigeru Ban (b.1957), based in Japan, is a rising star among young, world-class architects
- Documents 32 projects, including 15 new projects begun since 2001 in Japan, China, the US and France
- Ban is renowned for experimental structures built with paper and paper tubes
- Ban practises 'green' architecture, working with recyclable, affordable, natural materials
- Includes technical data sections documenting Ban's original research
- Unique design of book reflects Ban's experiments with paper

Matilda McQuaid is Exhibitions Curator and Head of the Textiles Department at the Cooper-Hewitt, National Design Museum in New York and until 2001 was an associate curator in the Department of Architecture and Design at the Museum of Modern Art, New York
Frei Otto is an eminent architect based in Germany; he pioneered research in lightweight membranes and innovative structures. He collaborated with Shigeru Ban on the Japan Pavillion for Expo 2000 in Hanover, Germany

Design

Fashion & Contemporary Culture

Decorative Arts

Music & Performing Arts

Video

Index

PAPER HOUSE

DESIGN DATES:
October, 1990–July, 1994
CONSTRUCTION DATES:
October, 1994–July, 1995
LOCATION:
Lake Yamanaka, Yamanishi, Japan
STRUCTURAL ENGINEER:
Gengo Matsui, Minoru Tezuka
GENERAL CONTRACTOR:
Marukaku Kenchiku
SITE AREA: 499m²
BUILT AREA: 100m²
TOTAL FLOOR AREA: 100m²

RIGHT: Paper House spheres

PAPER ART MUSEUM, A & B

DESIGN DATES:
October, 1990–July, 1994
CONSTRUCTION DATES:
October, 1994–July, 1995
LOCATION:
Zushi, Kanagawa, JP
STRUCTURAL ENGINEER:
Gengo Matsui, Minoru Tezuka
GENERAL CONTRACTOR:
Marukaku Kenchiku
SITE AREA: 100m²
BUILT AREA: 100m²
TOTAL FLOOR AREA: 100m²

LEFT: Paper House at night

This museum (I) and contemporary gallery (II) located two hours (check) outside of Tokyo, is devoted to the art and manufacture of paper. The client (TK) is a long established paper manufacturer in Japan and wanted to build a paper art museum, one of the few in the world, that presented not only the client's own collection of paper, but also an ongoing series of contemporary exhibitions on artists working in this medium.

The two buildings are connected by an entrance vestibule with the four-story museum on the west end of the site and the one-story contemporary gallery to the east. Each building is a steel frame construction, but they are differentiated by their exterior skin. For the museum, which has a total floor area of 2,400 square meters. But includes a double layer of glass-reinforced polycarbonate panels on the exterior with an interior of double layered glass and silica calcium board – used primarily for thermal insulation and fireproofing material (?). The ground floor exterior panels on the south side can be opened to create an awning or shitomido, a type of vertical shutter used centuries ago in Japanese

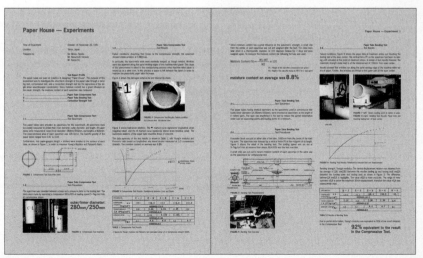

Paper House — Experiments

Paper House — Experiment (?)

General
Non-Fiction

Art

Photography

Collector's
Editions

Film

Architecture
NEW TITLE

290 × 250 mm
11³⁄₈ × 9⁷⁄₈ inches
272 pp
c.150 col, 100 b&w illus.,
150 line drawings

Hardback
0 7148 4045 9

£ **45.00** UK
$ **75.00** US
€ **75.00** EUR
$ **99.95** CAN
$ **129.95** AUS

Published October

Louis Kahn

Robert McCarter

- Louis Kahn (1901–74) is one of the most influential architects of the mid-20th century
- In-depth and scholarly monograph that documents in detail the most important works, both built and unbuilt
- Includes major US institutions such as the Kimbell Art Museum, the Yale Art Gallery and the Salk Institute, as well as the National Assembly Building at Dhaka, Bangladesh
- Includes previously unpublished photographs, archive materials and line drawings
- Contains a new comprehensive list of projects compiled by William Whitaker of the Louis I Kahn Collection at the University of Pennsylvania Archives, listing over 231 projects, at least 30 previously unattributed

Robert McCarter is a prominent architectural historian and practising architect, and Professor of Architecture at the University of Florida. He is the author of *Frank Lloyd Wright* (1999), also published by Phaidon

Design

Fashion &
Contemporary Culture

Decorative Arts

Music &
Performing Arts

Video

Index

Kahn's architecture is notable for its monumentality and dramatic forms. Spreads illustrated show (from top) the Jewish Community Center, Trenton, NJ; Salk Institute, La Jolla, CA; Yale Center for British Arts, New Haven, CT

General
Non-Fiction

Art

Photography

Collector's
Editions

Film

Architecture
NEW IN PAPERBACK

The Garden Book

Mini format
163 x 123 mm
6³⁄₈ × 4⁷⁄₈ inches
520 pp
c.445 col, 55 b&w illus.

Paperback
0 7148 4355 5
See also hardback on p.386

£ **6.95** UK
$ **9.95** US
€ **9.95** EUR
$ **14.95** CAN
$ **16.95** AUS

Published Fall

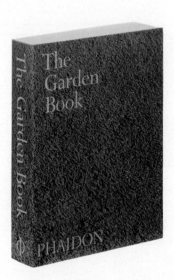

- A highly accessible overview of 500 garden designers organized in A-Z format now available in pocket format
- Presents a widely diverse range of gardens from ancient Persia to the classical gardens of Europe and the contemporary gardens of the US
- Each designer is represented by a garden that exemplifies their work and highlights their contribution to the history of the medium
- The featured gardens are famous, destroyed, mythical and private
- Includes an informative cross-referencing system linking designers who work in similar styles, movements or time periods
- Contains an essential glossary and directory of gardens

'A truly sumptuous encyclopedia … its range is magnificent – from ancient China and India to Renaissance Italy to modern Los Angeles.' (*Sunday Telegraph Magazine*)

Design

Fashion &
Contemporary Culture

Decorative Arts

Music &
Performing Arts

Video

Index

Hoare Henry — Stourhead

A Pantheon, a domed rotunda symbolising the classical ideal, is glimpsed across a lake lending a magical aspect to the surrounding landscape. The scene could be from an Old Master painting, but was the creation of Henry Hoare at Stourhead, his estate in Wiltshire. After the death of his second wife in 1743, Hoare threw himself into the job of improving Stourhead in the most fashionable manner. A large lake was formed from a series of ponds constituting the River Stour, and Hoare added a sequence of exceptionally fine buildings, by Henry Flitcroft, to its perimeter, punctuating a circular walk. Temples to Flora and Apollo are well placed and there is a delightful recessed grotto under the lip of the edge of the lake. The scion of a great London banking family, Hoare was closely connected with several leading early protagonists of the English landscape school, notably Lord Burlington, Alexander Pope and William Kent, as well as his West Country neighbour, Coplestone Warre Bampfylde of Hestercombe.

☛ Bingley, Bridgeman, Pope

Henry Hoare II. b London (UK), 1705. d London (UK), 1785. Stourhead, Wiltshire (UK).

Jencks Charles — Portrack

This sinuous 400ft- (120m) long terraced earthwork, twisting away from two crescent ponds, here viewed from the top of a 'snail mound', is the highlight of Charles Jencks' garden of cosmic speculation', created in Scotland in the 1990s. Jencks is a passionate advocate of the latest theories about the universe and its history, and several areas of his garden are designed as visual metaphors for these scientific theories. The twisting earthwork, for instance, is the most dramatic expression of a fractal – the irregular curves produced by repeated subdivision in mathematics – in the garden. Its form (but not its meaning) was inspired by the early experiments of Maggie Keswick, Jencks' late wife, into the feng shui principle of laying bare the 'bones of the earth'. Similar ideas occur in other parts of the garden. Jencks has made an unconventional potager called the Physics Garden, comprising six large metal sculptures that represent the double-helix structure of DNA, surrounded by a 'cell wall' of low box and swirling bands of lettuces. The garden is still being developed and enlarged.

☛ Hall, Kobori Enshu, Chien Lung

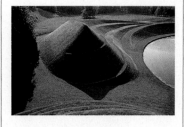

Charles Jencks. b (USA), 1945. Portrack, Scotland (UK).   381

Olmsted Frederick Law — Central Park

The curved walkways and roads of Olmsted's 1858 design for Central Park in New York are a triumph of landscape design and city planning, notable for their disruption of the city's grid street pattern. In collaboration with Calvert Vaux, Olmsted envisaged a park composed of various picturesque elements that complemented the natural landscape: rocky and wooded to the south, gently sloping to the north. Olmsted had to incorporate transverse roads into his park design, and to counter this intrusion he sunk the roads below the natural level of the land. Central Park has been much altered, and the advent of skyscrapers means that the city can now be seen from most areas of the park, but Olmsted's original vision of successive surprises, a plethora of discrete areas, and planned contrasts between open spaces and woodland, has largely survived. Olmsted was the USA's foremost nineteenth-century landscape architect, known chiefly for his large-scale public schemes, such as the Boston parks system, the Capitol landscape in Washington DC and Prospect Park, Brooklyn.

☛ Cleveland, Le Vaux, Mansard

Frederick Law Olmsted. b Hartford, CT (USA), 1822. d 1903. Central Park, New York, NY (USA).

Parsons Chris — Dew Garden

The only morning light illuminates an extraordinary abstract pattern in the dew at a bowling green in Aylesbury, Buckinghamshire, England. The pattern is the creation of Chris Parsons, a young groundsman, who rises before dawn and repeatedly sweeps a large rag brush over the close-cropped lawn. Parsons discovered the technique by accident one morning in 1991, and he has now made a wide variety of patterns, which he photographs from a nearby tree. The patterns last between three and five hours. 'Dew looks its best in the sun because it glitters,' Parsons says. 'From the moment the sun goes down, the dew starts to come down. You can feel the moistness in the air.' Parsons is also interested in the more conventional technique of creating patterns in lawns through different mowing regimes, and expresses an interest in land art and contemporary sculpture including Andy Goldsworthy. He also sees in his work a natural affinity with the Op Art style of Bridget Riley, and his recent work reflects this.

☛ Goldsworthy

Chris Parsons. b Kampala (UG), 1967. Dew Garden, Aylesbury, Buckinghamshire (UK).   381

Sackville-West Vita — Sissinghurst Castle Garden

White roses, clematis and honeysuckle combine to create a striking white colour scheme, which is harmoniously balanced by the background green. The white garden at Sissinghurst, Kent, England, is one of the most influential influence on gardening taste in the second half of the twentieth century, principally through Sissinghurst and her garden columns in the Observer newspaper. Planted in 1948, some twelve years after Vita Sackville-West and her diplomat husband Harold Nicolson arrived at the derelict Jacobean estate, the white garden started a cult in gardening taste that can still be discerned in gardens from Cape Town to Sydney.

The white garden is a small part of the Sissinghurst layout, based on a series of 'garden rooms' – formal in shape but informally planted – another influential concept, although not pioneered at this garden. Sackville-West had an enormous

☛ Hoare, Meyer

Vita (Victoria) Sackville-West. b Knole, Kent (UK), 1892. d Sissinghurst, Kent (UK), 1962.
Sissinghurst Castle Garden, Sissinghurst, Kent (UK).

Sitta Vladimir — Smith Residence

Black bamboo, Phyllostachys nigra, and tufts of mondo grass border a simple rectangular pool that culminates in a relief sculpture. At this private Sydney garden Vladimir Sitta has created a formal space with a strong Japanese tone. The Czechoslovakian-born designer has emerged over the last decade as one of the leading avant-garde designers currently working in Australia. His work often incorporates geologically inspired elements, such as fissures cracking through otherwise pristine stone, artificial mist and monolithic slabs. In the Smith Residence garden two jagged spears of stone bisect the reflections of the pool and lend it an elemental quality that compromises what would otherwise be an example of pristine Modernism. In the best Japanese tradition, Sitta explores this tension between order and untamed nature. Sitta's garden designs will be amongst the most closely followed of the next decade.

☛ Cao, Delaney, Schwartz

Vladimir Sitta. Smith Residence, Sydney (AUS).   381

On each page a short text describes the garden and its designer, while cross-referencing makes interesting links. Examples of gardens from around the world (from top, left to right) Stourhead in Wiltshire; Garden of Cosmic Speculation in Portrack; Central Park in New York; Dew Garden in Aylesbury; Sissinghurst Castle Garden in Kent; Smith Residence in Sydney

General Non-Fiction

Art

Photography

Collector's Editions

Film

Architecture NEW IN PAPERBACK

290 × 250 mm
11³⁄₈ × 9⁷⁄₈ inches
240 pp
315 col, 253 b&w illus.

Paperback
0 7148 4357 1

£ **19.95** UK
$ **29.95** US
€ **29.95** EUR
$ **49.95** CAN
$ **59.95** AUS

Hardback
0 7148 3950 7

£ **45.00** UK
$ **75.00** US
€ **75.00** EUR
$ **110.00** CAN
$ **125.00** AUS

Paperback published October

Greene & Greene

Edward R Bosley

- A critical monograph that charts the joint and independent careers of brothers Charles and Henry Greene, creators of the most iconic houses of the American Arts & Crafts movement
- Illustrated with new colour photography and draws on a wealth of previously unpublished archival material
- Examines in detail their most significant works, such as the Gamble, Blacker and Thorsen houses
- Showcases Californian architecture of the period, with its Asian influences and rich wood craftsmanship

Edward R Bosley is Director of the Gamble House in Pasadena, California. He has written and lectured widely on the work of the Greenes

Design

Fashion &
Contemporary Culture

Decorative Arts

Music &
Performing Arts

Video

Index

Spreads from Greene & Greene showing (from top, left to right) interiors of the Theodore Irwin, Jr., House, Pasadena, 1906–7; David B Gamble House, Pasadena, 1907–9; project for Mortimer Fleishhacker Townhouse, San Francisco, 1916; Henry Mather Greene, c.1935; project for Charles H Stoddard House, Burlingame, 1916, elevation and perspective; Walter L Richardson Ranch House, Porterville, 1929

General
Non-Fiction

Art

Photography

Collector's
Editions

Film

Architecture

245 × 210 mm
9⁵⁄₈ × 8¹⁄₄ inches
352 pp
199 col, 204 b&w illus.

Paperback
0 7148 3616 8

£ **16.95** UK
$ **24.95** US
€ **29.95** EUR
$ **39.95** CAN
$ **49.95** AUS

Hardback
0 7148 3615 X

£ **24.95** UK
$ **39.95** US
€ **39.95** EUR
$ **59.95** CAN
$ **65.00** AUS

The Story of Architecture

2nd edition
Patrick Nuttgens

- A comprehensive history of architecture from ancient times through to the present in a new edition
- Completely redesigned with more than 400 illustrations, new maps, time charts and architects' biographies
- Revised edition with updated text and expanded treatment of the modern and contemporary periods
- Each chapter charts a stage in the development of architecture, dividing the book into natural study units

Patrick Nuttgens is Honorary Professor at the University of York and a writer and broadcaster on architectural and educational subjects

'*The Story of Architecture* brings understanding and insight for those who have encountered the world's architectural heritage in their travels or through the media, and seek to explore it further.' *(Perspective)*

Design

Fashion & Contemporary Culture

Decorative Arts

Music & Performing Arts

Video

Index

290 × 250 mm
11³⁄₈ × 9⁷⁄₈ inches
512 pp
410 col, 90 b&w illus.

Hardback
0 7148 3984 1

£ **29.95** UK
$ **45.00** US
€ **49.95** EUR
$ **69.95** CAN
$ **79.95** AUS

Point of Sale
Book tower available

The House Book

- 500 of the most significant houses from the ancient to the new presented in A to Z order by the name of the designer
- Includes icons like Le Corbusier's Villa Savoye as well as stand-out designs by virtual unknowns
- An accessible and informative sourcebook for the architect as well as general interest reader
- Each house is represented by a full page reproduction
- Each page includes cross-references to other architects working in a similar style, movement or time period
- Includes easy-to-use glossary of architectural terms and movements and directory of houses open to the public with accompanying text about the building and its larger context

General
Non-Fiction

Art

Photography

Collector's
Editions

Film

Architecture

290 × 250 mm
11³⁄₈ × 9⁷⁄₈ inches
512 pp
445 col, 55 b&w illus.

Hardback
0 7148 3985 X
See also paperback mini
format on p.380

£ **29.95** UK
$ **45.00** US
€ **49.95** EUR
$ **69.95** CAN
$ **79.95** AUS

The Garden Book.

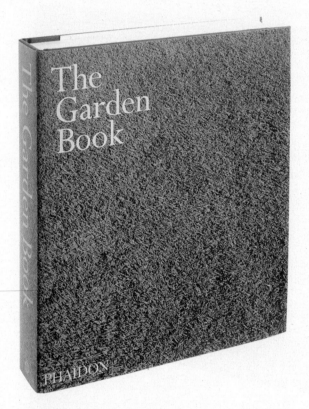

- A highly accessible overview of 500 garden designers organized in A-Z format now available in pocket format
- Presents a widely diverse range of gardens from ancient Persia to the classical gardens of Europe and the contemporary gardens of the US
- Each designer is represented by a garden that exemplifies their work and highlights their contribution to the history of the medium
- The featured gardens are famous, destroyed, mythical and private
- Includes an informative cross-referencing system linking designers who work in similar styles, movements or time periods
- Contains an essential glossary and directory of gardens

'A truly sumptuous encyclopedia … its range is magnificent – from ancient China and India to Renaissance Italy to modern Los Angeles.' (*Sunday Telegraph Magazine*)

Design

Fashion &
Contemporary
Culture

Decorative Arts

Music &
Performing Arts

Video

Index

'For a pictorial art history *The Garden Book* is unrivalled.'

The Washington Post

245 × 210 mm
9⅝ × 8¼ inches
736 pp
310 col, 367 b&w illus.
185 line drawings

Paperback
0 7148 3356 8

£ **24.95** UK
$ **39.95** US
€ **39.95** EUR
$ **59.95** CAN
$ **69.95** AUS

Hardback
0 7148 3524 2

£ **35.00** UK
$ **59.95** US
€ **59.95** EUR
$ **89.95** CAN
$ **95.00** AUS

Award

Winner in the Monographs category, American Institute of Architects International Architecture Book Awards, 1997

Modern Architecture Since 1900

3rd edition
William J R Curtis

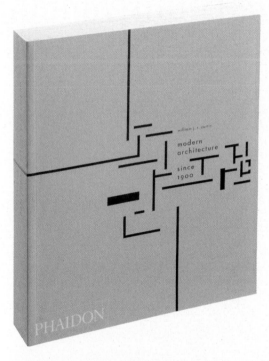

- This third edition of Curtis's classic text has been revised and expanded with new material, and a fresh appreciation of regional identity and variety
- Includes seven new chapters and covers recent world architecture
- Focuses on individual architects and the qualities that give their outstanding buildings lasting value
- Brings together technical, economic, social and intellectual developments in a comprehensive narrative
- Essential reading for an understanding of 20th-century architecture

William Curtis has won worldwide acclaim for his architectural writing. His books include *Le Corbusier: Ideas and Forms* and *Denys Lasdun,* both published by Phaidon

'As close to a definitive guide to the architecture of our century as we yet have.' *(The Sunday Times)*
'A book of this length and depth is an unimaginable achievement. Despite his immense knowledge he does not talk down to his audience; instead his enthusiasm is infectious.' *(Building Design)*
'This should be a standard volume in all architecture collections.' *(Library Journal)*
'Well established as the standard work on twentieth-century architecture, the new edition of this book has a fresh appreciation of the range and conplexity of modern architecture. This will become an essential textbook.' *(AIA Jury)*

Design

Fashion & Contemporary Culture

Decorative Arts

Music & Performing Arts

Video

Index

245 × 172 mm
9⅝ × 6¾ inches
352 pp
c.91 b&w illus.
111 line drawings

Hardback
0 7148 4080 7

£ **29.95** UK
$ **49.95** US
€ **49.95** EUR
$ **75.00** CAN
$ **89.95** AUS

Labour, Work and Architecture

Collected Essays on Architecture and Design
Kenneth Frampton

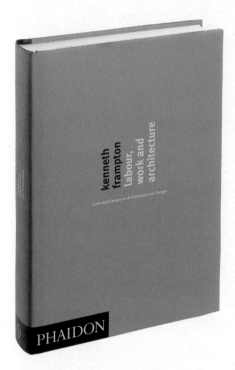

- An anthology of writings by esteemed architectural critic Frampton, containing his most influential essays from the last 35 years
- Includes Frampton's seminal critiques, reviews and theoretical and historical essays, along with three previously unpublished texts
- Presented in chronological order within three sections – Theory, History and Criticism
- Essays focus on 20th-century architecture, dealing with themes and movements, built works and architects

Kenneth Frampton is an internationally respected architectural critic who holds the Ware Professorship in Architecture at Columbia University, New York. He lectures extensively in the US and Europe, and has also written, edited and contributed to numerous publications on contemporary architecture. He is the author of *Modern Architecture: A Critical History* and *Studies in Tectonic Culture*

'For his entire career Mr Frampton has looked beneath the aesthetic surface of buildings in search of deeper meanings …' (Paul Goldberger, *The New York Times*)

General Non-Fiction

Art

Photography

Collector's Editions

Film

Architecture

290 × 250 mm
11³⁄₈ × 9⁷⁄₈ inches
512 pp
504 col, 14 b&w illus.

Paperback
0 7148 4097 1

£ 29.95   UK
$ 49.95   US
€ 49.95   EUR
$ 75.00   CAN
$ 85.00   AUS

Hardback
0 7148 3617 6

£ 45.00   UK
$ 69.95   US
€ 75.00   EUR
$ 98.00   CAN
$ 125.00   AUS

Point of Sale
15-copy tower available
0 7148 3703 2

Architecture Today

James Steele

- A clear and comprehensive guide to the prominent architectural styles and movements of the last 25 years
- Traces the work of leading contemporary architects around the world
- A primer of recent architectural history
- Essential reading for all those interested in architecture, the visual arts and modern culture

James Steele is Associate Professor of Architecture at the University of Southern California, Los Angeles. He has written a number of books, including *Pierre Koenig*, *Los Angeles Architecture* and *Queen Mary*, all published by Phaidon

'An ambitious guide to the trends in architecture over the last 25 years. In other words, a romp through all those tricky isms, from Vernacular to Deconstruction.' *(Sunday Times)*
'As a beginners' guide to the trends of the last 25 years, *Architecture Today* is invaluable. Accessible text and a preponderance of colour pictures go a long way toward doing for architecture what Gombrich did for art.' *(Creative Review)*

Design

Fashion & Contemporary Culture

Decorative Arts

Music & Performing Arts

Video

Index

290 × 250 mm
11³⁄₈ × 9⁷⁄₈ inches
512 pp
1001 col, 3 b&w illus.
208 line drawings

Paperback
0 7148 4203 6

£ **35.00** UK
$ **59.95** US
€ **59.95** EUR
$ **89.95** CAN
$ **120.00** AUS

Contemporary World Architecture

Hugh Pearman

- A comprehensive survey of recent architecture around the world
- Offers a critical study of the social, cultural and political changes – advances in building technology, shifting demographics and increasing levels of global communication – that are shaping today's built environment
- Thirteen chapters organized by building function: Visual Arts, Performance, Learning, Religion, Consumerism, Living, Workplace, Industry, Leisure, Transport, Sport, Civic Realm and Towers
- Presents over 660 recent public and private buildings from the late 1960s to the end of the 20th century

Hugh Pearman has been architecture and design critic for the *Sunday Times* since 1986, and contributes to numerous other newspapers, magazines and journals in Europe and America. He is also the author of *Equilibrium: The Work of Nicholas Grimshaw & Partners*, also published by Phaidon

'This is surely the most comprehensive guide we have to the recent history of architecture.' (*Architects' Journal*)

General
Non-Fiction

Art

Photography

Collector's
Editions

Film

Architecture

297 × 297 mm
12 × 12 inches
468 pp
c.1,000 col, 500 b&w illus.

Hardback
0 7148 3922 1

£ **45.00** UK
$ **69.95** US
€ **75.00** EUR
$ **99.95** CAN
$ **130.00** AUS

10 x 10

10 critics, 100 architects
Curated by Haig Beck & Jackie Cooper, Aaron Betsky, Roger Conah, Kristin Feireiss, Jorge Glusberg, Tom Heneghan, Moshen Mostavi, Terence Riley, Jaime Salazar and Neil Spiller

- A kaleidoscopic view of the work of 100 contemporary architects around the world selected by ten leading international curators and critics
- Features over 250 buildings and projects dating from 1990 to the present encompassing multimillion dollar schemes, small domestic projects and virtual technology
- Unique and innovative book design with a lenticular cover reflects the arresting visual imagery within, including over 1,500 images
- Presented alphabetically with four pages devoted to each architect
- Includes essays by each curator about the contemporary scene

'*10 x 10* is unchallenged as the architecture book of the year.' *(Washington Post)*
'The more you look, the more you find: *10 x 10* showcases the sly wit, depth and thought in the people behind today's best buildings.' *(HQ, Australia)*
'*10 x 10* truly delivers the promised overview of contemporary architecture. From its holographic cover to cultural references, it provides a body of work which offers fresh new ways of evaluating our built environment.' *(Baseline)*
'*10 x 10*'s claim to be the definitive contemporary architecture document would seem to be justified.' *(Blueprint)*

Design

Fashion &
Contemporary
Culture

Decorative Arts

Music &
Performing Arts

Video

Index

290 × 250 mm
11⅜ × 9⅞ inches
240 pp
300 col, 40 b&w illus.
100 line drawings

Hardback
0 7148 3987 6

£ **39.95** UK
$ **59.95** US
€ **65.00** EUR
$ **89.95** CAN
$ **120.00** AUS

Modern House 2

Clare Melhuish

- Similar format to Phaidon's hugely popular *Modern House*
- Features architects and practices such as Foster and Partners, Williams and Tsien, Günter Behnisch, Patkau Architects, SANAA, Herzog & de Meuron, Marcos Acayaba and Gabriel Poole
- Considers contemporary issues in architecture such as ecological concerns, changing patterns of living, building in dense cities
- Discusses concept houses and offers insight into possible future directions for domestic architecture

Clare Melhuish contributes regularly to the *Architects' Journal* and was formerly Reviews Editor for *Building Design*. She is the author of Phaidon's *Decq and Cornette* monograph

General
Non-Fiction

Art

Photography

Collector's
Editions

Film

Architecture

290 × 250 mm
11³⁄₈ × 9⁷⁄₈ inches
240 pp
215 col, 93 b&w illus.
148 line drawings

Paperback
0 7148 3837 3

£ **22.95** UK
$ **29.95** US
€ **39.95** EUR
$ **45.00** CAN
$ **55.00** AUS

Modern House

John Welsh

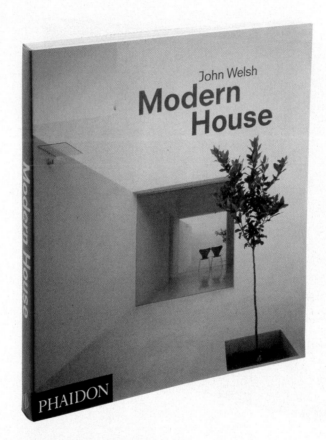

- Analysis of 30 recent houses by notable contemporary architects such as Glenn Murcutt, Richard Meier, OMA, Tadao Ando and Frank Gehry
- Variety reveals the importance of the house as a laboratory of design experimentation
- Demonstrates continuing links between contemporary innovation and the work of the early 20th-century masters

John Welsh is former Editor of the *RIBA Journal*. He was previously Buildings Editor of *Building Design*

'Give this book to potential clients.' *(Architects' Journal)*

Design

Fashion & Contemporary Culture

Decorative Arts

Music & Performing Arts

Video

Index

290 × 250 mm
11³⁄₈ × 9⁷⁄₈ inches
240 pp
c.300 col, c.50 b&w illus.
20 line drawings

Hardback
0 7148 4155 2

£ **45.00** UK
$ **75.00** US
€ **75.00** EUR
$ **99.95** CAN
$ **140.00** AUS

Modern Landscape

Michael Spens

- Features over 30 international projects, including schemes by both architects and landscape architects, often working in collaboration
- Extends the existing debate around landscape design to encompass the growing concern about the proper maintenance and enhancement of natural spaces
- Arranged thematically to analyse different aspects of landscape design, including parkland, architecture as landscape, garden landscapes and urban interventions

Michael Spens is Reader in Architecture at Dundee University. He has written extensively on the subject of landscape, focusing especially on the integration of buildings with landscape. His books include *Landscape Transformed* (editor, 1995), *The Complete Landscape Designs and Gardens of Geoffrey Jellicoe* (1994) and *Viipuri Library by Alvar Aalto* (1993)

General
Non-Fiction

Art

Photography

Collector's
Editions

Film

Architecture

290 × 250mm
11³⁄₈ × 9⁷⁄₈ inches
232 pp
156 col, 87 b&w illus.

Paperback
0 7148 3756 3

£ **19.95** UK
$ **29.95** US
€ **35.00** EUR
$ **45.00** CAN
$ **55.00** AUS

Los Angeles Architecture

The Contemporary Condition
James Steele

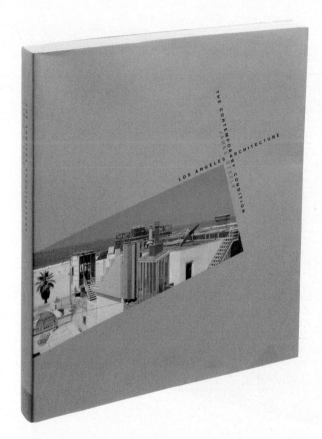

- Looks beneath the seductive surface of Los Angeles to reveal why the city's architectural scene is so fascinating
- Traces the energy of Los Angeles architecture from the American Arts & Crafts movement, through Frank Lloyd Wright and Rudolph Schindler, to Frank Gehry
- Investigates avant-garde institutions such as Sci-Arc as well as the development of specific zones, including downtown Los Angeles

James Steele is Associate Professor of Architecture at the University of Southern California, Los Angeles. His many books include *Architecture Today* and *Pierre Koenig*, both published by Phaidon

'This book proves to be far more than skin deep, thanks to a provocative and erudite text. An excellent insight.' *(Architectural Review)*
'Steele's rigorous examination of Los Angeles' contemporary condition looks at issues as well as influences, providing a timely portrait of a city often said to represent the urban typology of the future.' *(Perspectives)*

Design

Fashion & Contemporary Culture

Decorative Arts

Music & Performing Arts

Video

Index

250 × 290 mm
9⅞ × 11⅜ inches
320 pp
201 col, 76 b&w illus.
203 line drawings

Paperback
0 7148 4098 X

£ **29.95** UK
$ **49.95** US
€ **49.95** EUR
$ **75.00** CAN
$ **89.95** AUS

Awards

The Art Directors Club, Inc.

Merit Award
New York
Art Directors' Club, 1997

Winner in the Professional
Reference category, American
Institute of Architects
International Architecture
Book Awards, 1998

Glass in Architecture

Michael Wigginton

- The first comprehensive overview of the art and science of glass in architecture
- An essential manual for architects and constructors worldwide
- Spans the cathedrals of medieval Europe to the *grands projets* of Paris
- A central section presents 20 international case studies of contemporary glass architecture

Michael Wigginton is Professor of Architecture at the University of Plymouth and an architect in private practice. He has been responsible for some of the pioneering glass buildings of the last decade

'Immensely rewarding. The most important book on the subject.' *(Arq)*

General
Non-Fiction

Art

Photography

Collector's
Editions

Film

Architecture

245 × 210 mm
9⅝ × 8¼ inches
240 pp
330 col illus.

Hardback
0 7148 4172 2

£ **35.00** UK
$ **59.95** US
€ **59.95** EUR
$ **89.95** CAN
$ **120.00** AUS

Asymptote: Flux

Lise Anne Couture and Hani Rashid

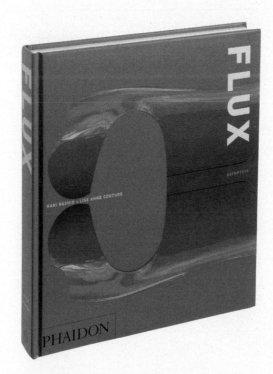

- A career overview designed and written by Asymptote partners Lise Anne Couture and Hani Rashid
- Documents Asymptote's first built works
- Includes diverse projects such as the trading floor for the New York Stock Exchange, a multimedia research park in Kyoto, and a modular furniture system for Knoll
- Illustrated with installation photographs, collaged photographs and computer-generated diagrams and environments
- Interspersed with descriptive text and the speculative writing characteristic of Asymptote

Hani Rashid and **Lise Anne Couture** combine their architectural practice with teaching, Rashid at Columbia University and Couture at Columbia and Parsons School of Design

Design

Fashion &
Contemporary
Culture

Decorative Arts

Music &
Performing Arts

Video

Index

290 × 250 mm
11³⁄₈ × 9⁷⁄₈ inches, 280 pp
c.350 col illus.
c.50 line drawings

Hardback
0 7148 4070 X

£ 45.00 UK
$ 75.00 US
€ 75.00 EUR
$ 99.95 CAN
$ 140.00 AUS

Morphosis

Thom Mayne and Val K Warke

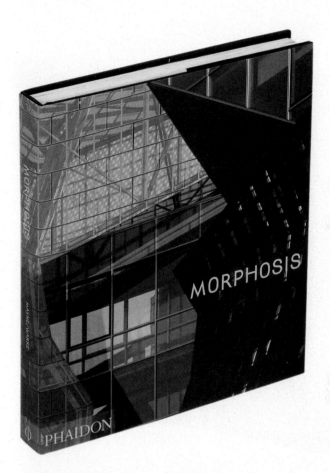

- The first monograph to document all of the key built works by Morphosis, a Los Angeles-based practice headed by Thom Mayne and founded in 1972
- One of the most influential architecture firms of the past 20 years
- Comprised of bold, documentary-style colour photographs of 35 completed buildings presented in an almost cinematic layout
- Covers the early projects in Los Angeles to recent large-scale work beyond California and the United States – in Canada, Taiwan, Korea, Japan and Austria

Val Warke is Associate Professor of Architecture at Cornell University in Ithaca, New York

General
Non-Fiction

Art

Photography

Collector's
Editions

Film

Architecture

290 × 250 mm
11³⁄₈ × 9⁷⁄₈ inches
208 pp
c.600 col, 100 b&w illus.

Paperback
0 7148 4320 2

£ **22.95** UK
$ **35.00** US
€ **39.95** EUR
$ **49.95** CAN
$ **59.95** AUS

Hardback
0 7148 4085 8

£ **39.95** UK
$ **59.95** US
€ **65.00** EUR
$ **89.95** CAN
$ **98.00** AUS

Imagination

With an introduction by Stephen Bayley

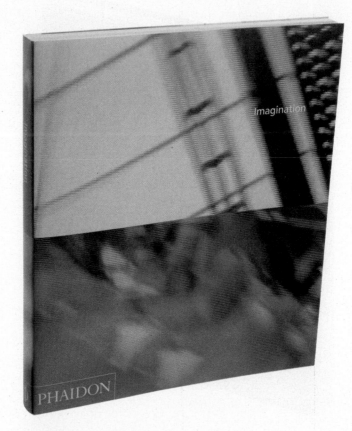

- A unique history of the communications and design agency Imagination, founded by Gary Withers in 1978
- Features over 30 projects organized into thematic chapters reflecting their aims: to inform, entertain, inspire, persuade and amaze
- With an introduction by design critic Stephen Bayley that assesses the significance of Imagination's approach to communication
- Includes insight by Mike Davies of the Richard Rogers Partnership, Sean Perkins of North, architect Lorenzo Apicella, Ian Liddell of Buro Happold and others
- An extensive interview with Gary Withers is illustrated with over 350 projects from the course of Imagination's history

Stephen Bayley was a founder of London's Design Museum and now works as a freelance writer and design consultant

Design

Fashion &
Contemporary
Culture

Decorative Arts

Music &
Performing Arts

Video

Index

290 × 250 mm
11³⁄₈ × 9⁷⁄₈ inches, 160 pp
181 col illus.
117 line drawings

Paperback
0 7148 3771 7

£ **19.95**   UK
$ **29.95**   US
€ **35.00** EUR
$ **45.00** CAN
$ **55.00** AUS

Hardback
0 7148 3343 6

£ **29.95**   UK
$ **49.95**   US
€ **49.95** EUR
$ **75.00** CAN
$ **85.00** AUS

Odile Decq
Benoît Cornette

Clare Melhuish

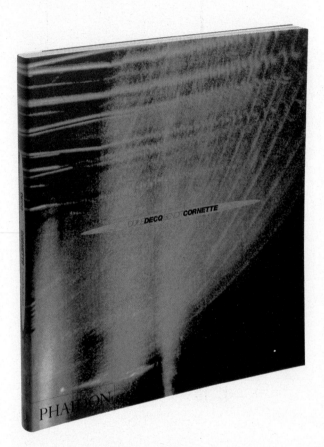

- An overview of the work of Decq and Cornette's work which is notable for its innovative use of metal and sophisticated engineering
- Decq (b.1950) and Cornette (b.1953) first rose to international prominence with their administrative and social building for the Banque Populaire de l'Ouest in Rennes in 1990, winner of many awards
- Charts the architects' working process in over 20 buildings and projects
- Features a range of visual material, including model images, sketches and computer renderings

Clare Melhuish contributes regularly to the *Architects' Journal* and was formerly Reviews Editor for *Building Design*. She is also the author of Phaidon's *Modern House 2*

'An intellectually demanding but ultimately rewarding study. A visually stunning publication.'
(Times Literary Supplement)

290 × 250 mm
11³⁄₈ × 9⁷⁄₈ inches
208 pp
c.200 col, 20 b&w illus.
100 line drawings

Hardback
0 7148 3831 4

£ **35.00** UK
$ **59.95** US
€ **59.95** EUR
$ **89.95** CAN
$ **99.95** AUS

Future Systems

Marcus Field

- Traces the continuing development of Future Systems, one of the most innovative and influential architectural practices on the current scene
- Examines over 30 recent projects, including designs for products and furniture
- Unique book design by Jan Kaplicky, one of the founders of Future Systems
- Contains a glossary of projects from 1958–92 including recent work such as the Hauer-King House, London, the Media Centre at Lords Cricket Ground and Comme des Garçons shops in New York, Paris and Tokyo

Marcus Field writes for the *Independent on Sunday*. He was previously Editor of *Blueprint*

Design

Fashion & Contemporary Culture

Decorative Arts

Music & Performing Arts

Video

Index

290 × 250 mm
11³⁄₈ × 9⁷⁄₈ inches
240 pp
375 col, 17 b&w illus.
40 line drawings

Hardback
0 7148 3830 6

£ **45.00** UK
$ **75.00** US
€ **75.00** EUR
$ **110.00** CAN
$ **125.00** AUS

You Are Here:

The Jerde Partnership International
Edited by Frances Anderton with essays by Ray Bradbury, Margaret Crawford,
Norman M Klein & Craig Hodgetts

- **The first monograph to examine the work of Jon Jerde (b.1940), the successful 'shopping and entertainment' architect**
- **Shows how the Jerde Partnership synthesizes commerce and public life to influence the design of 21st-century cities**
- **Closely examines 25 of the Jerde Partnership's most significant built and unbuilt projects**
- **Includes Jerde's evocative sketches**

Editor **Frances Anderton** is a Los Angeles-based journalist and a producer of the radio programme 'Which Way, LA?' Critical essays are by architectural historian Margaret Crawford, cultural historian Norman M Klein architect Craig Hodgetts. The foreword is by acclaimed author Ray Bradbury

General Non-Fiction

Art

Photography

Collector's Editions

Film

Architecture

245 × 210 mm
9⅝ × 8¼ inches
240 pp
250 col illus.
50 line drawings

Hardback
0 7148 3909 4

£ **39.95** UK
$ **59.95** US
€ **65.00** EUR
$ **89.95** CAN
$ **120.00** AUS

John Pawson Works

Deyan Sudjic

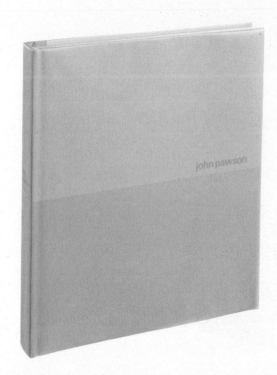

- A record of ten of Pawson's recent projects, showing in detail his unique approach to design
- Pawson (b.1940) is the highly acclaimed designer of the Calvin Klein flagship store in New York as well as other high-profile projects
- Incisive text and specially commissioned pictures explore Pawson's design process, working methods and philosophical approach

Deyan Sudjic was formerly Editor of *Blueprint* magazine. He is Editor of *Domus* magazine, was Director of 'Glasgow 1999: UK City of Architecture and Design', and has written many books, including *The 100 Mile City*

'As refined, precise and elegant as the buildings it describes.' *(LA Architecture)*

Design

Fashion & Contemporary Culture

Decorative Arts

Music & Performing Arts

Video

Index

245 × 172 mm
9⁵⁄₈ × 6³⁄₄ inches
128 pp
c.150 col, 50 b&w illus.

Hardback
0 7148 4237 0

£ **19.95** UK
$ **29.95** US
€ **35.00** EUR
$ **49.95** CAN
$ **59.95** AUS

John Pawson

Themes and Projects

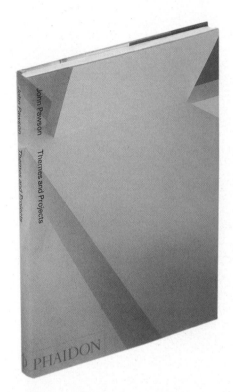

- A thematic overview of Pawson's (b.1940) work ideal for both architects and the general public interested in the Minimalist aesthetic
- Examines how Pawson's architecture is informed by light, mass and structure, ritual and order, and the interrelationship of indoor and outdoor spaces
- Includes six new projects: 'When Objects Work,' Calvin Klein Paris, Vacherin Constantin, the Marketmuseum, a private house in Germany and the Novy Dvur monastery
- With essays by Deyan Sudjic, Sam Hecht, Michael Craig-Martin, Phoebe Greenwood, Robert Winder, Kate Bucknell, Bruce Chatwin and Father Samuel, a monk of the Abbey of Notre-Dame de Sept-Fons

General
Non-Fiction

Art

Photography

Collector's
Editions

Film

Architecture

240 × 220 mm
9¹₂ × 8²₃ inches
524 pp
100 col, 370 b&w illus.
512 line drawings

Paperback
0 7148 3717 2

£ **29.95** UK
$ **45.00** US
€ **49.95** EUR
$ **69.95** CAN
$ **89.95** AUS

Tadao Ando

Complete Works
Edited by Francesco Dal Co

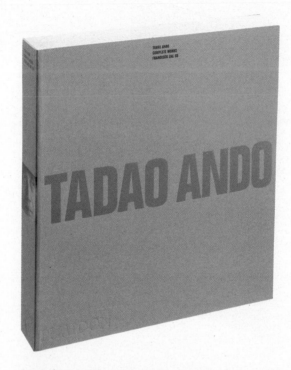

- A complete catalogue of the work of Ando (b.1941), Japan's leading architect
- Examines over 100 buildings and projects, illustrated by drawings, sketches, plans and documents from the architect's studio
- Comprehensive survey ranges from small private houses to major commissions like the Church on the Water, the Japanese Pavilion for the Expo 92 in Seville and the Naoshima Contemporary Art Museum
- With an introduction by Francesco Dal Co and an interview with Ando by Hiroshi Maruyama
- Includes essays on Ando's architecture by respected critics including Peter Eisenman, Kenneth Frampton, Tom Heneghan and François Chaslin, and selected writings by Ando himself

Francesco Dal Co is Professor of Architectural History at the University Institute of Architecture in Venice. He was Director of the architecture section of the 1991 Venice Biennale

'Wonderful plans, wonderful spaces, wonderful concrete, and now it is all wonderfully presented in this blockbuster monograph.' *(Interior Design)*
'A quite magnificent and massive collection.' *(Jerusalem Post)*

Design

Fashion &
Contemporary
Culture

Decorative Arts

Music &
Performing Arts

Video

Index

'The best book
to appear thus far
on this major artist.'

The New York Times

156 × 136 mm
6¹s × 5³s inches
284 pp
180 col illus.
27 b&w sketches

Hardback
0 7148 3999 X
See also collector's edition on p.364

£ **12.95** UK
$ **19.95** US
€ **22.95** EUR
$ **29.95** CAN
$ **35.00** AUS

Point of Sale
10-copy counterpack available

Tadao Ando, The Colours of Light

Photographs by Richard Pare, with an introduction by Tom Heneghan

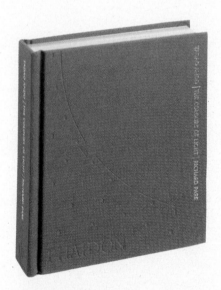

- The result of ten years' collaboration between photographer Pare and Japan's leading architect, Ando (b.1941)
- Includes 27 of Ando's buildings, including the notable Hidosaki House, Tokyo (1986), the Church on the Water, Hokkaido (1988) and the Meditation Space for UNESCO, Paris (1995)
- Pare's photographs distil the essence of Ando's buildings by concentrating on the subtle effects of natural light on architecture
- Introductory essay by Tom Heneghan, Professor at Kogakuin University in Tokyo
- Drawings by Ando accompany each project description

'An outstanding presentation of arguably the most significant body of work of the last 20 years.' *(Architects' Journal)*
'Exquisitely photographed by Richard Pare, the details of Mr Ando's houses, office buildings, meditation spaces and churches haunt the retina.' *(The New York Times)*
'This beguiling and vivacious book allows you to tune into Ando's work right away. In this book, every page raises your level of consciousness and I cannot say how much pleasure it gave.' *(Architectural Review)*

Design

Fashion & Contemporary Culture

Decorative Arts

Music & Performing Arts

Video

Index

290 × 250 mm
11³⁄₈ × 9⁷⁄₈ inches
620 pp
220 col, 145 b&w illus.
300 line drawings

Hardback
0 7148 4004 1

£ **60.00** UK
$ **95.00** US
€ **95.00** EUR
$ **140.00** CAN
$ **165.00** AUS

Álvaro Siza

Complete Works
Introduction by Kenneth Frampton

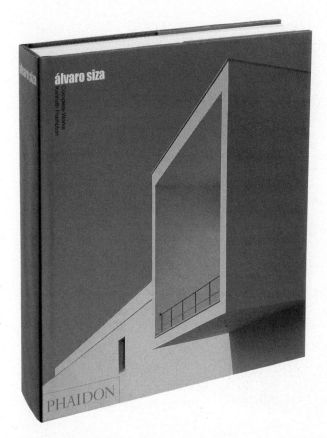

- Charts over 40 years of work by the Pritzker Prize-winning Portuguese architect Siza (b.1933)
- Covers Siza's earliest built work – the Boa Nova Tea House in Portugal (1958–63) as well as the recent projects
- Text by noted architectural critic Kenneth Frampton is interspersed with Siza's own writings
- Includes many of Siza's original sketches

Kenneth Frampton is Ware Professor at the Graduate School of Architecture and Planning, Columbia University, New York. He is well known for his writing on 20th-century architecture. His books include *Modern Architecture: A Critical History* (1980; revised 1985 and 1992) and *Studies in Tectonic Culture* (1997). His collected essays *Labour, Work and Architecture* are published by Phaidon

General Non-Fiction

Art

Photography

Collector's Editions

Film

Architecture

290 × 250 mm
11³⁄₈ × 9⁷⁄₈ inches
240 pp
283 col, 245 b&w illus.
205 line drawings

Paperback
0 7148 3898 5

£ 22.95 UK
$ 35.00 US
€ 39.95 EUR
$ 49.95 CAN
$ 59.95 AUS

Renzo Piano Building Workshop

Complete Works, Volume 1
Peter Buchanan

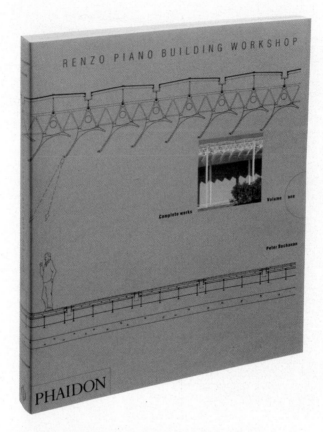

- The first volume of the complete works of Piano (b.1937)
- A detailed presentation of key early works including Piano's studio in Genoa, the Pompidou Centre (with Richard Rogers) in Paris, the Bari Sports Stadium in Italy and the early stages of the Kansai Airport International Terminal in Japan
- Specially prepared drawings and plans give new insight into well-known buildings

Peter Buchanan was formerly Deputy Editor of the *Architectural Review* and is now a freelance writer and lecturer

'This is the first book about the Building Workshop that is an accurate mirror of what we do and the way we do it.' *(Renzo Piano)*

Design

Fashion & Contemporary Culture

Decorative Arts

Music & Performing Arts

Video

Index

290 × 250 mm
11³⁄₈ × 9⁷⁄₈ inches
240 pp
592 col, 115 b&w illus.
224 line drawings

Paperback
0 7148 3899 3

£ **22.95** UK
$ **35.00** US
€ **39.95** EUR
$ **49.95** CAN
$ **59.95** AUS

Renzo Piano Building Workshop

Complete Works, Volume 2
Peter Buchanan

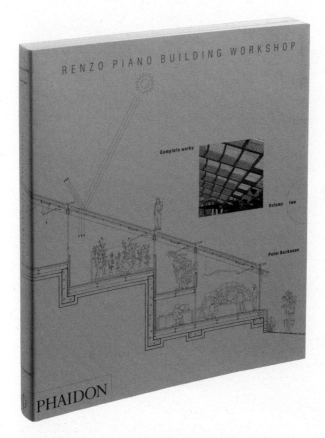

- The second volume of the complete works of Piano (b.1937)
- A detailed presentation of all buildings and projects from 1987 to 1993, many of them located in and around Piano's home town of Genoa
- Includes interview in which Piano discusses the development of his practice, his attitude towards technology and the continuing evolution of what Buchanan has called 'a natural architecture'

Peter Buchanan was formerly Deputy Editor of the *Architectural Review* and is now a freelance writer and lecturer

General Non-Fiction

Art

Photography

Collector's Editions

Film

Architecture

290 × 250 mm
11³⁄₈ × 9⁷⁄₈ inches
240 pp
385 col, 41 b&w illus.
200 line drawings

Paperback
0 7148 3933 7

£ 22.95 UK
$ 35.00 US
€ 39.95 EUR
$ 49.95 CAN
$ 59.95 AUS

Renzo Piano Building Workshop

Complete Works, Volume 3
Peter Buchanan

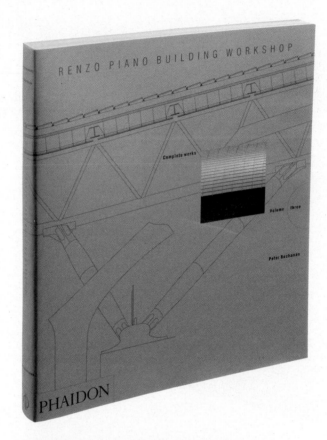

- The third volume of the complete works of Piano (b.1937)
- A detailed presentation of projects of the early 1990s, including the Kansai Airport in Japan from its initial design to the finished building; the Lingotto Factory renovation, Turin; the Cité Internationale, Lyons; the Cy Twombly Pavilion, Houston, Texas; the Rome Auditoria; the Saitama Arena in Japan; and L'Ile Seguin and Le Grand Stade, Paris
- Particular emphasis on Piano's innovative approach to lighting and curtain-wall construction

Peter Buchanan was formerly Deputy Editor of the *Architectural Review* and is now a freelance writer and lecturer

Design

Fashion &
Contemporary
Culture

Decorative Arts

Music &
Performing Arts

Video

Index

290 × 250 mm
11³⁄₈ × 9⁷⁄₈ inches
240 pp
430 col, 14 b&w illus.
113 line drawings

Paperback
0 7148 4287 7

£ 22.95 UK
$ 35.00 US
€ 39.95 EUR
$ 49.95 CAN
$ 59.95 AUS

Hardback
0 7148 3931 0

£ 45.00 UK
$ 75.00 US
€ 75.00 EUR
$ 110.00 CAN
$ 125.00 AUS

Renzo Piano Building Workshop

Complete Works, Volume 4
Peter Buchanan

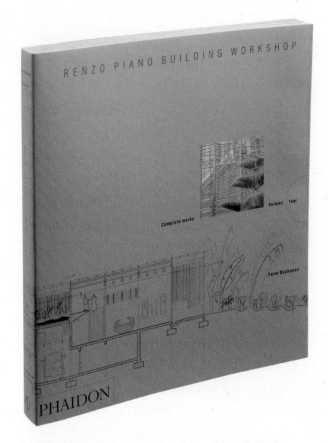

- The fourth volume of the complete works of Piano (b.1937)
- A detailed presentation of projects of the late 1990s, including the Potsdamer Platz masterplan in Berlin, a science museum in Amsterdam, high-rise towers in Rotterdam and Sydney, the acclaimed Beyeler Foundation, and the Jean-Marie Tjibaou Cultural Centre in New Caledonia
- Technical drawings and descriptive analysis explain innovative solutions to structural problems

Peter Buchanan was formerly Deputy Editor of the *Architectural Review* and is now a freelance writer and lecturer

General
Non-Fiction

Art

Photography

Collector's
Editions

Film

Architecture

290 × 250 mm
11³⁄₈ × 9⁷⁄₈ inches
320 pp
300 col, 250 b&w illus.

Hardback
0 7148 3746 6

£ **59.95** UK
$ **95.00** US
€ **95.00** EUR
$ **140.00** CAN
$ **175.00** AUS

Richard Rogers

Complete Works
Volume 1 – Team 4, Piano + Rogers, Richard Rogers and Partners
Kenneth Powell

- The first volume of the complete works of Rogers (b.1933)
- Covers 1961–88, including Roger's early work with Norman Foster and Team 4 and his partnerships with Su Rogers and Renzo Piano
- Examines each project in detail and includes new visual material from practice archives
- Highlights include Creek Vean in Cornwall (1966), the Rogers and Piano collaboration at the Pompidou Centre in Paris (1971–7) and Lloyd's of London (1978–86)
- With a complete list of works and interviews with key figures who have collaborated with Rogers throughout his career

Kenneth Powell, former Architecture Correspondent of the *Daily Telegraph,* is a contributor to many architectural journals and Consultant Director of the 20th Century Society. He has written extensively on the work of Richard Rogers

'An authoritative guide to every building and project of note from 1961 to 1988.'
(Building Design)

Design

Fashion & Contemporary Culture

Decorative Arts

Music & Performing Arts

Video

Index

290 × 250 mm
11³⁄₈ × 9⁷⁄₈ inches
320 pp
300 col, 150 b&w illus.
150 line drawings

Hardback
0 7148 3747 4

£ **59.95** UK
$ **95.00** US
€ **95.00** EUR
$ **140.00** CAN
$ **175.00** AUS

Richard Rogers

Complete Works
Volume 2
Kenneth Powell

- **The second volume of the complete works of Rogers (b.1933)**
- **Features over 50 projects from 1987–92**
- **Includes competition schemes for Terminal 5 at Heathrow Airport, the Tokyo International Forum, and buildings such as Channel 4 headquarters and the Strasbourg Court of Human Rights**

Kenneth Powell, former Architecture Correspondent of the *Daily Telegraph*, is a contributor to many architectural journals and Consultant Director of the 20th Century Society. He has written extensively on the work of Richard Rogers

'Solid and authoritative.' *(Architects' Journal)*

General Non-Fiction

Art

Photography

Collector's Editions

Film

Architecture

250 × 250 mm
9⅞ × 9⅞ inches
256 pp
190 col, 34 b&w illus.
143 line drawings

Paperback
0 7148 3934 5

£ **22.95** UK
$ **35.00** US
€ **39.95** EUR
$ **49.95** CAN
$ **59.95** AUS

Architecture, Industry and Innovation

The Early Work of Nicholas Grimshaw & Partners
Colin Amery

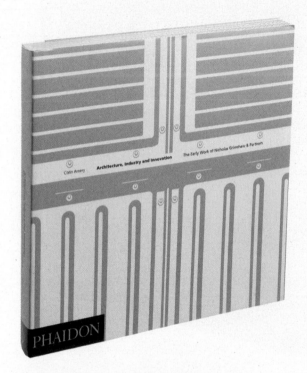

- Part of a series that details Grimshaw's (b.1939) practice
- Covers the years 1965–88, a period which saw him establish worldwide reputation
- Charts Grimshaw's development from his student days at the Architectural Association and gives critical insights into his design methodology
- Incorporates an examination of a family of buildings, from the 1965 Service Tower for student apartments to his 1988 Grand Union Walk housing and Sainsbury Superstore in Camden Town, north London

Colin Amery was formerly the Architecture Correspondent of the *Financial Times*

Design

Fashion &
Contemporary
Culture

Decorative Arts

Music &
Performing Arts

Video

Index

250 × 250 mm
9⅞ × 9⅞ inches
256 pp
152 col, 42 b&w illus.
117 line drawings

Paperback
0 7148 3457 2

£ **22.95** UK
$ **35.00** US
€ **39.95** EUR
$ **49.95** CAN
$ **59.95** AUS

Structure, Space and Skin

The Work of Nicholas Grimshaw & Partners
Introduced by Kenneth Powell, edited by Rowan Moore

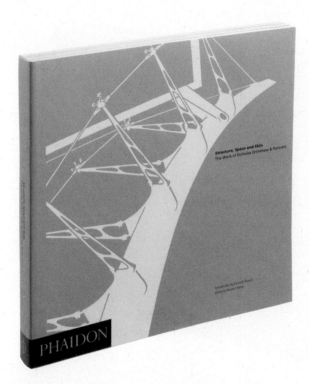

- **Part of a series that details Grimshaw's (b.1939) practice**
- **Covers late 1980s and through the 1990s**
- **Features the Financial Times printing plant and the acclaimed international railway terminal at Waterloo, London**

Kenneth Powell is the former Architecture Correspondent of the *Daily Telegraph* and a consultant editor of *Architectural Design*
Rowan Moore is a former editor of *Blueprint* and currently Architecture Correspondent of the *London Evening Standard*.

'The excellent mix of photographs and illustrations will be welcomed by students and practitioners alike.' *(Architects' Journal)*

General
Non-Fiction

Art

Photography

Collector's
Editions

Film

Architecture

250 × 250 mm
9⅞ × 9⅞ inches
256 pp
250 col, 100 b&w illus.

Hardback
0 7148 3958 2

£ **45.00** UK
$ **75.00** US
€ **75.00** EUR
$ **110.00** CAN
$ **125.00** AUS

Equilibrium

The Work of Nicholas Grimshaw & Partners
Hugh Pearman

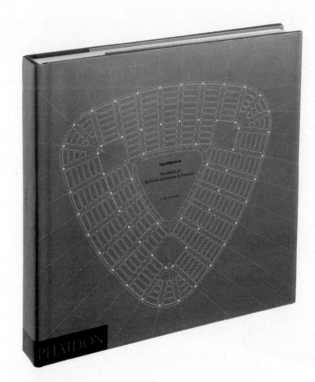

- Part of a series that details Grimshaw's (b.1939) practice
- Covers the late 1990s to the present day
- Focuses on the Eden Project in Cornwall, Ludwig Erhard Haus in Berlin, the Orange Call Centre in Darlington, the National Space Science Centre in Leicester and the redevelopment of Paddington Station

Hugh Pearman is a London-based writer, broadcaster and lecturer. He has been architecture and design critic for the *Sunday Times* since 1986 and contributes to many other newspapers, magazines and periodicals worldwide. He is also author of *Contemporary World Architecture* (Phaidon, 1998)

Design

Fashion &
Contemporary
Culture

Decorative Arts

Music &
Performing Arts

Video

Index

290 × 250 mm
11³⁄₈ × 9⁷⁄₈ inches
240 pp
250 col, 90 b&w illus.
80 line drawings

Paperback
0 7148 3456 4

£ **22.95** UK
$ **35.00** US
€ **39.95** EUR
$ **49.95** CAN
$ **59.95** AUS

Hopkins

The Work of Michael Hopkins and Partners
Colin Davies

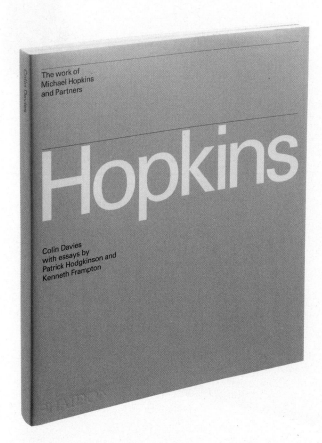

- Contains all the early built works and projects of Royal Gold Medal winner Hopkins (b.1935) and his firm
- Works featured include the Glyndebourne Opera House and the designs for the New Parliamentary Building
- With essays by Colin Davies, Kenneth Frampton and Patrick Hodgkinson

Colin Davies is an architect, a former editor of the *Architects' Journal* and teaches history of architecture at the University of North London

'The superb photography brilliantly conveys the Escorial-like severity and gravitas of much of their work.' *(The Times)*

General
Non-Fiction

Art

Photography

Collector's
Editions

Film

Architecture

290 × 250 mm
11³⁄₈ × 9⁷⁄₈ inches
240 pp
250 col, 20 b&w illus.
120 line drawings

Hardback
0 7148 3925 6

£ **45.00** UK
$ **69.95** US
€ **75.00** EUR
$ **99.95** CAN
$ **125.00** AUS

Hopkins 2

The Work of Michael Hopkins and Partners
Colin Davies

- Second volume of the architect's work containing 26 recent buildings and projects
- Extensive presentation of Hopkins' most important commission to date: the New Parliamentary Building in London
- A detailed discussion of the development of the architect's design vocabulary

Colin Davies is an architect, a former editor of the *Architects' Journal* and teaches history of architecture at the University of North London

'Excellent jargon-free essays by Colin Davies and Charles Jencks.' *(Architects' Journal)*

Design

Fashion & Contemporary Culture

Decorative Arts

Music & Performing Arts

Video

Index

290 × 250 mm
11³⁄₈ × 9⁷⁄₈ inches
240 pp
184 duotone illus.
63 line drawings

Paperback
0 7148 3902 7

£ 22.95 UK
$ 35.00 US
€ 39.95 EUR
$ 49.95 CAN
$ 59.95 AUS

Hardback
0 7148 2871 8

£ 45.00 UK
$ 75.00 US
€ 75.00 EUR
$ 98.00 CAN
$ 125.00 AUS

Denys Lasdun

Architecture, City, Landscape
William J R Curtis

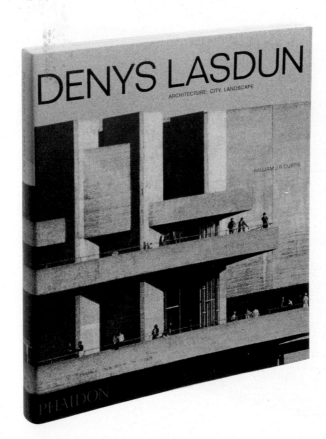

- Comprehensive study of the career of eminent British architect Lasdun (1914–2001) which spans the period of Modernism in British architecture
- Curtis offers a critical assessment of Lasdun's ideas and achievements, tracing the evolution of his architectural language
- Many outstanding illustrations from the architect's own archive
- Notable buildings include the Royal College of Physicians in Regent's Park, the University of East Anglia, the European Investment Bank in Luxembourg and the National Theatre on London's South Bank

William Curtis has won worldwide acclaim for his architectural writing. His books include *Le Corbusier: Ideas and Forms* and the best-selling *Modern Architecture Since 1900*, both also published by Phaidon

'At last we have a monograph worthy of the man.' *(Architectural Review)*
'A fine celebration and reappraisal of Lasdun's work.' *(Observer)*

General
Non-Fiction

Art

Photography

Collector's
Editions

Film

Architecture

290 × 250mm
11³⁄₈ × 9⁷⁄₈ inches
160 pp
84 col, 96 b&w illus.
98 line drawings

Paperback
0 7148 4096 3

£ **19.95** UK
$ **29.95** US
€ **35.00** EUR
$ **49.95** CAN
$ **59.95** AUS

Pierre Koenig

James Steele & David Jenkins

- The first monograph fully to document the pioneering architecture of Koenig (b.1925)
- Provides insight into the evolution of Modernism and the impact of the Case Study programme on the architecture of the West Coast of the US
- Includes newly commissioned and vintage photographs together with the architect's original drawings
- Looks at Koenig's first exposed steel house, built in 1950, as well as the iconic and innovative Case Study Houses #21 and #22, commissioned by *Arts and Architecture Magazine*

James Steele is Associate Professor of Architecture at the University of Southern California, Los Angeles. His many publications include *Los Angeles Architecture: The Contemporary Condition* and *Architecture Today,* both published by Phaidon
David Jenkins was Buildings Editor of the *Architect's Journal* and is currently with Foster Associates

Design

Fashion & Contemporary Culture

Decorative Arts

Music & Performing Arts

Video

Index

210×210 mm
8¼×8¼ inches
224 pp
250 b&w illus.

Hardback
0 7148 4063 7

£ **39.95** UK
$ **59.95** US
€ **59.95** EUR
$ **89.95** CAN
$ **120.00** AUS

Raphael Soriano

Wolfgang Wagener

- The first monograph on Soriano (1907-1988), one of the early Case Study architects in post-war Los Angeles
- Detailed descriptions of 30 key Soriano buildings, including important works that have been destroyed or remodelled beyond recognition
- Documents Soriano's innovations in steel construction and post-war housing, which influenced other architects such as Charles and Ray Eames, Pierre Koenig and Craig Ellwood
- With a listing of complete works that documents for the first time every known project in Soriano's archive
- Includes more than 100 classic period photographs by renowned architectural photographer Julius Shulman

Wolfgang Wagener is an architect and has written articles on 20th-century modern architecture. Since 1997 he has been a visiting professor at the University of Southern California, Los Angeles

General
Non-Fiction

Art

Photography

Collector's
Editions

Film

Architecture

210 × 210 mm
8¹⁄₄ × 8¹⁄₄ inches
272 pp
307 b&w illus.

Hardback
0 7148 4074 2

£ **39.95** UK
$ **59.95** US
€ **65.00** EUR
$ **89.95** CAN
$ **120.00** AUS

A Quincy Jones

Cory Buckner

- The first book published on Los Angeles architect Archibald Quincy Jones (1913–79), a pioneer in affordable housing designed with a modern aesthetic
- Introductory essay traces Jones's life and career, his post-war planning projects and his long association with Palo Alto building magnate Joseph Eichler
- Contains a catalogue of 60 of Jones's projects illustrated with high-quality black-and-white period photographs, plans and renderings by Jones
- Jones's projects are quintessential examples of mid-century American architecture

Cory Buckner is a practising architect and writer who bought a house designed by Jones and began to research his work. She obtained her architecture degree from the California Institute of the Arts and an MA in architectural history at the University of California at Los Angeles

Design

Fashion &
Contemporary
Culture

Decorative Arts

Music &
Performing Arts

Video

Index

210 × 210 mm
8¹₄ × 8¹₄ inches
304 pp
c.25 col, 250 b&w illus.
175 line drawings

Hardback
0 7148 3914 0

£ **39.95** UK
$ **59.95** US
€ **65.00** EUR
$ **89.95** CAN
$ **120.00** AUS

R M Schindler

Judith Sheine

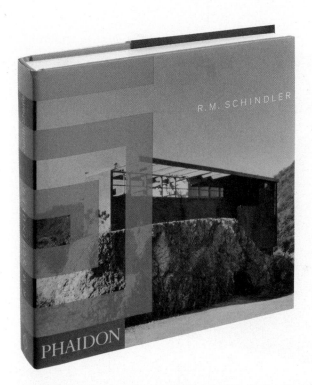

- A comprehensive overview of the pivotal Modernist architect R M Schindler (1887–1953) who has recently been rediscovered by critics
- Examines more than 75 of the 500 designs by Schindler, over 150 of which were built
- Focuses on Schindler's original approach, which he dubbed 'space architecture', influenced by the ideas of Loos, Wagner and Wright
- Includes rare archival material and new photography by Grant Mudford, as well as over 150 redrawn plans, sections and diagrams

Judith Sheine is a practising architect in Los Angeles and Associate Professor at California State Polytechnic University, Pomona

'A thorough, well-paced survey of his professional development, interweaving his biography and works to notable effect.' *(The New York Times)*

General
Non-Fiction

Art

Photography

Collector's
Editions

Film

Architecture

223 × 158 mm
8³⁄₄ × 6¹⁄₄ inches
80 pp
27 col, 24 duotone illus.

Hardback
0 7148 3960 4

£ **9.95** UK
$ **15.95** US
€ **16.95** EUR
$ **24.95** CAN
$ **27.95** AUS

Luis Barragán

René Burri

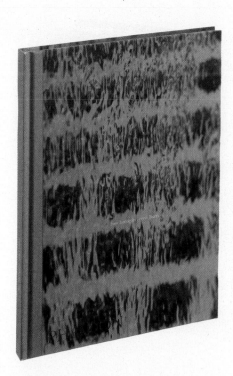

- A key figure in modern architecture, Barragán's (1902–88) influence has travelled far beyond his Mexican homeland
- Burri's photographs illustrate an architecture inspired by the vernacular style of Mexico, Barragán's love of Moorish architecture, and a desire for spiritual beauty and harmony with nature
- Unique union of two powerful visions – photographer and architect

René Burri, a photographer and film-maker, was born in Switzerland and studied at the Zurich School of Art. At the age of 23 he published his first story in *Life* and three years later, in 1959, he became a full member of the now legendary photo agency Magnum. A monograph that charts his entire career is also published by Phaidon

Design

Fashion &
Contemporary
Culture

Decorative Arts

Music &
Performing Arts

Video

Index

245 × 172 mm
9³⁄₈ × 6 inches
192 pp
31 b&w illus.
41 sketches by Niemeyer

Hardback
0 7148 4007 6

£ **14.95** UK
$ **24.95** US
€ **24.95** EUR
$ **35.00** CAN
$ **39.95** AUS

The Curves of Time

Oscar Niemeyer Memoirs
Oscar Niemeyer

- The first English-language edition of Niemeyer's memoirs
- Reveals the architect's many influences including his family, friends, women, art, literature
  and the sensuous landscapes of Brazil
- Niemeyer (b.1903) recounts his life in an informal, fluid narrative that moves from his
  childhood in Rio, through friendships with intellectuals and politicians such as Jean-Paul
  Sartre and Fidel Castro, to tales of adventurous road trips
- Includes 40 specially-made sketches by Niemeyer and a chronology of his life and career

'Superbly crafted … the unforgettable presence of an acute man who writes clearly and draws
like a Picasso angel.' *(Guardian)*

270 × 205 mm
10⁵⁄₈ × 8¹⁄₈ inches
272 pp
c.120 col, 200 b&w illus.

Hardback
0 7148 4289 3

£ **39.95** UK
$ **69.95** US
€ **69.95** EUR
$ **99.95** CAN
$ **120.00** AUS

Room 606

The SAS House and the Work of Arne Jacobsen
Michael Sheridan

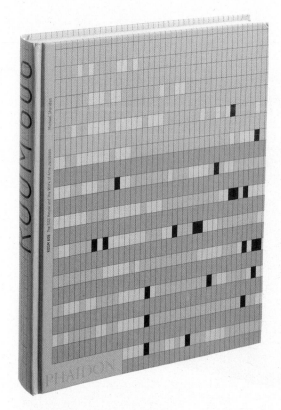

- An intriguing look at Danish architect Jacobsen (1902–71) through a detailed study of Room 606, the only preserved part of Jacobsen's masterwork, the SAS House in Copenhagen
- Exemplifies how Jacobsen dissolved the boundaries between architecture, interior and industrial design
- Organized in sections that alternately look at Room 606, reconstruct the original building and connect this masterpiece to other works
- Provides an overview of Jacobsen's entire career

Michael Sheridan is a practising architect in New York. He lived in Copenhagen during his youth and later studied architecture at the University of Minnesota and Columbia University in New York

Design

Fashion & Contemporary Culture

Decorative Arts

Music & Performing Arts

Video

Index

210 × 210 mm
8¹₄ × 8¹₄ inches
272 pp
296 b&w illus.
54 line drawings

Hardback
0 7148 3893 4

£ **39.95** UK
$ **59.95** US
€ **65.00** EUR
$ **89.95** CAN
$ **120.00** AUS

Breuer Houses

Joachim Driller

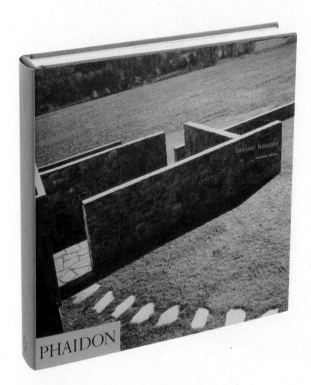

- **A comprehensive study of the houses designed by Hungarian-born architect Breuer (1902–81)**
- **Projects span 1923 to 1973**
- **Breuer became known for diverse and powerful designs for the Whitney Museum of American Art in New York, the UNESCO headquarters in Paris and the iconic 'Wassily' chair**
- **Richly illustrated with drawings, plans and archival photography**
- **Breuer has profoundly influenced residential architecture around the world and many generations of designers**

Joachim Driller is an expert on Breuer's work. He has taught and researched at the University of Pennsylvania and at Harvard, and currently teaches at the University of Wuppertal in Germany

General
Non-Fiction

Art

Photography

Collector's
Editions

Film

Architecture

280 × 215 mm
11 × 8¹₂ inches
240 pp
31 col, 212 b&w illus.

Paperback
0 7148 2790 8

£ **19.95** UK
$ **29.95** US
€ **35.00** EUR
$ **45.00** CAN
$ **55.00** AUS

Le Corbusier

Ideas and Forms
William J R Curtis

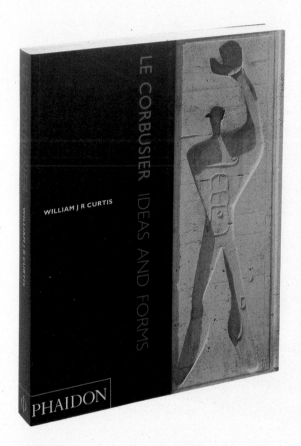

- A balanced perspective of the career of the most dominant force in early 20th-century architecture whose impact has had lasting effect on the architecture of the world
- Le Corbusier (1887–1965) developed many of the archetypes of Modernism and generated intense controversy
- Documents individual projects in detail while relating them to Le Corbusier's philosophy of life, his urban visions, his art and the cultural predicaments of his times

William Curtis has won worldwide acclaim for his architectural writing. His books include the best-selling *Modern Architecture Since 1900,* and *Denys Lasdun*, both also published by Phaidon

Design

Fashion & Contemporary Culture

Decorative Arts

Music & Performing Arts

Video

Index

210 × 210 mm
8¹₄ × 8¹₄ inches
256 pp
22 col, 200 b&w illus.
14 line drawings

Hardback
0 7148 3905 1

£ **39.95** UK
$ **59.95** US
€ **65.00** EUR
$ **89.95** CAN
$ **120.00** AUS

Eileen Gray

Caroline Constant

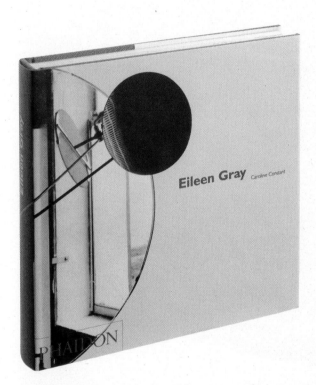

- An in-depth study of the Irish-born designer Eileen Gray (1878–1976)
- Examines her highly original furniture and interior design, including sumptuous lacquer furniture influenced by traditional French decorative arts, and wool carpets and draperies
- Explores nine realized buildings and more than 45 architectural projects from Gray's archive, including villa E. 1027 on the coast of southern France
- Places Gray in the context of contemporary movements in design and architecture and 20th-century social and cultural history
- Includes a wealth of archival material, plans, drawings and photographs, including many of Gray's own

Caroline Constant is Professor of Architecture at the University of Michigan

'An excellent and thought-provoking read.' *(Architects' Journal)*

General Non-Fiction

Art

Photography

Collector's Editions

Film

Architecture

210 × 210 mm
8¹⁴ × 8¹⁴ inches
256 pp
90 col, 160 b&w illus.

Hardback
0 7148 4043 2

£ **39.95** UK
$ **59.95** US
€ **65.00** EUR
$ **89.95** CAN
$ **120.00** AUS

Auguste Perret

Karla Britton

- The first monograph in English on the work of the architect Auguste Perret (1874–1954), a pioneering precursor to the Modern movement
- Looks at Perret's projects in France and abroad, such as the Musée des Travaux Publics in Paris, the Church of Notre-Dame at Raincy and other domestic, industrial and urban buildings, and his innovative use of structure and materials
- Richly illustrated with new colour photography as well as drawings and photographs from the Perret archive
- Includes an appendix of Perret's aphorisms and other writings

Karla Britton is Director of the New York/Paris programme of Columbia University's Graduate School of Architecture, Planning and Preservation in Paris

'[Perret] emerge[s] as witty, wise and social minded, the deft first user of concrete, justifiably admired by "Corb".' *(Art Newspaper)*

Design

Fashion & Contemporary Culture

Decorative Arts

Music & Performing Arts

Video

Index

290 × 250 mm
11³⁄₈ × 9⁷⁄₈ inches
240 pp
190 col, 160 b&w illus.
260 line drawings

Paperback
0 7148 3628 1

£ **22.95** UK
$ **35.00** US
€ **39.95** EUR
$ **49.95** CAN
$ **59.95** AUS

Hans Scharoun

Peter Blundell Jones

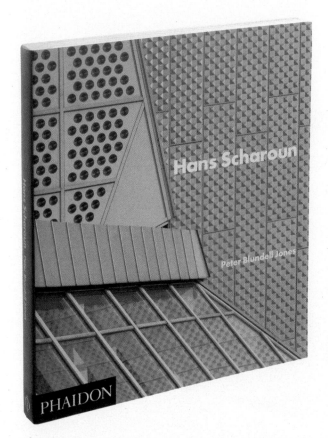

- Exhaustive study of Hans Scharoun (1893–1972), the most significant German architectural Modernist of the 1920s and exponent of organic architecture
- Provides a comprehensive overview of Scharoun's life and work
- Also explores his theoretical stance in relation to contemporaries such as Hugo Häring, Mies van der Rohe and Le Corbusier
- Highlights important projects such as the controversial house for the Stuttgart Weissenhofsiedlung in 1927 and Philharmonie concert hall in Berlin from 1956–63

Peter Blundell Jones is a Professor of Architecture at Sheffield University. In 1992 he was named Architectural Journalist of the Year for articles published in the *Architects' Journal*

'We will not see in our time a better (or more handsome) book on Scharoun than this.' (Professor Colin St John Wilson, *Architects' Journal*)

General
Non-Fiction

Art

Photography

Collector's
Editions

Film

Architecture

250 × 290 mm
9⁷⁄₈ × 11³⁄₈ inches
192 pp
240 b&w illus.
160 line drawings

Paperback
0 7148 3896 9

£ **19.95** UK
$ **29.95** US
€ **35.00** EUR
$ **45.00** CAN
$ **55.00** AUS

Mies van der Rohe at Work

Peter Carter

- Paperback reprint of classic text featuring enhanced reproductions of the original photography
- Analyses Mies's concepts through three building prototypes: the skeleton-frame building in its high- and low-rise manifestations, and the clear-span building
- Traces Mies's life from the son of a stonemason to his eventual emergence as the 20th century's master architect of steel and glass
- Devotes a section to the architect as educator, illustrated with examples drawn from Mies's students at IIT
- Includes statements by Mies and his colleagues

Peter Carter is an architect now living in London. In 1958 he joined Mies van der Rohe's office after studying with him in Chicago. He continued to work with Mies for 13 years and became an associate in the firm

Design

Fashion & Contemporary Culture

Decorative Arts

Music & Performing Arts

Video

Index

290 × 250 mm
11³⁄₈ × 9⁷⁄₈ inches
240 pp
185 col, 110 b&w illus.
140 line drawings

Paperback
0 7148 3710 5

£ **22.95** UK
$ **35.00** US
€ **39.95** EUR
$ **49.95** CAN
$ **59.95** AUS

Award

Sir Banister Fletcher
award for Excellence
in Architectural Book
Publishing, 1996

Alvar Aalto

Richard Weston

- An award-winning monograph on the internationally renowned architect Aalto (1898–1976), whose work is deeply rooted in the culture and landscape of his native Finland
- Places Aalto in the context of international Modernism and Finnish culture
- Explores Aalto's inspirations and the complete range of his work looking at key public institutions as well as social housing and private dwellings, from the Paimio Sanatorium to the Congress Centre, Helsinki

Richard Weston is an architect, teacher and writer. Formerly head of the University of Portsmouth School of Architecture, he has also taught at De Montfort University and the Welsh School of Architecture

'A handsome tome, well backed up with as many architect's drawings as you are likely to get today and exquisite photographs that bring Alvar Aalto's magic right into your lap.' *(Architects' Journal)*
'Essential for anyone interested in modern architecture.' *(Theme)*

General Non-Fiction

Art

Photography

Collector's Editions

Film

Architecture

290 × 250 mm
11³⁄₈ × 9⁷⁄₈ inches
368 pp
191 col, 226 b&w illus.

Paperback
0 7148 3854 3

£ 27.95 UK
$ 45.00 US
€ 49.95 EUR
$ 69.95 CAN
$ 75.00 AUS

Hardback
0 7148 3148 4

£ 59.95 UK
$ 79.95 US
€ 95.00 EUR
$ 100.00 CAN
$ 150.00 AUS

Frank Lloyd Wright

Robert McCarter

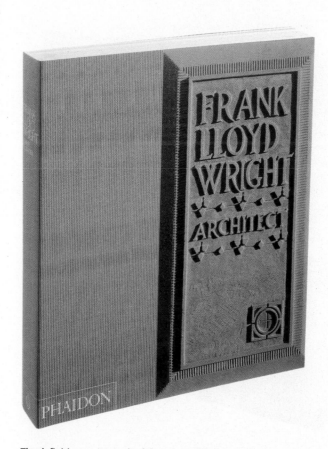

- The definitive monograph of the unparalleled 60-year career of Wright (1867–1959)
- Explores key themes in Wright's work and presents the consistent qualities that underlie his designs
- Includes an extensive selection of archival drawings, specially commissioned photographs, redrawn plans and detail drawings
- With a complete list of Wright's buildings and projects compiled by the Frank Lloyd Wright Archives

Robert McCarter is a practising architect and Professor of Architecture at the Department of Architecture, University of Florida. He is the author of *Unity Temple* and *Fallingwater* in Phaidon's Architecture in Detail series, and *Frank Lloyd Wright,* all published by Phaidon

'Robert McCarter's volume is a masterly achievement.' *(Times Literary Supplement)*
'As a presentation of Wright's complete career, it is difficult to imagine McCarter's book being bettered.' *(Architects' Journal)*
'An intensely human and at times poetically interpreted description of Wright's work and life.' *(World Architecture)*
'One of the handsomest books yet on America's architect of the century.' *(Sunday Times)*

Design

Fashion &
Contemporary
Culture

Decorative Arts

Music &
Performing Arts

Video

Index

Arts and Crafts Architecture

Peter Davey

290 × 250 mm
11³⁄₈ × 9⁷⁄₈ inches
256 pp
139 col, 178 b&w illus.

Paperback
0 7148 3711 3

£ **22.95** UK
$ **35.00** US
€ **39.95** EUR
$ **49.95** CAN
$ **59.95** AUS

Award

Winner History category
International Architecture
Book Awards
American Institute
of Architects, 1997

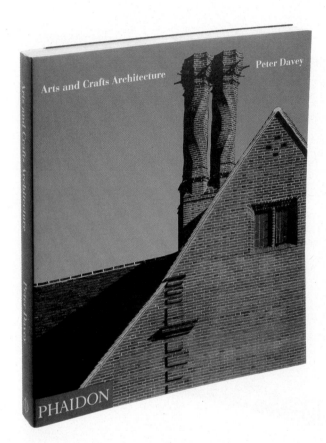

- Major survey of architects of the Arts and Crafts movement of the 1870s and 1880s
- Gives a critical account of the lives, ideological and egalitarian theories of the architects
- Tracing the contradictions of the high cost of materials and craftsmanship which forced them to work mainly for a wealthy élite class
- Explains how the movement influenced the California and Prairie Schools and Art Nouveau, ultimately leading to neo-Georgianism and the growth of the machine-worshipping Modern movement after the First World War

Peter Davey is an architect, historian and journalist, and Editor of the *Architectural Review*

'The most useful – and inspiring – work on the subject.' *(Architectural Review)*

General
Non-Fiction

Art

Photography

Collector's
Editions

Film

Architecture

290 × 250 mm
11³⁄₈ × 9⁷⁄₈ inches
240 pp
250 col, 90 b&w illus.

Paperback
0 7148 3712 1

£ **22.95** UK
$ **35.00** US
€ **39.95** EUR
$ **49.95** CAN
$ **59.95** AUS

C F A Voysey

Wendy Hitchmough

- The first definitive account of one of the most renowned British Arts and Crafts architects prior to the the First World War
- Combines contemporary sources – photographs, quotations, original wallpaper designs and watercolour perspectives – with specially commissioned photography of his houses
- Examines Voysey's role in linking the Arts and Crafts movement with Modernism

Wendy Hitchmough is a historian specializing in architecture of the late 19th and 20th centuries

'The Voysey book that we have been waiting for. A rounded and perceptive portrait.
It will remain the definitive biography.' *(Architectural Review)*

Design
Fashion & Contemporary Culture
Decorative Arts
Music & Performing Arts
Video
Index

255 × 250 mm
10 × 9⅞ inches
336 pp
16 col, 684 b&w illus.

Hardback
0 7148 2678 2

£ **45.00** UK
$ **75.00** US
€ **75.00** EUR
$ **120.00** CAN
$ **125.00** AUS

John Nash

A Complete Catalogue
Michael Mansbridge

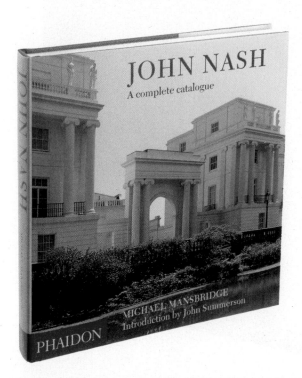

- Illustrated survey of the work of Nash (1752–1835), town-planner, landscape designer, bridge-builder, engineer and entrepreneur, and most successful architect of his time
- Includes all his known and attributed works
- Sets Nash's work in its historical context, including his patronage by George IV
- With an introduction by distinguished architectural historian Sir John Summerson

Michael Mansbridge studied architecture and photography before deciding to become an architect. He worked for Howard Lobb, and later joined Barry Webber and Partners

General Non-Fiction

Art

Photography

Collector's Editions

Film

Architecture

290 × 250 mm
11³⁄₈ × 9⁷⁄₈ inches
240 pp
152 col, 283 b&w illus.

Hardback
0 7148 3211 1

£ 45.00 UK
$ 75.00 US
€ 75.00 EUR
$ 110.00 CAN
$ 125.00 AUS

The Glasshouse

John Hix

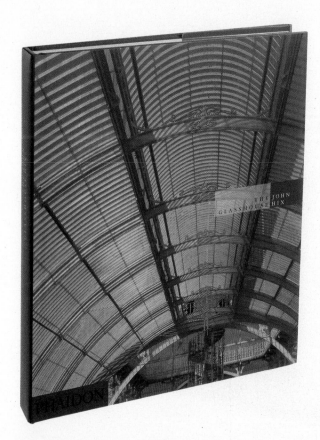

- Traces the evolution of the glass building from antiquity to the 20th century
- From early 16th-century orangeries to examples from the 18th and 19th centuries when increasingly more complex structures, incorporating iron and industrial construction techniques, were built
- Charts the contribution of innovators such as Joseph Paxton and J C Loudon and their influence on pioneers of 20th-century design such as Paul Scheerbart and Bruno Taut

John Hix studied architecture at Iowa and Pennsylvania Universities. Now in private practice in Toronto, he is the author of a number of books and a Fellow of the Royal Canadian Academy of Arts

'Well illustrated with photographs, plans, sections and etchings, the book is primarily a tribute to the wonderful glass palaces of the past. As such, it's a clear winner.' *(House & Garden)*

Design

Fashion &
Contemporary
Culture

Decorative Arts

Music &
Performing Arts

Video

Index

290 × 250 mm
11³⁄₈ × 9⁷⁄₈ inches
240 pp
191 col, 146 b&w illus.

Paperback
0 7148 4102 1

£ **19.95** UK
$ **29.95** US
€ **35.00** EUR
$ **45.00** CAN
$ **55.00** AUS

Hardback
0 7148 3467 X

£ **39.95** UK
$ **59.95** US
€ **65.00** EUR
$ **89.95** CAN
$ **98.00** AUS

Station to Station

Steven Parissien

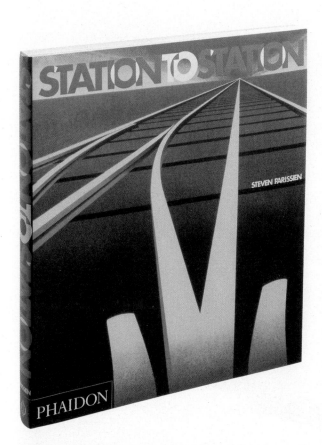

- Examines the fascinating and evocative history of the railway station and charts architectural developments over the past 150 years
- Highlights seminal examples such as London's St Pancras, Grand Central Station in New York, Nicholas Grimshaw's Waterloo International Terminal and Santiago Calatrava's Lyon Satolas
- A fascinating visual record with archive pictures, railway ephemera and new photography of the contribution the railway station makes to the life of our cities

Steven Parissien is the Director of Sotheby's Institute, London; and has previously worked for the Georgian Group and English Heritage. He is also the author of *Adam Style, Regency Style* and *Palladian Style,* all published by Phaidon

'Steven Parissien leads readers on an absorbing, copiously illustrated journey through the vaulted interiors of real-life rail terminals around the world. His graceful narrative encompasses major shifts in civic history, design, popular taste and passenger requirements.' *(Los Angeles Times)*

290 × 250 mm
11³⁄₈ × 9⁷⁄₈ inches
160 pp
67 duotone photographs

Hardback
0 7148 4003 3

£ **35.00** UK
$ **59.95** US
€ **59.95** EUR
$ **89.95** CAN
$ **95.00** AUS

Architecture of Truth

The Cistercian Abbey of Le Thoronet
Photographs by Lucien Hervé

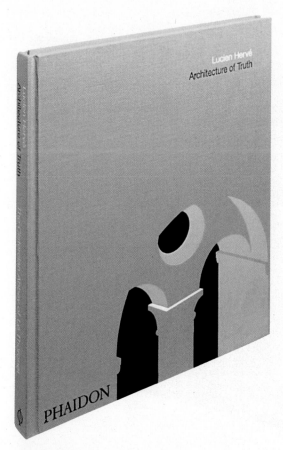

- A pictorial tribute to Le Thoronet Abbey in Provence, one of the wonders of 12th-century Cistercian architecture
- Photographs taken in the mid-1950s by Hervé, who used the changing effect of daylight to present the building over the course of one day
- Introduction by Le Corbusier
- Includes an essay by a monk of the Abbey of Notre-Dame de Sept-Fons, providing an insight into the Cistercian order
- Specially designed by John Pawson, who also contributes a short personal appreciation

Lucien Hervé (b.1910) is a French-Hungarian photographer, known for his architectural photographs, in particular those of buildings by Le Corbusier

'Lucien Hervé's amazing photographs of Le Thoronet Abbey have acquired mythical status in the profession. Now, these 50s images have been excellently reproduced in *Architecture of Truth*.' *(Architectural Review)*
'A work of meditation, an entrance into the particularly austere understanding of truth associated with the Cistercian Order.' *(Art Newspaper)*

Design

Fashion & Contemporary Culture

Decorative Arts

Music & Performing Arts

Video

Index

290 × 250 mm
11³⁄₈ × 9⁷⁄₈ inches
320 pp
213 col, 167 b&w illus.

Paperback
0 7148 3864 0

£ 24.95   UK
$ 39.95   US
€ 39.95   EUR
$ 59.95   CAN
$ 65.00   AUS

290 × 250 mm
11³⁄₈ × 9⁷⁄₈ inches
320 pp
213 col, 167 b&w illus.

Hardback
0 7148 3005 4

£ 45.00   UK
$ 75.00   US
€ 75.00   EUR
$ 115.00 CAN
$ 140.00 AUS

Venice: The City and Its Architecture

Richard Goy

- A truly comprehensive history of Venetian architecture
- Places Venice's buildings within their unique urban context
- Covers a wide range of buildings, from fishermen's cottages to the palazzi on the Grand Canal and from the simplest of early Christian basilicas to Palladio's masterpieces and Longhena's Santa Maria della Salute
- With colour photographs, original plans, contemporary drawings and paintings by the Venetian masters

Richard Goy is a practising architect and architectural historian. His three previous books are *Chioggia and the Villages of the Venetian Lagoon*, *Venetian Vernacular Architecture* and *The House of Gold*

'A handsome volume that far surpasses the routine tributes to "La Serenissima" that appear every season.' *(The New York Times)*
'Published in 1997, this book immediately became the benchmark. A book that does full justice to the richness and density of the Venetian cityscape – and the design and choice of pictures are exemplary.' *(Rough Guide to Venice and the Veneto)*

290 × 250 mm
11³⁄₈ × 9⁷⁄₈ inches
320 pp
220 col, 110 b&w illus.

Hardback
0 7148 3911 6

£ **45.00** UK
$ **75.00** US
€ **75.00** EUR
$ **115.00** CAN
$ **140.00** AUS

Florence: The City and Its Architecture

Richard Goy

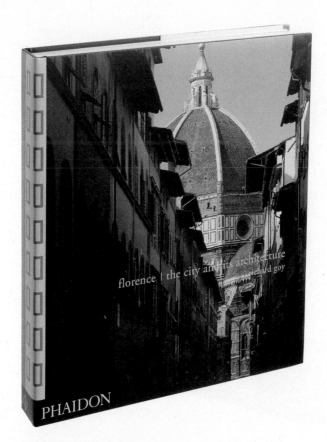

- A comprehensive account of the architecture of Florence, from the city's foundation by Julius Caesar in 59 BC to modern times
- Sets the political, economic and cultural contexts in which the major buildings of the city were constructed
- The historical overview examines architecture associated with the powers of Church and State and the practicalities of building
- Includes range of buildings from the Duomo and the Palazzo Pitti to neighbourhood churches and elegant lesser known piazzas
- Original plans and paintings by Florentine masters emphasize historical context

Richard Goy is a practising architect and an architectural historian. His previous books include the successful predecessor to this volume, *Venice: The City and Its Architecture*, also published by Phaidon

Design
Fashion & Contemporary Culture
Decorative Arts
Music & Performing Arts
Video
Index

245 × 210 mm
9⁵₈ × 8¹₄ inches
288 pp
c.300 col, 150 b&w illus.

Hardback
0 7148 4202 8

£ 35.00 UK
$ 59.95 US
€ 59.95 EUR
$ 89.95 CAN
$ 99.95 AUS

Dwellings: The Vernacular House Worldwide

Paul Oliver

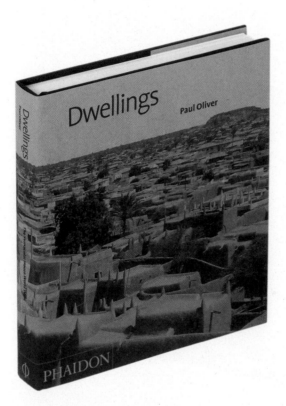

- An exploration of the types and forms of vernacular houses around the world and how they are constructed, decorated and inhabited by their occupants
- A revised and expanded edition of a classic text, containing new field research and scholarship
- Includes new academic developments in cultural geography, gender studies, sociology and anthropology
- Beautifully illustrated throughout, largely by photographs compiled in the course of the author's field research
- A useful survey of how different communities cope with issues of climate, migration, mass development and symbolic and cultural meaning in architecture

Paul Oliver is the Chair of the Master's course in International Studies in Vernacular Architecture at the School of Architecture, Oxford Brookes University. He is the author of numerous books, notably *Shelter and Society* and *Dunroamin: The Suburban Semi and its Enemies*, and is the editor of the three-volume *Encyclopedia of Vernacular Architecture of the World*

'To have steered a clear path through so many types of architecture, without flagging and without repetition, is a remarkable achievement. … What every architect can certainly learn here is that many hundreds of vernacular building types offer endless examples of commonsense building technology; and no lesson of this kind should ever be wasted.' (*Architectural Review*)

General Non-Fiction

Art

Photography

Collector's Editions

Film

Architecture

245 × 175 mm
9²₃ × 6³₄ inches
480 pp
240 b&w illus.
52 maps

Paperback
0 7148 2523 9

£ **16.95** UK
$ **24.95** US
€ **29.95** EUR
$ **39.95** CAN
$ **49.95** AUS

The Art and Architecture of London

An Illustrated Guide
Ann Saunders

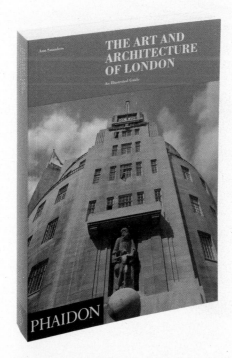

- A comprehensive guide that introduces the reader to the unparalleled visual wealth and historical interest of London art and architecture
- An enthusiastic narrative, enriched with wide-ranging historical detail, brings the topographical survey to life
- Invaluable for visitors and residents of London alike
- Winner of a London Tourist Board Award

Ann Saunders is a historian, lecturer and editor. A Fellow of the Society of Antiquaries, her publications include several books on the history and topography of London

Design

Fashion & Contemporary Culture

Decorative Arts

Music & Performing Arts

Video

Index

263 × 263 mm
10³⁄₈ × 10³⁄₈ inches
336 pp
96 col, 454 b&w illus.

Paperback
0 7148 2960 9

£ **24.95** UK
$ **39.95** US
€ **39.95** EUR
$ **59.95** CAN
$ **65.00** AUS

The History of Architecture in India

Christopher Tadgell

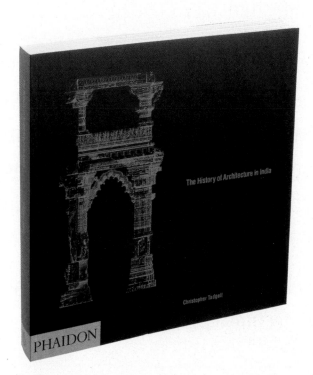

- The first book to draw together all the strands of India's architectural history
- Spans the Vedic and indigenous traditions of early India, Hindu, Buddhist, Islamic and secular architecture, and the eclecticism of the British Raj
- Contains historical and cultural background information on the role of invasions and migrations, dynasties, religion, symbolism and myth in the development of characteristic forms
- The hundreds of photographs, engravings, maps, plans and elevations are closely integrated with the text

Christopher Tadgell is Senior Lecturer in Architectural History at the Canterbury School of Architecture, Kent Institute of Art and Design. In 1985 he was Morgan Professor of Architectural Design at the University of Louisville, Kentucky

'Christopher Tadgell stands in the great tradition of European chroniclers of Indian culture.' *(Architects' Journal)*
'It should be studied before one's Indian visits.' *(New York Review of Books)*

General
Non-Fiction

Art

Photography

Collector's
Editions

Film

Architecture
Architecture 3

Architecture 3

'An endlessly fascinating encyclopedic tour of the world's best examples of domestic architecture.' *Town & Country Magazine*

'While many of the works are iconic, others are little-known and a revelation for the first-time viewer, particularly, I found, those from South America, Australia, India and Japan. Its selection of contemporary architecture is also impressive.'
Contemporary

'An elegant cheat sheet for residential architecture.' *Dwell Magazine*

- Award-winning series for students and professionals that celebrates some of the greatest works of architecture by some of the most important architects
- Each volume contains three buildings of related significance causing intriguing combinations that invite analysis and comparison
- Introductory essays by Beth Dunlop and James Russell explore the social, cultural and political issues that continue to shape architecture today
- Over 200 specially commissioned colour and black-and-white photographs
- Specially produced plans and technical drawings that reveal each building's structural virtuosity
- Highly readable and well-informed essays on each building

Design

Fashion & Contemporary Culture

Decorative Arts

Music & Performing Arts

Video

Index

297 × 297 mm
11⁵⁸ × 11⁵⁸ inches
180 pp
c.45 col, 165 b&w illus.
60 line drawings

Hardback
0 7148 3875 6

£ **19.95** UK
$ **29.95** US
€ **35.00** EUR
$ **45.00** CAN
$ **59.95** AUS

Arts & Crafts Houses I

Red House, Melsetter House, Goddards

With essays by Edward Hollamby, Trevor Garnham and Brian Edwards

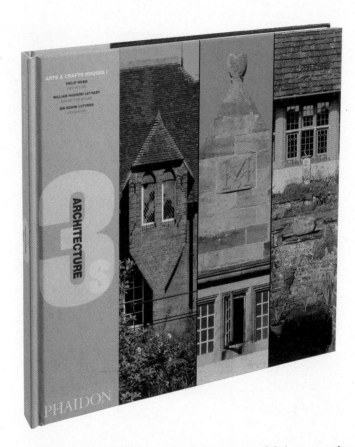

- **Studies three houses of the Arts & Crafts movement and their common themes**
- **Examines the seminally 'modern' Red House designed for William Morris in 1859 and the Melsetter House, designed by William Lethaby**
- **Concludes with Goddards, designed by Edwin Lutyens, who is notable for his subtle handling of materials and colour**

Edward Hollamby is an architect who has lived in the Red House since 1952, studying and restoring it. He has practised as a consultant specializing in historic buildings and conservation
Trevor Garnham is Senior Lecturer at Kingston University School of Architecture. He is author of *Oxford Museum* in the Architecture in Detail series, published by Phaidon
Dr Brian Edwards is Professor of Architecture at the University of Huddersfield and is an expert on the buildings of the Arts & Crafts movement

General
Non-Fiction

Art

Photography

Collector's
Editions

Film

Architecture
Architecture 3

297 × 297 mm
11⁵⁸ × 11⁵⁸ inches
180 pp
c.45 col, 165 b&w illus.
60 line drawings

Hardback
0 7148 3874 8

£ **19.95** UK
$ **29.95** US
€ **35.00** EUR
$ **45.00** CAN
$ **59.95** AUS

Arts & Crafts Houses II

Hill House, The Homestead, Gamble House
With essays by James Macaulay, Wendy Hitchmough and Edward Bosley

- **A close examination of three houses in the Arts & Crafts style by three experts in their field**
- **A companion volume to *Arts & Crafts Houses I***
- **Hill House, designed by Charles Rennie Mackintosh, combines Arts & Crafts honesty with Art Nouveau decoration and Scottish elements**
- **The Homestead, a private house built for entertaining, is one of C F A Voysey's finest achievements**
- **Greene & Greene's Gamble House represents the ennoblement of the California bungalow image, while maintaining a striking intimacy**

Dr James Macaulay, Senior Lecturer at the Mackintosh School of Architecture, has been Chairman of the Society of Architectural Historians of Great Britain and the Architectural Society of Scotland; he has written much on the work of Mackintosh
Wendy Hitchmough is an historian and writer. She is author of *Hoover Factory* in the Architecture in Detail series and the monograph *C F A Voysey*, both published by Phaidon
Edward Bosley is Associate Director of the Gamble House, and has written widely on Arts & Crafts architecture

Design

Fashion & Contemporary Culture

Decorative Arts

Music & Performing Arts

Video

Index

297 × 297 mm
11⁵⁄₈ × 11⁵⁄₈ inches
180 pp
c.45 col, 165 b&w illus.
60 line drawings

Hardback
0 7148 3876 4

£ **19.95** UK
$ **29.95** US
€ **35.00** EUR
$ **45.00** CAN
$ **59.95** AUS

Arts & Crafts Masterpieces

St Andrew's Church, Glasgow School of Art, First Church of Christ Scientist
With essays by Trevor Garnham, James Macaulay and Edward Bosley

- Enlists three outstanding 'public buildings' to demonstrate how Arts & Crafts architects worked within varying environments
- St Andrew's Church, Roker, is a striking creation – a collaboration of work by architect Edward Prior, artists and craftsmen builders
- Glasgow School of Art, designed by Charles Rennie Mackintosh, is a synthesis of opposites – austere and delicate, dark and light, derivative and innovative
- Bernard Maybeck's First Church of Christ Scientist, Berkeley, is versatile, colourful and inventive
- Describes how each building responds to its context, while retaining its unique character

Trevor Garnham is Senior Lecturer at Kingston University School of Architecture. He is author of *Oxford Museum* in the Architecture in Detail series, published by Phaidon
Dr James Macaulay, Senior Lecturer at the Mackintosh School of Architecture, has been Chairman of the Society of Architectural Historians of Great Britain and the Architectural Society of Scotland, and specializes in the work of Mackintosh
Edward Bosley is Associate Director of the Gamble House, and has written widely on Arts & Crafts architecture

General
Non-Fiction

Art

Photography

Collector's
Editions

Film

Architecture
Architecture 3

297 × 297 mm
11⁵⁄8 × 11⁵⁄8 inches
180 pp
c.45 col, 165 b&w illus.
60 line drawings

Hardback
0 7148 3873 X

£ **19.95** UK
$ **29.95** US
€ **35.00** EUR
$ **45.00** CAN
$ **59.95** AUS

City Icons

Expiatory Church of the Sagrada Familia, Grand Central Terminal, Sydney Opera House
With essays by Mark Burry, Kenneth Powell and Philip Drew

- Examines three innovative and iconic buildings that are symbols of national and metropolitan pride
- Looks at Antoni Gaudí's Expiatory Church of the Sagrada Familia, the Grand Central Terminal by Whitney Warren and Charles Wetmore, and the Sydney Opera House by Jørn Utzon

Mark Burry lectures at the School of Architecture, Victoria University of Wellington, New Zealand. He is currently working as an architect at the Sagrada Familia and is advising on its construction

Kenneth Powell is an architectural writer and a leading figure in the Twentieth Century Society. He was architectural correspondent for the *Daily Telegraph* and is author of *Richard Rogers Complete Works: Volume 1*, published by Phaidon

Philip Drew is an architectural writer and critic based in Australia. His previous books include *Leaves of Iron*, a monograph on the work of Glenn Murcutt

Design

Fashion &
Contemporary
Culture

Decorative Arts

Music &
Performing Arts

Video

Index

297 × 297 mm
11⁵⁄₈ × 11⁵⁄₈ inches
180 pp
c.45 col, 165 b&w illus.
60 line drawings

Hardback
0 7148 3871 3

£ **19.95** UK
$ **29.95** US
€ **35.00** EUR
$ **45.00** CAN
$ **59.95** AUS

Contemporary California Houses

Schnabel House, Lawson-Westen House, Drager House
With essays by James Steele and Aaron Betsky

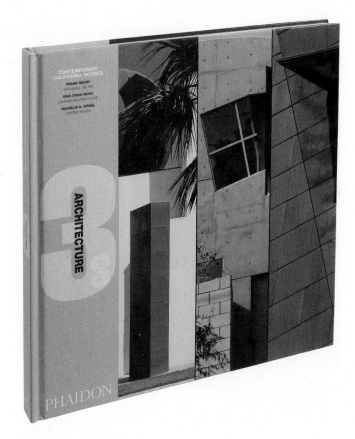

- Surveys the unique architectural style of California
- Examples of domestic architecture from three Los Angeles-based architects – Frank Gehry, Eric Owen Moss and the late Franklin Israel

James Steele is Associate Professor at the University of Southern California, Los Angeles, and has written frequently for *Architectural Design*, *Architectural Review* and *Mimar*
Aaron Betsky is the Director of the Netherlands Architecture Institute (Rotterdam) and the Director of the International Architecture Biennale (Rotterdam) 2001. He was formerly the Curator of Architecture, Design and Digital Projects at San Francisco Museum of Modern Art. In addition, he is also a practicing architect and has taught at a number of institutions. He is the author of *Landscrapers*, *Architecture Must Burn* and was a contributor to *10x10*.

General
Non-Fiction

Art

Photography

Collector's
Editions

Film

Architecture
Architecture 3

297 × 297 mm
11⁵⁄₈ × 11⁵⁄₈ inches
180 pp
c.15 col, 140 b&w illus.
80 duotone illus.
40 line drawings

Hardback
0 7148 3872 1

£ **19.95** UK
$ **29.95** US
€ **35.00** EUR
$ **45.00** CAN
$ **59.95** AUS

Lost Masterpieces

Crystal Palace, Palais des Machines, Pennsylvania Station
With essays by John McKean, Stuart Durant, Angus Low and Steven Parissien

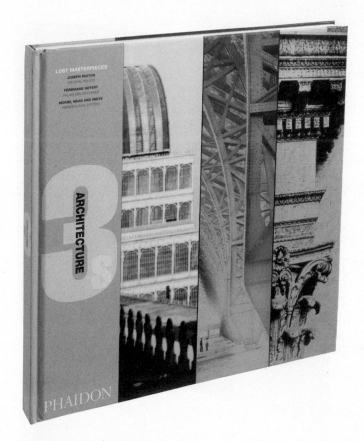

- An in-depth look at three of the grandest and most innovative buildings of the 19th and 20th centuries
- Joseph Paxton's Crystal Palace, the Palais des Machines by Ferdinand Dutert and Pennsylvania Station by McKim, Mead and White
- Charts their destruction in contrast to the confident innovative approaches to design and new technology during their construction

John McKean trained as both architect and historian. He is Head of Interior Design at the University of Brighton.
Stuart Durant lectures at Kingston University
Steven Parissien is Assistant Director of the Paul Mellon Centre for Studies in British Art in London, and the author of *Adam Style, Regency Style, Palladian Style* and *Station to Station*, all published by Phaidon

Design

Fashion & Contemporary Culture

Decorative Arts

Music & Performing Arts

Video

Index

297 × 297 mm
11⁵⁸ × 11⁵⁸ inches
180 pp
c.45 col, 165 b&w illus.
60 line drawings

Hardback
0 7148 3880 2

£ **19.95** UK
$ **29.95** US
€ **35.00** EUR
$ **45.00** CAN
$ **59.95** AUS

Pioneering British 'High Tech'

Engineering Department Building, Willis Faber Dumas Building, The Lloyd's Building
With essays by John McKean, Gabriele Bramante and Kenneth Powell

- A survey of three highly fêted and ground-breaking Modern British buildings
- Begins with the Leicester University Engineering Department Building, which established the worldwide reputation of James Stirling
- Includes the commanding glass façade of Norman Foster's building for Willis Faber Dumas in Ipswich
- Concludes with the 'mechanical cathedral' of Lloyd's in the heart of London, epitomizing Richard Rogers's concern with flexibility and technical imagery

John McKean trained as both architect and historian. He is Head of Interior Design at the University of Brighton
Gabriele Bramante is an architect, teacher, writer and journalist. She has been a regular contributor to the *Architectural Review*
Kenneth Powell is an architectural writer and a leading figure in the Twentieth Century Society. He was architectural correspondent for the *Daily Telegraph* and is author of *Richard Rogers Complete Works: Volume 1*, published by Phaidon

General
Non-Fiction

Art

Photography

Collector's
Editions

Film

Architecture
Architecture 3

297 × 297 mm
11⁵⁄₈ × 11⁵⁄₈ inches
180 pp
c.45 col, 165 b&w illus.
60 line drawings

Hardback
0 7148 3877 2

£ **19.95** UK
$ **29.95** US
€ **35.00** EUR
$ **45.00** CAN
$ **59.95** AUS

Places of Worship

St Paul's Cathedral, Church of the Sacred Heart, Church on the Water & Church of the Light
With essays by Vaughan Hart, Ivan Margolius and Philip Drew

- Chooses three extraordinary and disparate churches to demonstrate varying approaches taken by architects to create sacred space
- St Paul's Cathedral, designed by Christopher Wren, is an iconic British building combining Renaissance and Baroque elements
- The Church of the Sacred Heart is a key representative of the Modern movement in Prague, designed by Joze Plecnik
- Tadao Ando's Church on the Water and Church of the Light complement each other in a synthesis of opposites

Vaughan Hart has taught at the universities of Bath and Cambridge and at the Architectural Association, London
Ivan Margolius, an architect of Czech origin working in London, has contributed to various magazines and has edited an architectural guide to Prague
Philip Drew is an architectural writer and critic based in Australia. He has written widely on Japanese architecture

Design

Fashion & Contemporary Culture

Decorative Arts

Music & Performing Arts

Video

Index

297 × 297 mm
11⅝ × 11⅝ inches
180 pp
c.45 col, 165 b&w illus.
60 line drawings

Hardback
0 7148 3868 3

£ 19.95 UK
$ 29.95 US
€ 35.00 EUR
$ 45.00 CAN
$ 59.95 AUS

Twentieth-Century Classics

Bauhaus Dessau, Unité d'Habitation, Salk Institute
With essays by Dennis Sharp, David Jenkins and James Steele

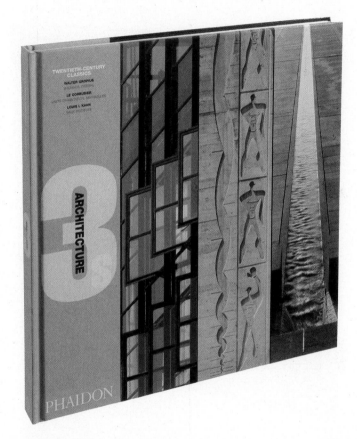

- Juxtaposes three pivotal buildings by renowned architects Walter Gropius, Le Corbusier and Louis Kahn
- From the building for the pioneering Bauhaus School to the universally cited Marseilles Unité d'Habitation and the monastic cloisters of the Salk Institute laboratories

Dennis Sharp is a Vice President of RIBA and Director of the International Committee of Architectural Critics. He writes regularly for *Building Design, A+U* and *Architectural Review*, and was Executive Editor of *World Architecture*
David Jenkins was buildings editor of the *Architects' Journal* and a commissioning editor at Phaidon Press. He is currently employed at Foster Associates
James Steele is Associate Professor at the University of Southern California, Los Angeles, and has written frequently for *Architectural Design, Architectural Review* and *Mimar*

General
Non-Fiction

Art

Photography

Collector's
Editions

Film

Architecture
Architecture 3

297 × 297 mm
11⅝ × 11⅝ inches
180 pp
c.45 col, 165 b&w illus.
60 line drawings

Hardback
0 7148 3870 5

£ **19.95** UK
$ **29.95** US
€ **35.00** EUR
$ **45.00** CAN
$ **59.95** AUS

Twentieth-Century Houses

Fallingwater, Villa Mairea, Eames House
With essays by Robert McCarter, Richard Weston and James Steele

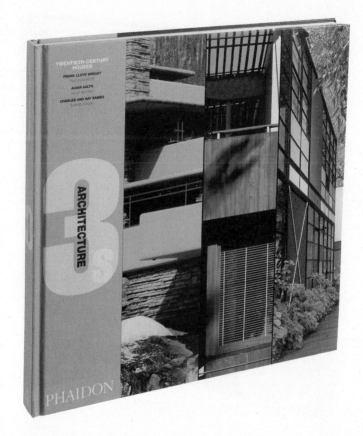

- Explores three buildings that represent responses to problems of residential design by three of the world's most influential architects
- Fallingwater is one of Frank Lloyd Wright's most inventive houses
- The rich and lyrical Villa Mairea draws on Alvar Aalto's deep understanding of vernacular building, classicism and modernism
- The house built by Charles and Ray Eames was assembled entirely from standardized industrial components

Robert McCarter is a practising architect and Professor of Architecture at the Department of Architecture, University of Florida. He is the author of *Unity Temple* in Phaidon's Architecture in Detail series and *Frank Lloyd Wright,* both published by Phaidon
Richard Weston is head of the Portsmouth Polytechnic School of Architecture and writes for the *Architectural Review* and the *Architects' Journal*
James Steele is Associate Professor at the University of Southern California, Los Angeles, and has written frequently for *Architectural Design, Architectural Review* and *Mimar*

Design

Fashion & Contemporary Culture

Decorative Arts

Music & Performing Arts

Video

Index

297 × 297 mm
11⁵⁸ × 11⁵⁸ inches
180 pp
c.45 col, 165 b&w illus.
60 line drawings

Hardback
0 7148 3878 0

£ **19.95** UK
$ **29.95** US
€ **35.00** EUR
$ **45.00** CAN
$ **59.95** AUS

Twentieth-Century Museums I

New National Gallery, Kimbell Art Museum, Museum für Kunsthandwerk
With essays by Maritz Vandenberg and Michael Brawne

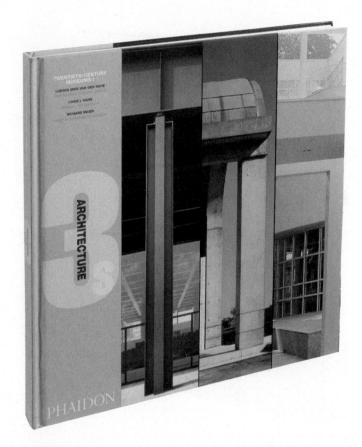

- Spans three different decades to show striking examples of modern museum design
- The Berlin Gallery was Mies van der Rohe's last great building, a 'temple' to art in glass and steel
- Louis Kahn's Kimbell Art Museum is a building of severity and restraint, with rhythmical spaces and a refined treatment of materials
- Richard Meier's Museum für Kunsthandwerk is a subtle and intricate building of shifted grids and superimposed planes

Maritz Vandenberg was the founding Publisher of Architecture and Technology Press and has worked as Technical Editor on the *Architects' Journal*
Professor Michael Brawne is an architect and former head of the University of Bath School of Architecture. An expert on museum design, he is also author of *Getty Center* in the Architecture in Detail series, published by Phaidon

General
Non-Fiction

Art

Photography

Collector's
Editions

Film

Architecture
Architecture 3

297 × 297 mm
11⅝ × 11⅝ inches
180 pp
c.45 col, 165 b&w illus.
60 line drawings

Hardback
0 7148 3879 9

£ **19.95** UK
$ **29.95** US
€ **35.00** EUR
$ **45.00** CAN
$ **59.95** AUS

Twentieth-Century Museums II

Museum of Modern Art, Clore Gallery & Tate Gallery, United States Holocaust Memorial Museum

With essays by Philip Drew, David Jenkins and Adrian Dannatt

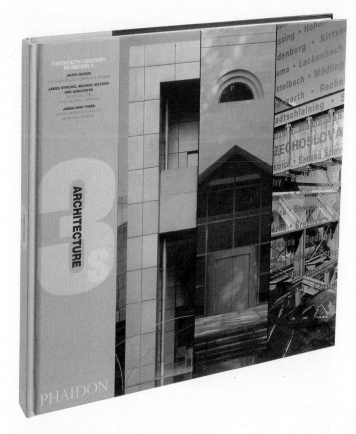

- Considers three seminal museums together to show varying approaches taken by different architectural practices
- The Museum of Modern Art in Gunma, Japan, is the most complete realization by Arata Isozaki of a conceptual approach to museum design
- Examines the Clore Gallery, London, and the Tate in Liverpool within the context of James Stirling & Michael Wilford's oeuvre at the time of construction
- James Ingo Freed's United States Holocaust Memorial Museum in Washington DC manages subtly and symbolically to disengage itself from the city in which it stands

Philip Drew is an architectural writer and critic based in Australia. He has written widely on Japanese architecture

David Jenkins was buildings editor of the *Architects' Journal* and a commissioning editor at Phaidon Press. He is currently employed at Foster Associates

Adrian Dannatt is London correspondent for *Flash Art International*, contributing editor of *Lacanian Ink*, and editor-at-large of *Open City* magazine

Design

Fashion & Contemporary Culture

Decorative Arts

Music & Performing Arts

Video

Index

297 × 297 mm
11⁵⁄₈ × 11⁵⁄₈ inches
180 pp
c.45 col, 165 b&w illus.
60 line drawings

Hardback
0 7148 3869 1

£ **19.95** UK
$ **29.95** US
€ **35.00** EUR
$ **45.00** CAN
$ **59.95** AUS

Frank Lloyd Wright

Unity Temple, Barnsdall (Hollyhock) House, Johnson Wax Administration Building & Research Tower

With essays by Robert McCarter, James Steele and Brian Carter

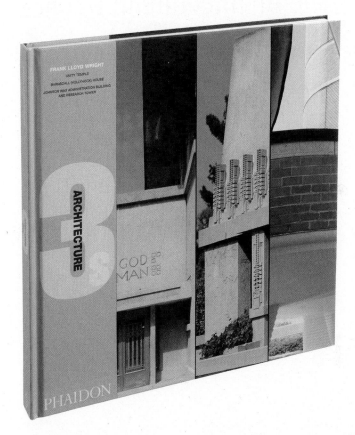

- **Focuses on three important buildings by Frank Lloyd Wright to provide insight into the versatility and breadth of Wright's career – Unity Temple, Barnsdall House and the Johnson Wax Administration Building and Research Tower**
- **Examples of Wright's architectural oeuvre across iconic office, residential and church designs**

Robert McCarter is a practising architect and Professor of Architecture at the Department of Architecture, University of Florida. He is the author of *Fallingwater* and *Unity Temple* in Phaidon's Architecture in Detail series

Brian Carter is an architect and academic. He is currently Professor and Chair of the Architecture Department at the University of Michigan at Ann Arbor

James Steele is Associate Professor at the University of Southern California, Los Angeles, and has written frequently for *Architectural Design*, *Architectural Review* and *Mimar*

General Non-Fiction

Art

Photography

Collector's Editions

Film

Architecture Architecture in Detail

Architecture in Detail

'The Architecture in Detail series is without question one of the most beautifully illustrated and well-documented collections of monographs on individual buildings produced anywhere in the world.'

Jury of the American Institute of Architects

- Award-winning architectural series for students and professionals
- Each volume focuses on a single celebrated building
- Series covers a wide range of periods and building types from houses to public buildings and from the majesty of St Paul's Cathedral to the intimacy of contemporary homes in California
- Each building selected for its exceptional character, innovative design or technical virtuosity
- Each volume contains a detailed introductory essay and over 100 photographs and line drawings
- With specially commissioned photography, technical drawings and working details

Design

Fashion &
Contemporary
Culture

Decorative Arts

Music &
Performing Arts

Video

Index

Each volume
250 × 250 mm
9⁷₈ × 9⁷₈ inches
60 pp
c.20 col, 60 b&w illus.
24 line drawings

Paperback

£ **9.95** UK
$ **14.95** US
€ **16.95** EUR
$ **24.95** CAN
$ **29.95** AUS

Awards

Winner of Series Award,
American Institute
of Architects
International Architecture
Book Awards,
95, 1996, 1997 and 1998

Farnsworth House
Hardback

250 × 250 mm
9⁷₈ × 9⁷₈ inches
60 pp
c.40 col, c.10 b&w illus.,
30 line drawings

£ **14.95** UK
$ **19.95** US
€ **22.95** EUR
$ **29.95** CAN
$ **39.95** AUS

Bauhaus, Dessau
Dessau 1925–6
Walter Gropius
Dennis Sharp
0 7148 4217 6 (NF)

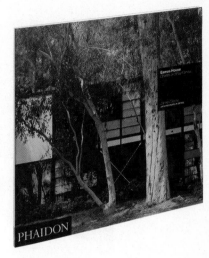

Eames House
Pacific Palisades 1949
Charles and Ray Eames
James Steele
0 7148 4212 5

Fallingwater
Bear Run, Pennsylvania 1935
Frank Lloyd Wright
Robert McCarter
0 7148 4213 3

Farnsworth House
Mies van der Rohe
Maritz Vandenberg
0 7148 3152 2

General
Non-Fiction

Art

Photography

Collector's
Editions

Film

Architecture
Architecture
in Detail

Gamble House
Pasadena 1907–8
Greene and Greene
Edward R Bosley
0 7148 4218 4

Glasgow School of Art
Glasgow 1897–1909
Charles Rennie Mackintosh
James Macaulay
0 7148 4221 4

Salk Institute
La Jolla 1959–65
Louis I Kahn
James Steele
0 7148 4214 1

Sydney Opera House
Sydney 1957–73
Jørn Utzon
Philip Drew
0 7148 4215 X

Design

Fashion & Contemporary Culture

Decorative Arts

Music & Performing Arts

Video

Index

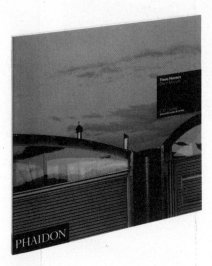

Three Houses
New South Wales 1974–84
Glenn Murcutt
E M Farrelly
0 7148 4219 2

The United States Holocaust Memorial Museum
Washington DC 1993
James Ingo Freed
Adrian Dannatt
0 7148 4220 6

Villa Mairea
Noormarkku 1938–9
Alvar Aalto
Richard Weston
0 7148 4216 8

General
Non-Fiction

Art

Photography

Collector's
Editions

Film

Architecture
Architecture
in Detail

Each volume
297 × 297 mm
11⁵⁄₈ × 11⁵⁄₈ inches
60 pp
c.20 col, 60 b&w illus.
24 line drawings

Paperback

£ **19.95** UK
$ **29.95** US
€ **35.00** EUR
$ **45.00** CAN
$ **55.00** AUS

Awards

Winner of Series Award,
American Institute
of Architects
International Architecture
Book Awards,
1995, 1996, 1997 and 1998

British Pavilion
Seville Exposition 1992
Nicholas Grimshaw & Partners
Colin Davies
0 7148 2747 9

California Aerospace Museum
Los Angeles 1982–4
Frank Gehry
James Steele
0 7148 2781 9

Church of the Sacred Heart
Prague 1922–33
Jože Plečnik
Ivan Margolius
0 7148 3351 7

**Church on the Water
and Church of the Light**
Hokkaido, Japan 1988 and Osaka, Japan
1989
Tadao Ando
Philip Drew
0 7148 3268 5

Clore Gallery
London 1987
Tate Gallery, Liverpool
Liverpool 1988
James Stirling, Michael Wilford and
Associates
David Jenkins
0 7148 2762 2

Drager House
Berkeley, California 1994
Franklin D Israel
Aaron Betsky
0 7148 3382 7

**Expiatory Church of
the Sagrada Família**
Barcelona 1884–
Antoni Gaudí
Mark Burry
0 7148 2849 1

Getty Center
Los Angeles 1997
Richard Meier & Partners
Double Length Issue
Michael Brawne
120 pp, 147 illus.
0 7148 3799 7

First Church of Christ, Scientist
Berkeley 1910
Bernard Maybeck
Edward R Bosley
0 7148 2997 8

Design

Fashion &
Contemporary
Culture

Decorative Arts

Music &
Performing Arts

Video

Index

Grand Central Terminal
New York City 1903–13
Warren and Wetmore
Kenneth Powell
0 7148 3346 0

The Homestead
Frinton-on-Sea 1905
C F A Voysey
Wendy Hitchmough
0 7148 3153 0

Igualada Cemetery
Barcelona 1986–90
Enric Miralles and Carme Pinós
Anatxu Zabalbeascoa
0 7148 3281 2

Imagination Headquarters
London 1990
Herron Associates
Sutherland Lyall
0 7148 2764 9

**Johnson Wax Administration Building
and Research Tower**
Racine, Wisconsin 1936–44
Frank Lloyd Wright
Brian Carter
0 7148 3282 0

Lawson-Westen House
Brentwood, California 1993
Eric Owen Moss
James Steele
0 7148 3259 6

**Leicester University Engineering
Building**
Leicester 1959–63
James Stirling and James Gowan
John McKean
0 7148 3154 9

Melsetter House
Orkney 1898
William Lethaby
Trevor Garnham
0 7148 2776 2

Münster City Library
Münster 1993
Architekturbüro
Bolles-Wilson + Partner
Francisco Sanin
0 7148 2996 X

467

General
Non-Fiction

Art

Photography

Collector's
Editions

Film

Architecture
Architecture
in Detail

Museum für Kunsthandwerk
Frankfurt am Main 1984
Richard Meier
Michael Brawne
0 7148 2765 7

Museum of Modern Art, Gunma
Takasaki, Gunma Prefecture, Japan
1971–4
Arata Isozaki
Philip Drew
0 7148 3549 8

National and University Library, Ljubljana
Ljubljana, Slovenia 1936–9
Jože Plečnik
Mel Gooding
0 7148 2938 2

New National Gallery, Berlin
Berlin 1962–8
Ludwig Mies Van Der Rohe
Maritz Vandenburg
0 7148 3763 6

Palais des Machines
Paris 1889
Ferdinand Dutert
Stuart Durant and Angus Low
0 7148 2930 7

Renault Centre
Swindon 1982
Foster Associates
Chris Abel
1 85454 776 3

Royal Festival Hall
London County Council 1948–51
Refurbishment 1993–2001
Allies & Morrison
Revised and Expanded Edition
John McKean
20 col, 70 b&w illus.s
28 line drawings; 72 pp
0 7148 4160 9

St Andrew's Church, Roker
Roker, Sunderland 1905
Edward Prior
Trevor Garnham
0 7148 3344 4

St Paul's Cathedral
London 1675–1710
Sir Christopher Wren
Vaughan Hart
0 7148 2998 6

Design

Fashion &
Contemporary
Culture

Decorative Arts

Music &
Performing Arts

Video

Index

**Schlumberger Cambridge
Research Centre**
Cambridge 1985
Michael Hopkins and Partners
David Jenkins
0 7148 2774 6 ((OF)

Schnabel House
Brentwood, California 1990
Frank Gehry
James Steele
0 7148 2749 5

Unity Temple
Oak Park, Illinois 1905
Frank Lloyd Wright
Robert McCarter
0 7148 3629 X

**The United States Holocaust
Memorial Museum**
Washington DC 1993
James Ingo Freed
Adrian Dannatt
0 7148 4220 6

**University of
Pennsylvania Library**
Philadelphia 1888–91
Frank Furness
Edward R Bosley
0 7148 3389 4

University of Virginia
Charlottesville 1817–26
Thomas Jefferson
Michael Brawne
0 7148 2752 5

Willis Faber & Dumas Building
Ipswich 1974
Foster Associates
Gabriele Bramante
0 7148 2772 X

Design

Graphics

Product

Graphics

Advertising

General
Non-Fiction

Art

Photography

Collector's
Editions

Film

Architecture

290 × 250 mm
11³⁄₈ × 9⁷⁄₈ inches
448 pp
c.1500 col illus.

Hardback
0 7148 4325 3

£ **39.95** UK
$ **69.95** US
€ **69.95** EUR
$ **99.95** CAN
$ **119.95** AUS

Marketing information
Simultaneous international
launch events in New York,
London, Paris and Berlin

Published September

area

100 graphic designers, 10 curators, 10 classics
Curated by Anthon Beeke, Nick Bell, Ken Cato, Shigeo Fukuda, Fernando Gutierrez, Werner Jeker, Uwe Loesch, Stefan Sagmeister, Serge Serov, Omar Vulpinari

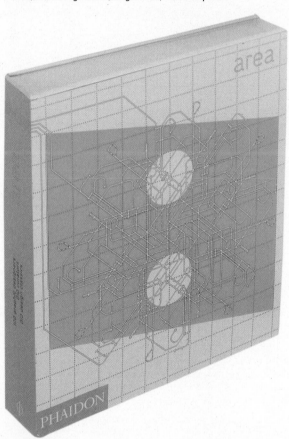

- A global up-to-the-minute overview of contemporary printed graphic design
- Following in the footsteps of *cream*, *10x10*, *BLINK*, and *Spoon*, *area* presents 100 of the most interesting graphic designers who have emerged internationally over the last five years, chosen by ten influential curators
- From corporate identity to posters, typefaces to compact discs, *area* presents trends and talents in visual communication in an entirely new format
- More than 1500 colour images illustrate the designers' projects, accompanied by concise, illuminating texts by the selecting curators

Anthon Beeke (Netherlands) heads his own design company and teaches at the Design Academy in Eindhoven. **Nick Bell** (UK) is Director of UNA designers and Art Director of *Eye* magazine. **Ken Cato** (Australia) is Chairman of Cato Purnell Partners. **Shigeo Fukuda** (Japan) is a visual artist and a visiting professor at Tokyo National University of Fine Arts and Music. **Fernando Gutierrez** (UK/Spain) is a partner of design firm Pentagram, and Creative Director of *Colors* and *Matador*. **Werner Jeker** (Switzerland) is Chair of the Visual Communications department at HGKK in Bern. **Uwe Loesch** (Germany) is a professor of Communication Design at the University of Wuppertal. **Stefan Sagmeister** (USA) is the award-winning Director of Sagmeister Inc. **Serge Serov** (Russia) is the founder and Director of the international Golden Bee graphic design biennale, Moscow. **Omar Vulpinari** (Italy) heads the department of Visual Communication Design at Fabrica in Treviso, Italy.

Design Graphics NEW TITLE | Fashion & Contemporary Culture | Decorative Arts | Music & Performing Arts | Video | Index

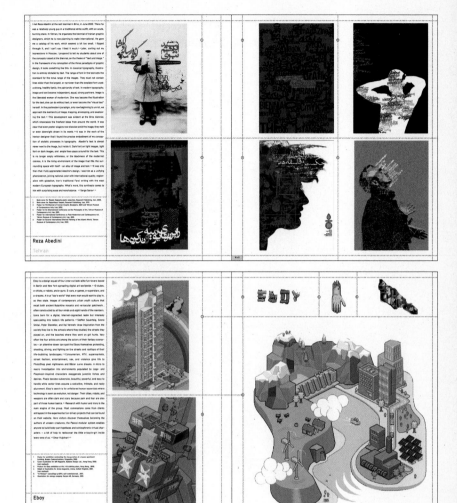

Reza Abedini
Tehran

Eboy
Berlin/New York

The work of each graphic designer is presented on two double-page spreads introduced with a short text by the selecting curator. The name and place of work of the designer reappears on each spread

100 designers Majid Abbasi, Reza Abedini, Aficionado, Kumnam Baik, André Baldinger, Jop van Bennekom, Andrew Blauvelt, Blue Source, Tom Bodkin, Günter Karl Bose, Mayo Bucher, Vladimir Chaika, Coma, Chaz Maviyane-Davies, Das Haus Rüegger + Albisetti, Delaware, De Designpolitie, Chis Dixon, Daniel Eatock/Foundation 33, Eboy, Dave Eggers, Jonathan Ellery Experimental Jetset, Sara Fanelli, Isidro Ferrer, Laurent Fétis, Field Study, Lizzie Finn, Amy Franceschini, Vince Frost, Tom Gauld, Juli Gudehus, Yuri Gulitov, Julia Hasting, Fons Hickmann, Kim Hiorthøy, Keiko Hirano, Hon Bing-wah, Inkahoots, Karlssonwilker, Siobhan Keaney, Kerr/Noble, Rene Knip, Elisabeth Kopf, Ji Lee, Ken-tsai Lee, Anette Lenz, Apex Lin, Andrey Logvin, Victor Hugo Marreiros, Malte Martin, Kei Matsushita, Ung Vai Meng, Saed Meshki, Mooren + van der Velden, Peter Moser, Müller + Hess, Melanie Mues, Hideki Nakajima, Dylan Nelson, Yves Netzhammer, Christoph Niemann, Nagi Noda, Norm, Nowakteufelknyrim, Fabio Ongarato, Tania Prill, Qwer, Reala, Casey Reas, David Richmond, Sanja Rocco, Gabriela Rodriguez, Joe Sacco, Ahn Sang-soo, Yasuhiro Sawada, Claudia Schmauder, Nico Schweizer, Chen Shaohua, So Man-yee, Leonardo Sonnoli, Jennifer Sterling, Remo Stoller, Kosta Stratigos, Yuri Surkov, Swip Stolk, Thonik, True, 2 x 4, Tycoon Graphics, Rick Valicenti, Alberto Vieceli, Garth Walker, Chris Ware, Martin Woodtli, Michael Worthington, Wang Xu, Catherine Zask, 032c, Viola Zimmermann

473

General
Non-Fiction

Art

Photography

Collector's
Editions

Film

Architecture

245 × 210 mm
9⅝ × 8¼ inches
208 pp
c.300 col illus.

Hardback
0 7148 4318 0

£ **29.95** UK
$ **49.95** US
€ **49.95** EUR
$ **75.00** CAN
$ **89.95** AUS

Related exhibitions
Major show at MOCA,
Los Angeles, opening
in spring 2004

Published October

Ronan and Erwan Bouroullec

Texts by Ronan and Erwan Bouroullec, Giulio Cappellini, Rolf Fehlbaum and Issey Miyake

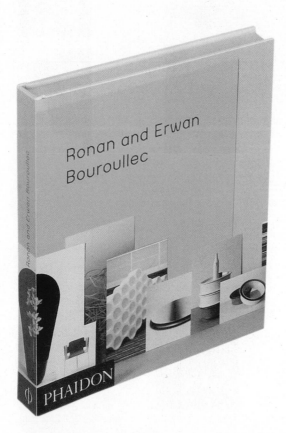

- Erwan (b.1976) and Ronan (b.1971) Bouroullec are perhaps the youngest, most established stars of international product design
- Based in Paris, they work for many of the most important furniture manufacturers in the world
- The first book to cover their entire career
- A showcase of their work, detailing their products (manufactured and prototypes) as well as their working practices through drawings, sketches, models and photographs, mostly published here for the first time
- With explanations of each product's development from commission to realization
- Texts by leading design entrepreneurs

Giulio Cappellini is a founding member of furniture manufacturer Cappellini and works with young designers all over the world. He first discovered the Bouroullecs
Rolf Fehlbaum is Chairman of furniture manufacturer Vitra and commissioned the Bouroullecs to develop a revolutionary new office system
Issey Miyake, renowned fashion designer, commissioned the brothers to design the A-POC shop in Paris and other showrooms

Design
Product
NEW TITLE

Fashion &
Contemporary
Culture

Decorative Arts

Music &
Performing Arts

Video

Index

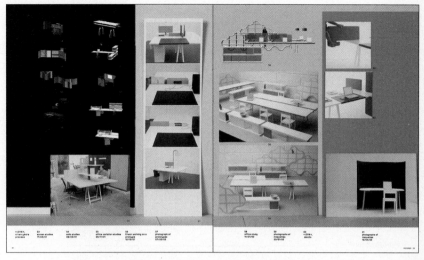

spreads from Ronan
and Erwan Bouroullec
showing (from top)
Joyn, office system
for Vitra: drawings,
studies and
maquettes; Joyn,
large table; Vase,
Galerie kreo;
1 et Demi, sofa,
Domeau et Pérès

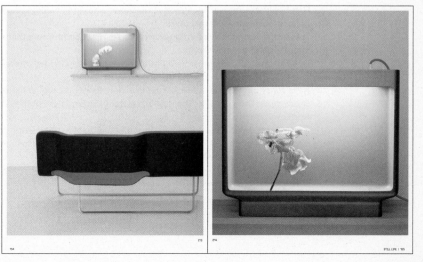

General
Non-Fiction

Art

Photography

Collector's
Editions

Film

Architecture

Hella Jongerius

Texts by Hella Jongerius and Louise Schouwenberg

245 × 210 mm
9⅝ × 8¼ inches
144 pp
252 col, 43 b&w illus.

Hardback
0 7148 4305 9

£ **24.95** UK
$ **39.95** US
€ **39.95** EUR
$ **59.95** CAN
$ **69.95** AUS

Related exhibitions
Solo exhibition at the
Design Museum, London,
July–October 2003,
to travel to other
international venues

Published July

- First book on a young Dutch product designer whose innovative creations have garnered acclaim in the international press
- Products featured include unique ceramics, textiles and furniture that emphasize organic materials and sensuous form
- Includes specially commissioned photographs and an extended interview with Jongerius

Hella Jongerius (b.1963) is head of her own firm, JongeriusLab, and has worked with renowned Dutch group Droog Design. She is Director of the Design Atelier at the Design Academy in Eindhoven, the Netherlands
Louise Schouwenberg is a Dutch artist, writer and publicist. She writes for the Dutch art magazine Metropolis M, is a contributing editor of FRAME magazine and tutors at the Design Academy in Eindhoven

Design
Product
NEW TITLE

Fashion &
Contemporary
Culture

Decorative Arts

Music &
Performing Arts

Video

Index

Louise **Do your attempts to convince the industry ever come up against a brick wall?**

Hella **On a good day, I'm pretty good at getting them to see things my way. But now and then my efforts are in vain.** It regularly happens that the company directors are enthusiastic, but the design falls afoul of the marketing department at the last fence because they fear a commercial flop. Good design isn't necessarily good merchandise.

ROYAL
TICHELAAR }
MAKKUM
B-Set, Red/White Vase, Big White Pot,
B-Set Repeat Series

Louise **You did the same thing with *Blizzard Bulbs*.**

Hella **There I was playing with the form vocabulary of traditional lampshades by putting handblown glass shapes on butane-gas bottles.**

Nearly 300 photographs show how Jongerius' work is designed, manufactured, exhibited and used. Here, vases are photographed in a shop vitrine, and felt stools are being prepared for shipping. An interview with Jongerius runs through the book in metallic text from cover to cover. Two critical essays are printed in blue ink on vellum pages sandwiched between the colour pages

General Non-Fiction

Art

Photography

Collector's Editions

Film

Architecture

156 × 136 mm
6¹₄ × 5¹₂ inches
328 pp plus 4 fold-outs
145 illus. reproduced
in six cols

Hardback
0 7148 3817 9

£ **12.95** UK
$ **19.95** US
€ **22.95** EUR
$ **29.95** CAN
$ **35.00** AUS

Point of Sale
10-copy counterpack
available
0 7148 5011 X

Minimum

John Pawson

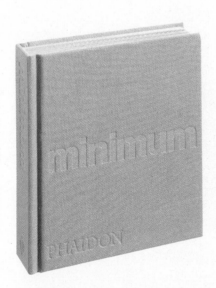

- An extraordinary visual essay that explores the notion of minimum as applied to architecture, art and design
- Compiled by the Minimalist architect John Pawson, *Minimum* captures the essential qualities of buildings and objects that have been reduced to their bare essentials
- Includes work as diverse as buildings from prehistoric Mexico to Le Corbusier and Mies van der Rohe, art by Donald Judd, photography, furniture and pottery

John Pawson is a renowned architect and designer specializing in the Minimalist aesthetic. He has designed interiors for Calvin Klein, B&B Italia and the Cathay Pacific Lounge at the Hong Kong International Airport. His own work is the subject of two books *John Pawson Works* and *John Pawson Themes and Projects,* both published by Phaidon

Design

Fashion &
Contemporary
Culture

Decorative Arts

Music &
Performing Arts

Video

Index

'A book to inspire its owner to throw out all others.' *I-D*

'A searching discourse on the appeal of minimalism.'

Financial Times

General Non-Fiction

Art

Photography

Collector's Editions

Film

Architecture

210 × 300 mm
8¹4 × 117⁄8 inches
448 pp
c.1,000 col illus.

**Specially bound
with a formed steel cover**
0 7148 4251 6

£ **45.00** UK
$ **75.00** US
€ **75.00** EUR
$ **99.95** CAN
$ **140.00** AUS

Spoon

100 designers, 10 curators, 10 design classics
*Curated by Ron Arad, Giulio Cappellini, Ultan Guilfoyle, Brooke Hodge, Laura Houseley,
Hansjerg Maier-Aichen, Ryu Niimi, Ramon Ubeda, Stefan Ytterborn and Lisa White*

- An up-to-the-minute, global overview of contemporary industrial design
- Following the mould of *cream*, *10x10* and *Blink*, showcases 100 of the most interesting product designers who have emerged internationally in the last five years, chosen by 10 influential curators
- 400 pages of designers' projects, extensively illustrated with over 1,000 colour photographs, sketches and drawings
- A beautiful design object in its own right
- Includes 10 design 'classics' chosen by each curator, to illustrate their concept of 'good design'

'If you care about what's great in contemporary product design and you want a reason to buy *Spoon*, you've got exactly 100' *(Blueprint)*
'Finally, a design book that is truly reflective of its content — as much a designed product as the artefacts it promotes.' *(Graphics International)*

Design
Product

Fashion &
Contemporary
Culture

Decorative Arts

Music &
Performing Arts

Video

Index

'Definitely the book to have for anyone practising, curious about, interested in or just plain infatuated with industrial design.' *I.D.*

General Non-Fiction

Art

Photography

Collector's Editions

Film

Architecture

290 × 250 mm
11³⁄₈ × 9⁷⁄₈ inches
272 pp
c.275 col, 75 b&w illus.

Hardback
0 7148 4163 3

£ **45.00** UK
$ **75.00** US
€ **75.00** EUR
$ **99.95** CAN
$ **140.00** AUS

Alexey Brodovitch

Kerry William Purcell

- Most comprehensive monograph in print on Alexey Brodovitch's life and work
- Highlights Brodovitch's major achievements as Art Director of *Harper's Bazaar*, his collaboration with Richard Avedon and André Kertész, and his role as educator to a young generation of photographers and designers
- Draws on interviews with a wide range of colleagues and collaborators
- Includes rare, previously unpublished material from archives and private collections around the world
- Reproduces in full three photography books designed by Brodovitch, including the extremely rare *Ballet*, and three issues of *Portfolio* magazine, a much-heralded journal that is now a cult collectable

Kerry William Purcell is a writer, lecturer and freelance picture editor. A former archivist at The Photographers Gallery in London, he has written widely on film and photography

Design
Graphics

Fashion &
Contemporary
Culture

Decorative Arts

Music &
Performing Arts

Video

Index

290 × 250 mm
11³⁄₈ × 9⁷⁄₈ inches
256 pp
302 col, 145 b&w illus.

Paperback
0 7148 3994 9

£ **22.95** UK
$ **35.00** US
€ **39.95** EUR
$ **49.95** CAN
$ **59.95** AUS

Paul Rand

Steven Heller, with texts by Armin Hofmann, George Lois and Jessica Helfand

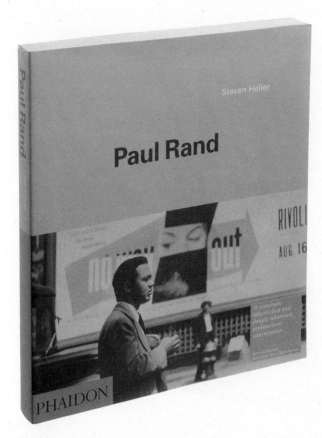

- Art director, teacher, writer and design consultant to companies including IBM and UPS, Paul Rand (1914–96) was a major influence in the field of graphics and visual communication
- Foreword by distinguished Swiss graphic designer Armin Hofmann, who taught with Rand at Yale University
- Inspiring introduction by George Lois, one of the most eminent figures in advertising
- With a concluding essay capturing Rand's educational achievements by Jessica Helfand, a former student of Rand
- First complete retrospective, organized by medium to explore the full range of advertising, publishing and corporate identity work

Steven Heller is a Senior Art Director at the *New York Times* and co-chair of the MFA/Design Program of the School of Visual Arts in New York. A respected authority in the design world, he has written and co-authored numerous publications, including *Merz To Emigre and Beyond*, also published by Phaidon

280 × 220 mm
11¼ × 8¾ inches
272 pp
400 col, 40 b&w illus.

Hardback
0 7148 3716 4

£ **39.95** UK
$ **59.95** US
€ **65.00** EUR
$ **89.95** CAN
$ **99.95** AUS

Tanaka Ikko

With an introduction by Gian Carlo Calza

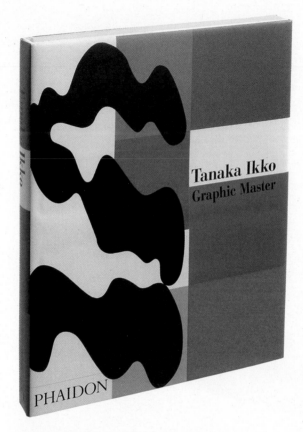

- An extensive monograph on the career of Tanaka Ikko (b. 1930), the established master of Japanese graphic design
- Tanaka's work draws together influences from both East and West, while remaining characteristically Japanese
- Covers entire career from late 1950s and includes Tanaka's graphic design and art direction, editorial and interior design
- With a critical anthology including contributions from leading commentators on contemporary graphic design, together with an extensive bibliography

Gian Carlo Calza is Professor of East Asian Art History at the University of Venice and Director of the International Hokusai Research Centre in Milan. He is the author of many books and articles on Japanese art, including *Hokusai,* also published by Phaidon

Design
Graphics

Fashion &
Contemporary
Culture

Decorative Arts

Music &
Performing Arts

Video

Index

245 × 210 mm
9²³ × 8¹₄ inches
266 pp
250 col illus.

Hardback
0 7148 3354 1

£ **39.95** UK
$ **59.95** US
€ **65.00** EUR
$ **89.95** CAN
$ **120.00** AUS

Beware Wet Paint

Designs by Alan Fletcher, commentary by Jeremy Myerson, with an interview by Rick Poynor and a pen portrait by David Gibbs

- The only monograph on the international graphic master Alan Fletcher
- Over one hundred design solutions each with a commentary to show how the graphic idea was developed, giving insights into the individual project and the design process
- Grouped into thematic chapters for easy reference
- Demonstrates Fletcher's unique lithe and lateral jumps, his skills and techniques and his ease in fusing aesthetics with function

Jeremy Myerson, former Editor of *Design Week* and of *Creative Review*, writes about Fletcher's life and works
Rick Poynor, former Editor of *Eye* magazine, interviews Fletcher
David Gibbs, editor of *Pentagram: The Compendium,* also published by Phaidon, offers a retrospective appreciation

'Fletcher probably gets bored with always being on the receiving end of praise, but his work is simply terrific – buy this book.' *(FX)*
'One of the best graphic design books ever published.' *(Critique)*

245 × 210 mm
9⁵⁸ × 8¹⁴ inches
624 pp
c.1000 col, 100 b&w illus.

Hardback
0 7148 3827 6

£ **45.00** UK
$ **69.95** US
€ **75.00** EUR
$ **99.95** CAN
$ **140.00** AUS

Life Style

Bruce Mau

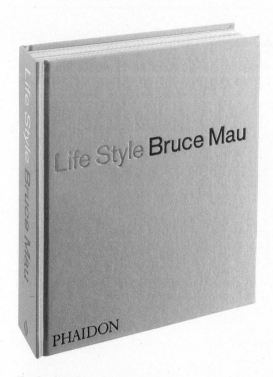

- First book to document the creative process and studio practice of Bruce Mau, one of the world's most sought-after designers
- Written by Mau and designed by his studio collaborators, with over 1,000 images
- A collection of perceptive, often playful statements about the visual and cultural trends that influence today's design culture
- Expresses the methods and convictions of Bruce Mau Design, a 'multidisciplinary think-tank' that includes artists, film-makers and writers
- Includes work such as the highly acclaimed *Zone* books, *S, M, X, XL* which he co-authored with Rem Koolhaas and his collaborations with Frank Gehry, the Netherlands Architecture Institute and the Getty Center
- Available in a variety of coloured and patterned binding materials

'An insightful and exhilarating analysis of image culture.' *(Dazed and Confused)*
'A 624-page strip tease performed with an endless variety of veils … the book tantalizes readers with glimpses into the thinking of one of the most creative minds at work in design today.' *(New York Times)*
'A book form that's partly a journal of ideas, creative anthology, social critique, manifesto for change — and a superlative piece of design.' *(Blueprint)*

Design
Graphics

Fashion &
Contemporary
Culture

Decorative Arts

Music &
Performing Arts

Video

Index

324 × 244 mm
12³⁄₄ × 92/3 inches
304 pp
300 col, 50 b&w illus.

Paperback
0 7148 3769 5

£ **24.95**   UK
$ **39.95**   US
€ **39.95**   EUR
$ **59.95**   CAN
$ **65.00**   AUS

Pentagram

The Compendium
Edited by David Gibbs

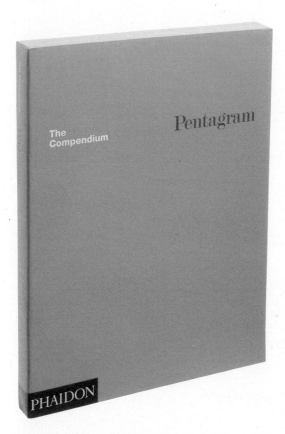

- An overview of one of the best known and most influential design agencies in the world
- Offers a rare and important insight into Pentagram's creative durability and documents work from its agencies in London, New York and San Francisco
- Explores the knowledge and thought processes behind the ideas that are the foundation of the group's reputation
- With essays by all of the Pentagram partners
- Special sections examine the client-designer relationship and the company's structure and methodology

David Gibbs has been editorial consultant to Pentagram since the 1970s. His understanding of the design process has been developed through extensive work with designers on publications and films worldwide. As a writer he contributes to journals in North America, South East Asia and the Middle East, as well as Europe

'Intelligently laid out examples of the company's work, organized in a user-friendly style, provide an overview of excellent design from the early 1960s to the present.' *(Graphis)*

290 × 250 mm
11³⁄₈ × 9⁷⁄₈ inches
512 pp
c.1000 col, 300 b&w illus.

Hardback
0 7148 4271 0

£ **45.00** UK
$ **75.00** US
€ **75.00** EUR
$ **99.95** CAN
$ **140.00** AUS

Rewind

Forty Years of Design and Advertising
Edited and written by Jeremy Myerson and Graham Vickers, with introductory texts by Jeremy Bullmore, Alan Fletcher, Richard Seymour, John Webster and Peter York

- An international survey of the history of design and advertising of the last 40 years
- Includes texts by leading practitioners within the creative industries
- Features a range of high-profile designs and advertising campaigns, including British Airways, Nike, Time Out, Levi Strauss, Habitat, Greenpeace and Volvo
- Presents the work of leading practitioners and design agencies, including the Conran Design Group, CDP, Saatchi's and Pentagram
- Covers a broad range of design disciplines including graphic design, TV, press and poster advertising, product design, new media and retail packaging

Jeremy Myerson is a writer and editor. He co-founded *Design Week* and is currently Co-Director of the Helen Hamlyn Research Centre at the Royal College of Art, London
Graham Vickers is a freelance journalist and author. He is a contributing editor to *Creative Review* and regularly writes for a number of trade publications. His books include *Style in Product Design* and *Key Moments in Architecture: The Evolution of the City*

Design
Graphics

Fashion &
Contemporary
Culture

Decorative Arts

Music &
Performing Arts

Video

Index

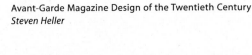

290 × 250 mm
11³⁄₈ × 9⁷⁄₈ inches
240 pp
c.550 col illus.

Hardback
0 7148 3927 2

£   45.00 UK
$ 75.00 US
€   75.00 EUR
$ 99.95 CAN
$ 140.00 AUS

Merz to Emigre and Beyond

Avant-Garde Magazine Design of the Twentieth Century
Steven Heller

- A historical survey of avant-garde cultural and political magazines and journals of the 20th century
- Features magazines from all over the globe linked to controversial art, literary and political movements such as Dada, Surrealism, the New Left and Deconstruction
- Contains the work of many experimental artists and designers of their time – from Kurt Schwitters and El Lissitzky in the 1920s and 30s, to Art Spiegelman and Rudy VanderLans in the 1980s and 90s
- Illustrated with over 500 newly photographed original magazine covers and inside spreads

Steven Heller is a Senior Art Director at the *New York Times* and Co-Chair of the MFA/Design Program of the School of Visual Arts in New York. A respected authority in the design world, he has written and co-authored numerous publications, including *Paul Rand*, also published by Phaidon

General
Non-Fiction
Art
Photography
Collector's
Editions
Film
Architecture

290 × 250 mm
11³⁄₈ × 9⁷⁄₈ inches
240 pp
260 col, 331 b&w illus.

Paperback
0 7148 3838 1

£ 22.95 UK
$ 35.00 US
€ 39.95 EUR
$ 49.95 CAN
$ 59.95 AUS

Marks of Excellence

The history and taxonomy of trademarks
Per Mollerup

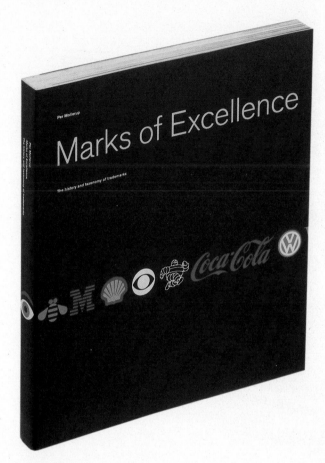

- An exploration of the trademark: its history, development, style, classification and relevance in today's world
- Includes discussions of its origins in heraldry, monograms, owner's marks and certificates of origins
- With a comprehensive taxonomy of trademarks, which makes this book an invaluable reference tool for design students and graphic designers

Per Mollerup is the founder of *Designlab,* a leading Scandinavian consultancy in visual communication, information design and corporate identity

Design
Graphics

Fashion &
Contemporary
Culture

Decorative Arts

Music &
Performing Arts

Video

Index

290 × 250 mm
11³⁄₈ × 9⁷⁄₈ inches
240 pp
427 col, 197 b&w illus.

Paperback
0 7148 3812 8

£ **22.95** UK
$ **35.00** US
€ **39.95** EUR
$ **49.95** CAN
$ **59.95** AUS

A Smile in the Mind

Witty thinking in graphic design
Beryl McAlhone and David Stuart, with a foreword by Edward de Bono

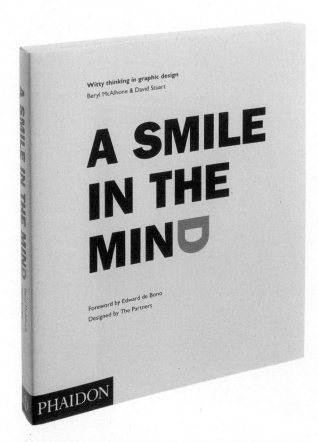

- An exploration of witty thinking – the most entertaining area of graphic design
- An analysis of the thought processes behind the image
- Includes interviews with some of the world's top designers
- Contains the best examples of graphic wit over the past 30 years with work from over 300 designers in the US, Britain, Europe and Japan

Beryl McAlhone is a writer with a special interest in design
David Stuart is a founding member of the international design company The Partners

'Beautifully edited, lovingly and carefully compiled … both intellectually and aesthetically stimulating. Oh, and it's funny too.' *(Graphics International)*

General
Non-Fiction

Art

Photography

Collector's
Editions

Film

Architecture

245 × 210 mm
9⁵⁄₈ × 4¹⁄₄ inches
288 pp
c.500 col, 150 b&w illus.

Hardback
0 7148 4174 9

£ **29.95** UK
$ **49.95** US
€ **49.95** EUR
$ **75.00** CAN
$ **89.95** AUS

Problem Solved

A Primer for Design and Communications
Michael Johnson

- A manual for students and professionals that offers solutions to design problems
- A guide to interpreting design briefs and producing new solutions to familiar problems
- Brings together discussions and case studies that illustrate the working methods of major advertising and graphic design firms
- Themes include: avoiding repetition, standing out in the market place, reinventing a tired brand, dealing with propaganda, communicating the essential facts
- Examples from international designers and agencies such as Chermeyeff and Geismar, Saatchi and Saatchi, BMP, Minale Tattersfield, Derek Birdsall, Niklaus Troxler, Bob Gill, Wieslan Walkuski, Makoto Saito, Paul Fishlock and Pentagram

Michael Johnson is Creative Director of Johnson Banks, which was voted most creative consultancy in Britain in 1999. He is Chairman of Education for British Design and Art Direction (D&AD) and lectures regularly on design theory and practice
'For once we have a graphics book that isn't just a parade of stunning imagery –
impressive though its visual content is. A challenging theory underpins each wittily titled chapter, promoting brave and contentious ideas. It also pushes the importance of words in communication – a rare treat from a serious graphics tome.' *(Design Week)*
'Not just an important textbook, but an ode to creative intelligence.' *(Magma)*
'A real *tour de force*. It covers an amazing amount of projects (and problems) and Johnson tackles them in an unpretentious and erudite way.' *(Graphics International)*

Design Graphics

Fashion & Contemporary Culture

Decorative Arts

Music & Performing Arts

Video

Index

280 × 215 mm
11 × 8½ inches
224 pp
113 col, 241 b&w illus.

Paperback
0 7148 3851 9

£ **14.95** UK
$ **24.95** US
€ **24.95** EUR
$ **35.00** CAN
$ **39.95** AUS

Design Writing Research

Writing on graphic design
Ellen Lupton and J Abbott Miller

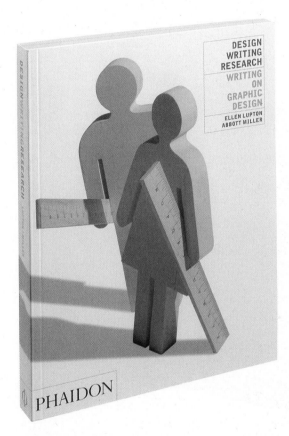

- A highly acclaimed critical study of graphic design and typography
- Invaluable for anyone interested in art and the history of books, advertising and visual and verbal communication
- Examines the history of punctuation, the origins of pictograms and the structure of modern typography and mass communication
- A time-line spanning 200 years of design in the US shows how modern graphic design has emerged as a response to culture, politics and economics

Abbott Miller is the Director of Design/Writing/Research, an award-winning multidisciplinary design studio, and also sits on the board of the American Center for Design
Ellen Lupton is the Curator of Contemporary Design at Cooper-Hewitt, National Design Museum in New York and has lectured widely on design and contemporary culture

'At last, an analysis of the design of writing … sophisticated, penetrating, incisive' (Rosalind Krauss)
'This book provides essential background in current design theory and opens the way to a broader awareness of the fundamental role of graphic design in our time.' (Mildred Friedman)

General
Non-Fiction

Art

Photography

Collector's
Editions

Film

Architecture

250 × 250 mm
9⁷₈ × 9⁷₈ inches
160 pp
180 col illus.

Paperback
0 7148 3461 0

£ **19.95** UK
$ **29.95** US
€ **35.00** EUR
$ **45.00** CAN
$ **55.00** AUS

Award

Winner of the silver
award from the
prestigious Design
and Art Directors'
Association (D&AD)

Paperwork

The potential of paper in graphic design
Nancy Williams

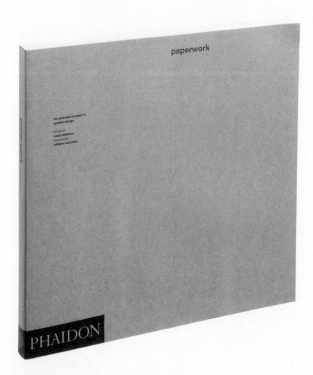

- *Paperwork* reveals the huge potential of paper by examining its usage and highlighting its amazing versatility
- Only book on paper to address all the special needs and interests of the print and design industries
- With sections on paper qualities, print effects, embossing, die-cutting, binding and pop-up effects
- Includes a glossary of terms and techniques and practical advice on types of paper suitable for various print and finishing processes

Nancy Williams founded Williams & Phoa with Phoa Kia Boon in 1984, after working with Pentagram. The company has received many design awards and has been nominated one of the top dozen graphic design companies in the UK

Winner of the silver award from the prestigious Design and Art Directors' Association (D&AD)

Design
Graphics

Fashion &
Contemporary
Culture

Decorative Arts

Music &
Performing Arts

Video

Index

250 × 250 mm
9⅞ × 9⅞ inches
160 pp
200 col illus.

Paperback
0 7148 2909 9

£ **19.95** UK
$ **29.95** US
€ **35.00** EUR
$ **45.00** CAN
$ **55.00** AUS

Letterwork

Creative letterforms in graphic design
Brody Neuenschwander

- An inspirational guide to the creation and adaptation of letterforms
- Draws on examples from packaging, posters, TV sequences and book design from around the world
- Demonstrates the principles of letterforms, the use of basic tools and many varied techniques which allow students and professionals to create unique lettering effects

Brody Neuenschwander is a lettering artist, graphic designer and lecturer in calligraphy. His work has been frequently reproduced in books and magazines and is represented in public and private collections

'High-quality production and thoughtful commentary make this book a must-have for the interested designer.' *(Step by Step Graphics)*

General
Non-Fiction

Art

Photography

Collector's
Editions

Film

Architecture

290 × 250 mm
11³⁄₈ × 9⁷⁄₈ inches
240 pp
551 col, 182 b&w illus.

Paperback
0 7148 3458 0

£ **22.95** UK
$ **35.00** US
€ **39.95** EUR
$ **49.95** CAN
$ **59.95** AUS

Graphic Agitation

Social and political graphics since the sixties
Liz McQuiston

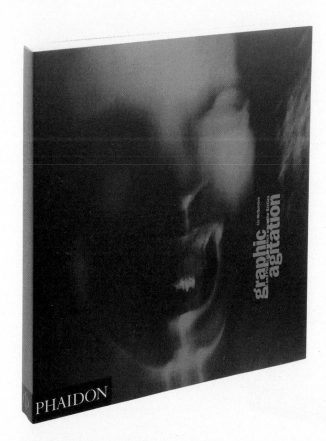

- An exploration of how graphic art and design have addressed social and political issues from the sixties to the present day
- Covers a broad range of subject areas including war, peace, ecology, health and sexual politics
- Features the work of some of the design world's best-known personalities as well as the graphics of anonymous protest
- With over 600 images that are visually striking and reflect the protest, propaganda, shock and subversion of graphic art

Liz McQuiston divides her time between graphic design practice, teaching and writing. Her most recent book is *Suffragettes to She-Devils,* also published by Phaidon

'This ambitious chronicle is a must for the scholars, students and practitioners of alternative media.' *(The New York Times)*

Design
Graphics

Fashion &
Contemporary
Culture

Decorative Arts

Music &
Performing Arts

Video

Index

290 × 250 mm
11³⁄₈ × 9⁷⁄₈ inches
240 pp
418 col, 24 b&w illus.

Paperback
0 7148 3993 0

£ **19.95** UK
$ **29.95** US
€ **35.00** EUR
$ **45.00** CAN
$ **55.00** AUS

Hardback
0 7148 3008 9

£ **39.95** UK
$ **59.95** US
€ **65.00** EUR
$ **89.95** CAN
$ **98.00** AUS

Comics, Comix & Graphic Novels

A history of comic art
Roger Sabin

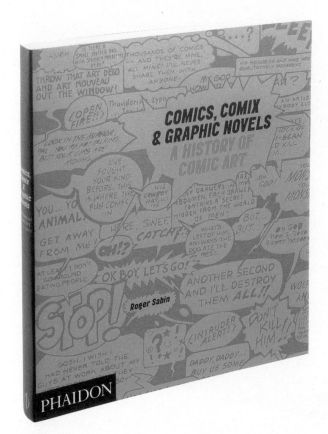

- Traces the history of the comic from the 19th century cartoon-like woodcuts to the graphic strips of today
- Encompasses traditions from the US, Britain, Europe and Japan
- Organized thematically, it includes genres such as humour, adventure, girls' comics, underground and alternative
- Examines the careers of the creators of the best-known characters, from Superman and Tintin to Tank Girl and Sgt Rock

Roger Sabin is an arts journalist and lecturer at Central St Martin's College of Art, London. He is the author of the highly acclaimed *Adult Comics: An Introduction*

'Here at last is an authoritative and beautifully produced history of this vigorous and versatile art form, which covers as much of the whole field as a single book could.' *(Guardian)*

General
Non-Fiction

Art

Photography

Collector's
Editions

Film

Architecture

290 × 250 mm
11³⁄₈ × 9⁷⁄₈ inches
240 pp
443 col, 174 b&w illus.

Hardback
0 7148 3619 2

£ **39.95** UK
$ **59.95** US
€ **65.00** EUR
$ **89.95** CAN
$ **120.00** AUS

Suffragettes to She-Devils

Women's Liberation and Beyond
Liz McQuiston, with a foreword by Germaine Greer

- Explores the developing role of graphics and related media in the struggle for women's liberation
- Spans from the vibrant visual identity of militant Suffragettes, through 1960s Women's Lib, to virtual-reality cyberfeminists
- Addresses issues such as rights in the workplace, gay rights, gay pride and questions of identity, race, violence and welfare
- Illustrated with a variety of posters, billboards, logos and computer graphics

Liz McQuiston divides her time between graphic design practice, teaching and writing. She is the author of *Graphic Agitation: Social and Political Graphics since the Sixties*, also published by Phaidon

'A fascinating and thought-provoking journey through visual feminist publishing and activity. Humour pervades much of the book, which is reassuring since humour is not an emotion that many people associate with feminism. Every home should have a copy.' *(Creative Review)*

Design
Graphics/Advertising

Fashion &
Contemporary
Culture

Decorative Arts

Music &
Performing Arts

Video

Index

245 × 210 mm
9⅝ × 8¼ inches
272 pp
190 col, 80 b&w illus.

Hardback
0 7148 4284 2

£ 24.95 UK
$ 39.95 US
€ 39.95 EUR
$ 59.95 CAN
$ 69.95 AUS

$ellebrity

My Angling and Tangling with Famous People
George Lois

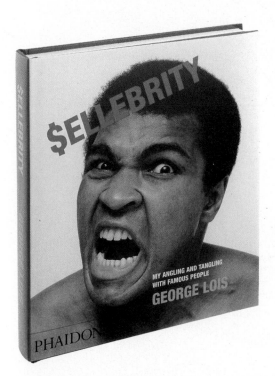

- Showcases the unforgettable career of legendary American adman George Lois (b.1931), a leader of the Creative Revolution
- Reproduces over 130 of Lois's most memorable print and TV campaigns with celebrities such as Andy Warhol, Frank Sinatra and Muhammad Ali
- Explains how each ad was conceived and produced, and tells of the unexpected pitfalls, scuffles and friendships that ensued
- Includes dozens of Lois's controversial covers for *Esquire* magazine during the 1960s and 70s
- Illustrated with memorable, humorous images from classic American advertisements

George Lois, a native New Yorker, joined Doyle Dane Bernbach as an art director in 1958 and started his first agency in 1960. He is the recipient of an AIGA Gold Medal, among other honours, and the author of two books on advertising. He continues to consult for major corporations

'At the pulsating intersection of 60s iconography and iconoclasm stood George Lois, genius adman, who went on to sock it to the nation's eyeballs as *Esquire*'s cover designer. As he publishes his visual memoir, Lois says he has no heirs. He may be right. *$ELLEBRITY* toots its horn as loud and proud as the photo of Muhammad Ali that shouts from the cover.' (James Wolcott, *Vanity Fair*, February 2003)

General Non-Fiction

Art

Photography

Collector's Editions

Film

Architecture

290 × 250 mm
11³⁄₈ × 9⁷⁄₈ inches
512 pp
408 col, 63 b&w illus.

Hardback
0 7148 3923 X

£ **45.00** UK
$ **75.00** US
€ **75.00** EUR
$ **110.00** CAN
$ **125.00** AUS

Advertising Today

Warren Berger

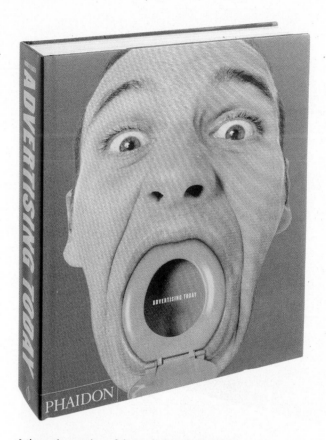

- A thematic overview of the evolution of advertising around the world over the past 30 years
- Includes over 500 advertisements in a wide range of media: print, television, billboards, the Internet and even very recent, so-called 'guerrilla' advertising
- Charts influences from the Creative Revolution of the early 1960s to the political and social upheavals of the 1970s to the Internet impact in the 1990s
- Each chapter features an interview with a key figure in advertising, including Benetton's Oliviero Toscani, American-Express spokesperson Jerry Seinfeld and John Hegarty, creator of the world-famous Levi's ads
- Acts as a history of global pop culture and a record of social, cultural and geo-political temperature-changes

Warren Berger is a journalist who is particularly well-known for his writing on advertising. He has written for industry publications such as *Advertising Age, Adweek, Graphis* and *Communication Arts*, and for the mainstream press, including *The New York Times, The Los Angeles Times, GQ* and *Wired*, where he is currently a contributing editor

'A fastidiously researched, visually delicious tome that media archaeologists will pour over for decades to come.' *(Village Voice)*

Design
Advertising

Fashion &
Contemporary
Culture

Decorative Arts

Music &
Performing Arts

Video

Index

290 × 250mm
11³⁄₈ × 9⁷⁄₈ inches
240 pp
553 col, 35 b&w illus.

Hardback
0 7148 3635 4

£   **45.00**   UK
$ **75.00**   US
€   **75.00**   EUR
$ **98.00**   CAN
$ **125.00**   AUS

Advertising Outdoors

Watch this Space!
David Bernstein

- An in-depth study of the art and ingenuity of those who devise large-scale artwork and ideas for outdoor advertising
- Explores many media including billboards, transit shelters, bus sides, taxis, airships and other location opportunities
- Discusses the rise of 'commercial art' and the exponential growth in advertising, making reference to successful advertising campaigns
- A work of enormous interest to designers, advertising professionals and clients

David Bernstein was Creative Director of three major international agencies before founding his own agency, The Creative Business. He has been awarded the Advertising Association's Mackintosh Medal for professional and public services to advertising

'A masterpiece. It's an Everything You Ever Wanted to Know About Posters But Were Too Busy Producing a Sub-Standard TV Commercial to Ask sort of book. Bernstein understands posters. He understands advertising. And he presents his case with consummate wit and precision.' *(Campaign)*

General
Non-Fiction

Art

Photography

Collector's
Editions

Film

Architecture

The Fashion Book

Hardback
290 × 250 mm
11³⁄₈ × 9⁷⁄₈ inches
512 pp
264 col, 236 b&w illus

0 7148 3808 X

£ **29.95** UK
$ **45.00** US
€ **49.95** EUR
$ **69.95** CAN
$ **79.95** AUS

Paperback mini format
163 × 123 mm
6³⁄₈ × 4⁷⁄₈ inches
520 pp
264 col, 236 b&w illus

0 7148 4118 8

£ **6.95** UK
$ **9.95** US
€ **11.95** EUR
$ **14.95** CAN
$ **16.95** AUS

- A-Z guide to 500 clothes and accessory designers, photographers, models and iconic figures who make up the fashion industry
- Spans 150 years and represents the entire industry – from pioneering designers, including Coco Chanel and Issey Miyake, to influential photographers such as Richard Avedon and Helmut Newton and the people they photographed
- Easy to use and filled with inspirational images
- Available in both pocket-sized and original formats

'The fashion bible.' *(Vogue)*
'The ultimate fashion reference book.' *(Elle)*
'A must for every self-respecting and dedicated follower of fashion.' *(Sunday Telegraph Magazine)*
'An A–Z of everything you could wish to know about the past 140 years of fashion. Models, moguls, designers and photographers are profiled and cross-referenced in this indispensable survey.' *(Harpers & Queen)*
'It is probably the most comprehensive fashion encyclopedia for general consumption available. A must-buy for the fashion obsessive'. *(Independent)*

Design

Fashion &
Contemporary
Culture

Decorative Arts

Music &
Performing Arts

Video

Index

290 × 250 mm
11³⁄₈ × 9⁷⁄₈ inches
512 pp
405 col, 200 b&w illus.

Paperback
0 7148 4334 2

£ **24.95** UK
$ **39.95** US
€ **39.95** EUR
$ **59.95** CAN
$ **69.95** AUS

Hardback
0 7148 3897 7

£ **39.95** UK
$ **69.95** US
€ **69.95** EUR
$ **98.00** CAN
$ **99.95** AUS

Fashion Today

Colin McDowell

- A kaleidoscopic, colourful and provocative survey of the fashion world from the introduction of Dior's New Look in 1947 to the present day
- Ranges from haute couture to street-style, from the one-off to the mass market
- Shows how fashion has reflected and influenced 20th-century attitudes from the sexual revolution in the 1960s to the consumerism of the 1980s and 1990s
- McDowell places current fashion in the context of previous fashion movements

Colin McDowell is a fashion historian and a Senior Fashion writer for the *Sunday Times*. He is the author of many books on the subject, including *Literary Companion to Fashion* (1995) and *Galliano* (1997)

'McDowell deconstructs fashion with insight, humour, verve ... One of the best books on the subject in recent years.' *(Chicago Tribune)*

245 × 172 mm
9⁵⁄₈ × 6³⁄₄ inches
224 pp
c.20 illus.

Hardback
0 7148 3887 X

£ 19.95 UK
$ 29.95 US
€ 35.00 EUR
$ 45.00 CAN
$ 55.00 AUS

A Dedicated Follower of Fashion

Holly Brubach

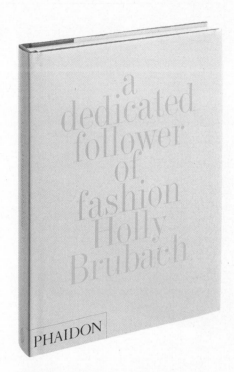

- A collection of 28 incisive essays by noted critic and 'fashion anthropologist' Holly Brubach
- Looks at clothing and the fashion industry as barometers of cultural and aesthetic change
- Subjects range from designers such as Saint Laurent, Gaultier and Versace to formal French style and the advent of casual athletic clothing
- Witty commentaries weave connections between fashion and the larger world around us
- An essential book for fashion insiders as well as anyone interested in popular culture and style

Holly Brubach is a journalist and consultant on fashion and the arts and Director of the Sport Collection and Home Collection for Prada. She was Style Editor of the *New York Times Magazine*, 1994–8, and was previously a writer for the *New Yorker*, the *Atlantic* and *Vogue* magazines

'Brubach's acutely observed snapshots deliver more than the usual kitten-heeled fluff we have come to expect from fashion writing.' *(The Face)*
'[This] book is like the friend who dares to be honest confirming that we're beautiful but flawed and smart enough to live well in spite of it.' *(New York Observer)*

Design

Fashion &
Contemporary
Culture

Decorative Arts

Music &
Performing Arts

Video

Index

195 × 140 mm
7⅝ × 5½ inches
560 pp
1,332 b&w photographs

Hardback
0 7148 4106 4

£ 24.95 UK
$ 39.95 US
€ 39.95 EUR
$ 59.95 CAN
$ 69.95 AUS

Halston

Edited by Steven Bluttal, with text by Patricia Mears

- A visual anthology of the life and legacy of Halston (1932–90), a name that became synonymous with American style
- Includes previously unpublished catwalk photographs, rare archival photographs by Warhol, behind-the-scenes images of fashion shows and parties, sketches and specially commissioned photographs of the collections
- Spans his career in Chicago in the late 1950s to being named 'the premier fashion designer of all America' by *Newsweek*

Steven Bluttal is an independent curator, archivist and photography editor based in New York
Patricia Mears is Assistant Curator in the Division of Costumes & Textiles at the Brooklyn Museum of Art, New York

'Visually, this book is spot-on. Its clean typeface and layouts mirror Halston's honed style … stuffed with lavish, informative pictures.' *(Blueprint)*
'Three years in the making *Halston* … is good news.' *(New York Times)*

General
Non-Fiction

Art

Photography

Collector's
Editions

Film

Architecture

220 × 160 mm
8³⁄₄ × 6¹⁄₄ inches
272 pp
268 col illus.

Flexibound
0 7148 4083 1

£ **19.95** UK
$ **29.95** US
€ **35.00** EUR
$ **45.00** CAN
$ **55.00** AUS

New York Public
Library's Books
for the Teenage List

Fruits

Shoichi Aoki

- A collection of Tokyo street fashion portraits from Japan's premier street fanzine of the same name, first established by photographer Shoichi Aoki in 1994
- With an extensive collection of portraits and cult images that uniquely documents the changing face of street fashion throughout the last decade
- Features kids aged on average between twelve and eighteen, wearing clothes that are a mixture of high fashion and home-made ensembles, creating a novel, if not hysterical, effect

'... A funky, funny look at Tokyo's teen street fashion — all Vivienne Westwood and DIY chic. Guaranteed to give you that happy-all-over feeling.' (Eithne Farry, *Elle*)

Design

**Fashion &
Contemporary
Culture**

Decorative Arts

Music &
Performing Arts

Video

Index

Box dimensions
197 × 138 mm
7⁶₈ × 5³₈ inches

0 7148 4335 0

incl. VAT £ **9.95** UK
$ **14.95** US
€ **14.95** EUR
$ **22.95** CAN
$ **24.95** AUS

Point of Sale
20-copy counterpack
0 7148 5276 7

Fruits Postcards

Shoichi Aoki

- A specially designed plastic, moulded, fluorescent box containing 45 of the best images from Aoki's best-selling book *Fruits*
- 45 teenage fashion setters from spikeys to fluffies
- Packaged in brightly coloured, fruity, fluorescent, plastic moulded boxes
- Cards are perfect to send to friends or pin on the wall
- Box comes in a range of 'fruity' fluorescent colours
- Box contains 45 postcards of 45 different images

General
Non-Fiction

Art

Photography

Collector's
Editions

Film

Architecture

245 × 175 mm
9⁵⁸ × 6⁷⁸ inches
304 pp
48 col portraits
49 col, 24 b&w illus.

Hardback
0 7148 3955 8

£ **24.95** UK
$ **39.95** US
€ **39.95** EUR
$ **59.95** CAN
$ **65.00** AUS

Star Culture

Collected interviews from *Dazed & Confused* magazine
Edited and introduced by Jefferson Hack

- A compilation of the best interviews and imagery from the archive of *Dazed & Confused* –
  the leading independent style magazine of its generation
- Contains a selection of new commissions especially for this book, and includes their radical
  use of the two-way interview
- Interviews range from Damien Hirst to Kate Moss, Keith Richards to Noam Chomsky
- Provides a definitive insight into modern style culture

Jefferson Hack is a co-publisher and editor who, through *Dazed & Confused* magazine and other
diverse media, has pioneered new approaches to journalism, film, photography and television.
In 1991 Jefferson co-founded *Dazed & Confused* with the photographer Rankin

Design

Fashion & Contemporary Culture

Decorative Arts

Music & Performing Arts

Video

Index

185 × 260 mm
7¼ × 10¼ inches
176 pp
88 col illus.

Specially hand bound
0 7148 4012 2

£ **49.95** UK
$ **75.00** US
€ **79.95** EUR
$ **115.00** CAN
$ **140.00** AUS

Special circular binding
0 7148 4012 2

The Order of Things

Photographs by Norbert Schoerner, edited by David James

- **A collection of exclusively commissioned work by fashion photographer Norbert Schoerner**
- **Presented in a book without a spine, *The Order of Things* is an art object in its own right**
- **Incorporates fashion images from Tokyo and London alongside portraits and personal stories**

Norbert Schoerner is internationally recognized as one of the most proficient and talented contemporary fashion photographers. His work for Prada and Miu Miu have been highly acclaimed within the industry.
David James was Art Director for Prada and Miu Miu.

General
Non-Fiction

Art

Photography

Collector's
Editions

Film

Architecture

245 × 172 mm
9⅝ × 6¾ inches
320 pp
c.30 illus.

Hardback
0 7148 4071 8

£ 24.95 UK
$ 39.95 US
€ 39.95 EUR
$ 59.95 CAN
$ 69.95 AUS

Cyber Reader

Critical writings for the digital era
Edited by Neil Spiller

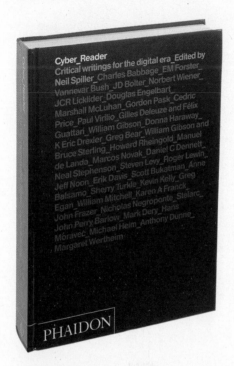

- An anthology of extracts from key texts related to the themes of cyberspace
- An essential source book for students and researchers
- Approaches the subject from a variety of fields, including science, philosophy, metaphysics, sexual politics, art, architecture and science fiction
- Includes over 40 texts arranged in chronological order
- Offers a wide range of approaches to the subject, including writings by Charles Babbage, Alan Turing and E M Foster

Neil Spiller is Reader in Architecture and Digital Theory at the Bartlett School of Architecture, University College, London. He has written widely on cyberspace and is also author of *Digital Dreams: Architecture and the New Alchemic Technologies* (1998)

Design

**Fashion &
Contemporary
Culture**

Decorative Arts

Music &
Performing Arts

Video

Index

250 × 250 mm
9⅞ × 9⅞ inches
224 pp
607 col, 54 b&w illus.

Paperback
0 7148 3267 7

£ **19.95** UK
$ **29.95** US
€ **35.00** EUR
$ **39.95** CAN
$ **55.00** AUS

The Cyberspace Lexicon

An illustrated dictionary of terms from multimedia to virtual reality
Bob Cotton and Richard Oliver

- A guide through the maze of existing and emerging technologies
- Addresses interactive video and multimedia, hypermedia, arcade games, high-band networks and virtual reality
- An invaluable source book for all those using electronic media
- Defines techniques and technologies, explains key concepts and clarifies 'buzzwords'
- In-depth illustrated features covering major issues complement clear, concise entries designed for quick reference

Bob Cotton and **Richard Oliver** are independent media consultants. They are the authors of *Understanding Hypermedia 2.0,* also published by Phaidon

'An excellent illustrated dictionary dedicated to technobabble.' *(Observer)*
'Nothing else in print will give you such a good idea of multimedia's overall look and feel. Well-conceived and ably written, designed and produced.' *(Wired)*
'This beautifully illustrated paperback is just the thing to help you keep abreast of all those new terms. An essential guide.' *(Library Journal)*

General
Non-Fiction

Art

Photography

Collector's
Editions

Film

Architecture

250 × 250mm
9⁷⁄₈ × 9⁷⁄₈ inches
192 pp
206 col, 52 b&w illus.

Paperback
0 7148 3740 7

£ **24.95** UK
$ **39.95** US
€ **39.95** EUR
$ **59.95** CAN
$ **65.00** AUS

Understanding Hypermedia

Multimedia origins, internet futures
Bob Cotton and Richard Oliver

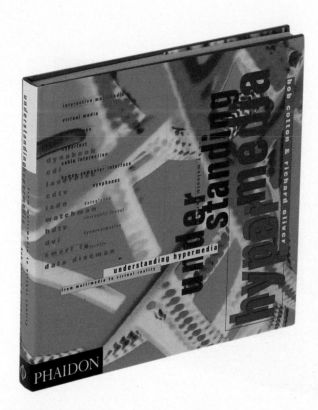

- A guide through the maze of existing and emerging technologies
- Addresses interactive video and multimedia, hypermedia, arcade games, high-band networks and virtual reality
- An invaluable source book for all those using electronic media
- Defines techniques and technologies, explains key concepts and clarifies 'buzzwords'
- In-depth illustrated features covering major issues complement clear, concise entries designed for quick reference

Bob Cotton and **Richard Oliver** are independent media consultants. They are the authors of *Understanding Hypermedia 2.0*, also published by Phaidon.

'An excellent illustrated dictionary dedicated to technobabble.' *(Observer)*
'Nothing else in print will give you such a good idea of multimedia's overall look and feel. Well-conceived and ably written, designed and produced.' *(Wired)*
'This beautifully illustrated paperback is just the thing to help you keep abreast of all those new terms. An essential guide.' *(Library Journal)*

Design

Fashion and
Contemporary
Culture

Decorative Arts

Music &
Performing Arts

Video

Index

250×250mm
9⅞×9⅞ inches
192 pp
206 col, 52 b&w illus.

Hardback
0 7148 3657 5

£ 24.95 UK
$ 39.95 US
€ 39.95 EUR
$ 59.95 CAN
$ 65.00 AUS

Understanding Hypermedia 2.0

Multimedia origins, internet futures
Bob Cotton and Richard Oliver

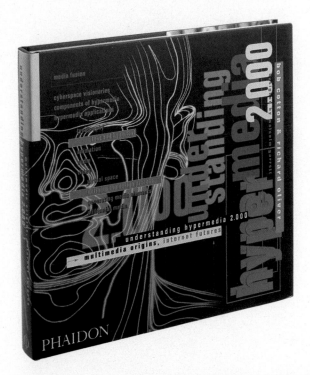

- A must-have guide to digital media, from websites and CD-Roms to satellite communications
- Gives practical information on design and production
- Includes an extensive glossary of technical terms
- Concludes with a look towards the digital future of the new millennium

Bob Cotton and **Richard Oliver** are independent media consultants. They are the authors of *The Cyberspace Lexicon*, also published by Phaidon

'A beautiful book whose words thankfully keep pace with its flowing kinetic images. An excellent introduction, perfect for students or anyone who wants to keep pace with a fast moving cultural field.' *(Guardian)*

Decorative Arts

General
Non-Fiction

Art

Photography

Collector's
Editions

Film

Architecture

290 × 250 mm
11³⁄₈ × 9⁷⁄₈ inches
240 pp
c.100 col, 200 b&w illus.

Hardback
0 7148 4030 0

£ **39.95** UK
$ **69.95** US
€ **69.95** EUR
$ **99.95** CAN
$ **119.95** AUS

Published October

Gustav Stickley

David Cathers

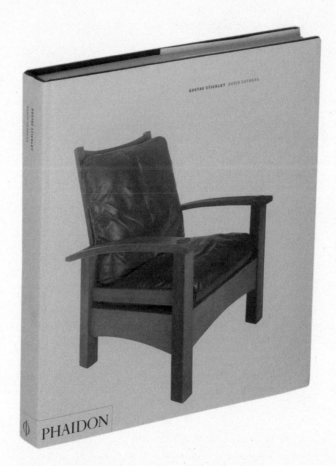

- First comprehensive monograph on Stickley (1858–1942), a pivotal figure of the American Arts & Crafts movement, covering all facets of his career
- Cathers is one of the most distinguished and widely consulted scholars on Stickley
- An indispensable research volume, includes chronology, bibliography and appendix on Stickley's significant collaborators
- Must-have book for collectors, auction houses, museums and students and scholars of the American Arts & Crafts movement and 20th-century decorative arts
- Generously illustrated with archival and specially commissioned photographs of furniture and objects, as well as people and places central to Stickley's life

David Cathers is a researcher, lecturer and writer on the Arts & Crafts movement, and a frequently consulted expert and lecturer on Gustav Stickley. He is the author of *Furniture of the American Arts and Crafts Movement* and *Stickley Style*, and editor of *Gustav Stickley's Craftsman Farms: A Pictorial History*

Design

Fashion & Contemporary Culture

Decorative Arts
NEW TITLE

Music & Performing Arts

Video

Index

The author's text is integrated with the illustrations in ten chapters, with the introduction and endmatter appearing on a tinted background. Illustrations include new colour photographs of Stickley furniture, period colour renderings of Stickley interiors and archival images including Craftsman houses, interiors, furniture, fabrics and lamps

General Non-Fiction
Art
Photography
Collector's Editions
Film
Architecture

290 × 250 mm
11³⁄₈ × 9⁷⁄₈ inches
240 pp
c.220 col, 30 b&w illus.

Hardback
0 7148 3957 4

£ **45.00** UK
$ **75.00** US
€ **75.00** EUR
$ **99.95** CAN
$ **129.95** AUS

Published October

Byzantium Rediscovered

J B Bullen

- This book charts the revival of the art and architecture of the Byzantine Empire that took place across Europe and North America in the 19th and early 20th centuries
- A highly decorative style, originally produced in Byzantium (modern day Istanbul), it inspired the works of designers, artists and patrons such as Louis Comfort Tiffany, Gustav Klimt, Edward Burne-Jones and Ludwig I of Bavaria
- This original and pioneering interdisciplinary study presents the first coherent account of the varied manifestations of Byzantinism in Germany, Austria, France, Britain and America
- Richly illustrated with Byzantine originals and the works they inspired
- Covering politics, religion and literature as well as the arts, this is an exemplary study in cultural history

J B Bullen is Professor of English at the University of Reading. He has a long-standing interest in interdisciplinary studies, and his books include *The Expressive Eye: Vision and Perception in the Work of Thomas Hardy* (1986), *The Myth of the Renaissance in Nineteenth-Century Writing* (1995) and *The Pre-Raphaelite Body: Fear and Desire in Painting, Poetry and Criticism* (1998)

Design

Fashion & Contemporary Culture

Decorative Arts NEW TITLE

Music & Performing Arts

Video

Index

great dome, which became established as a standard feature of Byzantine architecture, was mythologised to represent the arch of heaven itself, and the church interior not simply a microcosm, but a literal glimpse of heaven and divine order. Hagia Sophia had been the cathedral church of Constantinople for more than a thousand years when in 1453 it was taken by the Turks and turned into a mosque. In the succeeding centuries it was difficult to visit. Complicated systems or permits were in place to inhibit the curious, and in the first half of the nineteenth century the turbulent political climate discouraged visits to Constantinople. The story of the restoration of Hagia Sophia begins with the young Sultan Abdülmecid. The fabric of the building had been neglected and was in a very dilapidated state when in 1846 the Sultan decided to intervene. No substantial restoration had been done since the repairs of 1573 and none has taken place on this scale since. Earthquake tremors had caused superficial damage to the building, but many of the cracks and holes in the walls and domes had been generated by the slow processes of erosion and decay. A strange pair were commissioned to take on the task, the brothers Gaspare and Giuseppe Fossati – strange because they had no special training in the restoration of ancient buildings. But nonetheless they had made substantial careers for themselves in Constantinople. They came originally from Ticino in Switzerland, had studied architecture at the Brera Academy of Milan and were brought up in the austere neoclassical tradition of the period. Gaspare was more highly qualified than Giuseppe, who played a secondary role to his brother. In 1833 Gaspare had gone to St Petersburg to find work. Ever since its foundation by Peter the Great, St Petersburg had been a fruitful source of employment

30 | 31   Bavaria, Prussia and Austria: Friedrich Wilhelm IV of Prussia

14 (left) Hagia Sophia, Istanbul, 532–7
15 (opposite) Interior of Hagia Sophia, Istanbul, 532–7

137 Edward Burne-Jones, The Tree of Life, 1894, Mosaic, St Paul's American Church, Rome

Jacket image:
A G Walker, dome mosaic, Aghia Sophia, Moscow Road, London, 1874
Spreads from Byzantium Rediscovered showing (from top, left to right) Hagia Sophia, Istanbul, 532–7, exterior and interior; Edward Burne-Jones, The Tree of Life, 1894, mosaic, St Paul's American Church, Rome; Bertram Goodhue, St Bartholomew's, New York, 1915; Stanford White, Vanderbilt Portal, St Bartholomew's, New York, 1902; St-Gilles-du-Garde, France, c.1170

6 | Bertram Goodhue   The last decade of the nineteenth century and the first decade of the twentieth produced some important, if unusual, examples of building in North America that combined Byzantine and Romanesque. One of the most outstanding was Louis Sullivan's Transportation Building at the World's Fair (or Columbian Exposition) in Chicago. This was a huge cathedral-like structure with numerous arches containing every kind of conveyance from around the world, ranging from wagons and balloons to a model of the first railway to run between Manchester and Liverpool. This design went against the grain of the 'White City', the name by which the Exposition was known because it was built mainly in a severe Beaux-Arts style – clean, rational, centralized, classical and 'profane'. Instead, Sullivan's was a long rectangular construction, basilican in sectional form, with wide aisles flanking a central rectangular core that was illuminated by clerestory windows. Its clear allusion to Richardson and Romano-Byzantine building was confirmed by the grand entrance (fig. 224) consisting of a large, square block of richly detailed terracotta that framed a low-canted and deeply recessed arched doorway. This was named 'The Golden Doorway' on account of the reds, yellows and ochres of the coloured terracotta and the extensive use of gold leaf. Just as Tiffany had carried off many medals from this Exposition, so Sullivan's Transportation Building (much to the embarrassment of local architects) was awarded the gold medal of merit by the French government. As La Farge's St Matthew's Catholic Cathedral was nearing completion in Washington, D.C., the enigmatic choice of the Byzantine style for an Anglican church north of the border in Toronto was causing something of a stir. In 1907 the Building Committee of St Anne's decided to replace their small Gothic Revival church with a new one. A local architect, William Ford Howland, in conjunction with the Revd Lawrence Skey, drew up plans for a centralized building in the shape of a Greek cross, with a plain brick exterior and a central dome sixty feet high resting on pendentives. This was the first church in Canada to adopt the salient features of Byzantine architecture, yet paradoxically the congregation, which was

224 (opposite) Bertram Goodhue, St Bartholomew's, New York, 1915
225 (left) Portico, St-Gilles-du-Garde, c.1170
226 (above) Stanford White, Vanderbilt portal, St Bartholomew's, New York, 1902

General
Non-Fiction

Art

Photography

Collector's
Editions

Film

Architecture

290 × 250 mm
11³⁄₈ × 9⁷⁄₈ inches
240 pp
180 col, 63 b&w illus.

Paperback
07148 4329 6

£ 19.95 UK
$ 29.95 US
€ 29.95 EUR
$ 49.95 CAN
$ 59.95 AUS

Hardback
0 7148 2932 3

£ 39.95 UK
$ 59.95 US
€ 65.00 EUR
$ 89.95 CAN
$ 120.00 AUS

Paperback published
July

The Synagogue

Harold A Meek

- An engaging exploration of synagogues, their history and decoration, representing an illuminating record of the cultural and artistic history of the Jewish people
- Explores the symbolic and practical significance of the synagogue as a focal point for the community as well as a spiritual centre
- Meek examines the fascinating story of the building central to every Jewish community from its origins in the Tabernacle, through the exuberant Venetian synagogues of the Renaissance, to the often stark simplicity of modern buildings
- A spirited narrative shows the ways in which a vast array of cultural influences have merged to produce a rich and coherent heritage in the fields of architecture and decoration

Harold A Meek read architecture at Manchester University. After serving 12 years as Ancient Monuments Architect to the Government in Northern Ireland, Dr Meek lectured on the history of architecture at Queen's University, Belfast

Design

Fashion &
Contemporary
Culture

Decorative Arts
NEW IN PAPERBACK

Music &
Performing Arts

Video

Index

Spreads from The
Synagogue showing
(from top, left
to right)
Silver Torah case by
Maurice Mayer, Paris,
1860; silver Chanukah
lamp from Brody,
Galicia, 1787; Scola
Italiana, Padua,
founded 1548, interior
and exterior; ark and
detail of ark curtain;
the bimah in the Scola
Spagnola, Venice,
founded 1555,
with detail

General
Non-Fiction

Art

Photography

Collector's
Editions

Film

Architecture

290 × 250 mm
11³⁄₈ × 9⁷⁄₈ inches
240 pp
224 col, 64 b&w illus.

Hardback
0 7148 3000 3

£ **39.95** UK
$ **69.95** US
€ **69.95** EUR
$ **98.00** CAN
$ **120.00** AUS

The Aesthetic Movement

Lionel Lambourne

- An examination of the Aesthetic Movement, which touched every sphere of the fine and decorative arts in late 19th-century England
- Charts the transformation of architecture and interior design, as heavy Victorian forms were replaced by lighter, fresher, Japanese-inspired shapes
- Also covers the graphic arts, where innovative methods and a new approach to form revitalized illustration and design
- Examines how the movement – personified by such colourful figures as James McNeill Whistler, Oscar Wilde and Aubrey Beardsley – was held together by the coherence of its philosophy and its belief in elegance and richness

Lionel Lambourne, OBE, was Head of Paintings at the Victoria and Albert Museum from 1986 to 1993. His publications include *Utopian Craftsmen* (1980) and *Victorian Painting*, also published by Phaidon

'A volume to be read for its witty prose as well as to feast on with the eyes. A delightful book about artists who placed beauty above all.' *(New York Times)*

Design

Fashion & Contemporary Culture

Decorative Arts

Music & Performing Arts

Video

Index

280 × 215 mm
11 × 8½ inches
208 pp
64 col, 146 b&w illus.

Paperback
0 7148 2952 8

£ **19.95** UK
$ **29.95** US
€ **35.00** EUR
$ **49.95** CAN
$ **59.95** AUS

Christopher Dresser

A pioneer of modern design
Widar Halén

- The first book published on the life and career of Christopher Dresser (1834–1904), a pioneer of modern design
- Arguably Europe's first industrial designer, Dresser enthusiastically promoted machines and mass-production in his work and through his writings
- Documents Dresser's entire creative output – works in ceramics, glass, metal, furniture, carpets, textiles and wallpapers, which are now widely collected
- Explores the influence that Dresser's designs have had on modern taste, with their bold shapes, angular geometry and rich colours

Widar Halén is a Norwegian collector and scholar who graduated from the Universities of Oslo and Oxford. He studied archaeology and 19th-century design history

'This is the most thorough study to date on Dresser. The chronological recordings of Dresser's professional activities will prove of lasting worth and the illustrations are simply superb.'
(*Journal of Design History*)

General Non-Fiction

Art

Photography

Collector's Editions

Film

Architecture

246 × 189 mm
9²₃ × 7¹₂ inches
326 pp
8 col, 160 b&w illus.

Paperback
0 7148 2954 4

£ 17.95 UK
$ 24.95 US
€ 29.95 EUR
$ 39.95 CAN
$ 49.95 AUS

Antique Maps

3rd edition
Carl Moreland and David Bannister

- Firmly established as both a standard reference work and a collectors' guide to old maps
- Provides a historical background to the subject, and offers practical advice on starting and maintaining a collection
- A biographical section lists major map makers between 1450 and 1850, with key dates and works
- Ideal for experts and novices alike

Carl Moreland was a Fellow of the Royal Geographical Society
David Bannister has been a dealer in antique maps, prints and atlases for many years. He regularly lectures on the subject and has made a number of television appearances and radio broadcasts

'An absolute winner of a book. An excellent general introduction to antique map collecting.'
(*Books, Maps and Prints*)

Design

Fashion & Contemporary Culture

Decorative Arts

Music & Performing Arts

Video

Index

290 × 250 mm
11³⁄₈ × 9⁷⁄₈ inches
240 pp
240 col, 5 b&w illus.

Paperback
0 7148 3862 4

£ 22.95 UK
$ 35.00 US
€ 39.95 EUR
$ 49.95 CAN
$ 59.95 AUS

Tapestry

Barty Phillips

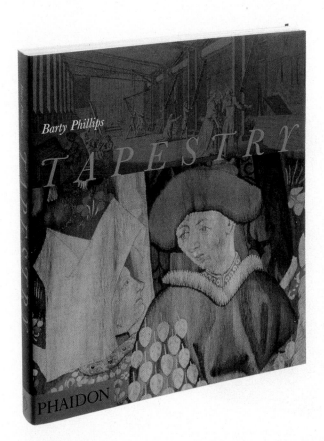

- Traces the history of tapestry, from the earliest examples to modern times
- Illustrations reveal the beauty of tapestries in detail and show them in the settings in which they are used
- Discusses different forms of tapestry associated with nomadic life and the developed world, as a practical craft and art form
- Offers advice on where to see the most interesting collections, how to buy antique or modern tapestry and how to care for it

Barty Phillips is the author of many books on gardening and the home. She was the Home Editor and Design Correspondent for the *Observer* for many years and has also written for the *Daily Telegraph, The Times* and the *New York Times*, among others

'A stunning showcase.' *(Publishers Weekly)*
'Sumptuous illustrations and an in-depth history of a visually stunning, eminently tactile art form.' *(Booklist)*
'*Tapestry* ... is probably one of the finest books ever published on this art form.'
(Sunday Star-Ledger)

General
Non-Fiction

Art

Photography

Collector's
Editions

Film

Architecture

250 × 290 mm
9⁷⁸ × 11³⁸ inches
224 pp
169 col illus.

Paperback
0 7148 3863 2

£ **19.95** UK
$ **29.95** US
€ **35.00** EUR
$ **45.00** CAN
$ **55.00** AUS

Dashboards

David Holland

- Celebrates the allure of the classic car through one of its quintessential features: the dashboard
- Features a cavalcade of design elements from some of the most exceptional cars ever made, from the engine-turned metal of the 1937 Cord to the sporting pedigree of the 1953 Aston Martin DB 2/4
- Expert photography of more than fifty cars seduces the reader with a combination of luxury and innovation

David Holland's lifelong passion for the motor vehicle became a full-time hobby upon his retirement from the business world. He combines restoration and research with active participation in historic racing and contact with collectors and enthusiasts all over the world

'An inspired edition.' *(Classic and Sportscar)*
'The book to end all books for anyone interested in classic vehicles.' *(Limited Edition)*
'Soft porn for hard petrolheads.' *(Independent on Sunday)*
'A delightful companion.' *(Los Angeles Times)*

290 × 250 mm
11³⁄₈ × 9⁷⁄₈ inches
240 pp
100 col, 200 b&w illus.
s fold-out cut-away guide
to the ship's interiors

Paperback
0 7148 4101 3

£ **19.95** UK
$ **29.95** US
€ **35.00** EUR
$ **45.00** CAN
$ **55.00** AUS

Hardback
0 7148 2891 2

£ **35.00** UK
$ **55.00** US
€ **59.95** EUR
$ **85.00** CAN
$ **95.00** AUS

Queen Mary

James Steele

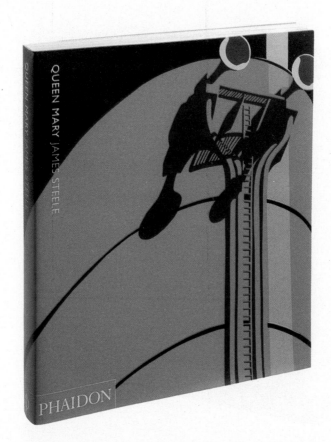

- The most complete record available of the world's largest and fastest ocean liner
- Recounts the history of the *Queen Mary*, from her maiden voyage in 1936 as a luxury passenger liner to her military services to her final journey to Long Beach, California, in 1967
- Showcases the aesthetic sophistication of sleek lines, Art Deco interiors and exquisite detailing that encapsulate the spirit of the era
- Illustrated with specially commissioned colour photographs and much previously unpublished archival material, including detailed drawings and plans

James Steele is an architectural writer and historian based in Los Angeles, close to where the Queen Mary is currently moored. His books include *Architecture Today* and *Los Angeles Architecture*, both published by Phaidon

'The wish book of the year.' *(Time)*
'Wonderfully detailed. Scrupulous research.' *(New York Times)*
'Anyone who has ever wondered if architecture floats will be convinced by this beautiful, fact-filled book about the last and grandest architecture ever to sail the bounding main. With Steele's intense research, we almost feel like we're there.' *(AIA Jury)*

General Non-Fiction

Art

Photography

Collector's Editions

Film

Architecture

290 × 250 mm
9⁷⁸ × 11³⁸ inches
240 pp
223 col illus.

Hardback
0 7148 2890 4

£ **29.95** UK
$ **49.95** US
€ **49.95** EUR
$ **75.00** CAN
$ **89.95** AUS

London Architecture

With text by Ben Weinreb and photographs by Matthew Weinreb

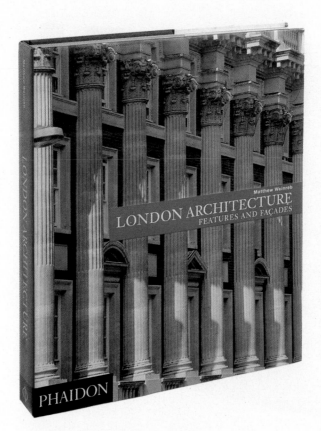

- **A powerful celebration of Paris's buildings and their features, punctuated by anecdotes from centuries of Parisian architectural history**
- **Extraordinary photography provides a refreshingly different approach, throwing a new and startling light on even the most familiar sites**
- **Also available in a handy, portable miniature format**

Matthew Weinreb, a native Londoner and prize-winning photographer, specializes in architecture, interiors and cityspaces. He has received commissions from many of the leading design and architectural firms, and was the first recipient of the prestigious 'Tectonic Award' for the best work in architectural photography

Ben Weinreb, father to photographer Matthew Weinreb, is co-author of *The Encyclopedia of London* and owns an internationally renowned architectural bookshop next door to the British Museum

'By concentrating on architecture, not people, Matthew Weinreb produces a city crackling with formal energy … the photographs have a quality that is both rigorous and emphatic.' *(New York Times)*

Design
Fashion & Contemporary Culture
Decorative Arts
Music & Performing Arts
Video
Index

Each volume
156 × 136 mm
6¹₄ × 5¹₂ inches
240 pp
223 col illus.

Paperback
London 0 7148 3859 4
Paris 0 7148 3455 6

Each volume
£ 6.95 UK
$ 9.95 US
€ 9.95 EUR
$ 14.95 CAN
$ 16.95 AUS

Point of Sale
10-copy counterpack
0 7148 5112 4

London: Portrait of a City
Paris: Portrait of a City

With texts by Ben Weinreb and Fiona Biddulph, and photographs by Matthew Weinreb

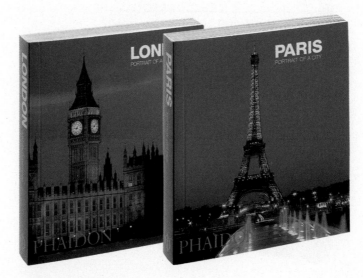

- Two pocket-sized books that celebrate the hidden secrets, architectural details and ornaments of two of the world's most visited cities
- Specially commissioned photography provides a refreshingly different approach, throwing light on even the most familiar sites
- With series of essays that explore the distinctive characteristics of both cities through their diverse and beautiful architectural features and material

Ben Weinreb, father to photographer Matthew Weinreb, is co-author of *The Encyclopedia of London* and owns an internationally renowned architectural bookshop next door to the British Museum
Fiona Biddulph is a writer specializing in art, architecture and interior design
Matthew Weinreb, a native Londoner and prize-winning photographer, specializes in architecture, interiors and cityspaces. He has received commissions from many of the leading design and architectural firms, and was the first recipient of the prestigious 'Tectonic Award' for the best work in architectural photography

General Non-Fiction

Art

Photography

Collector's Editions

Film

Architecture

245 × 210 mm
9⅝ × 8¼ inches
352 pp
c.200 col, c.50 b&w illus.

Hardback
0 7148 3774 1

£ **24.95** UK
$ **39.95** US
€ **39.95** EUR
$ **59.95** CAN
$ **69.95** AUS

The Book

A History of the Bible
Christopher de Hamel

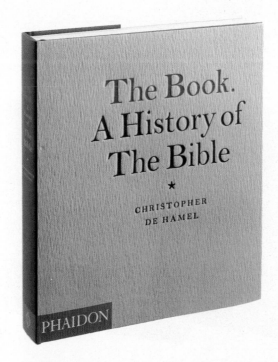

- This important volume tells for the first time the story of the Bible as a book, tracing its publication in endless forms and numerous languages from its origins to the present day
- Covers the original languages of Hebrew and Greek, the Latin Vulgate translation of Saint Jerome, the manuscript Bibles of the Middle Ages, the first printing and the translations of Protestant reformers, right up to the flood of new versions in the 20th century
- Concludes with the modern discovery of papyrus fragments and Dead Sea Scrolls which have cast important new light on the origins of the Bible
- With more than 200 rich, fascinating and varied illustrations of Bibles from all times and places

Christopher de Hamel is Fellow Librarian of Corpus Christi College, Cambridge. For many years he was head of the Western Manuscripts department at Sotheby's in London. His *History of Illuminated Manuscripts*, also published by Phaidon, has become a standard work

'Lively, fascinating and eminently readable.' *(History Today)*

Design

Fashion &
Contemporary
Culture

Decorative Arts
The Art
of the Book

Music &
Performing Arts

Video

Index

290 × 250 mm
11³⁄₈ × 9⁷⁄₈ inches
272 pp
175 col, 70 b&w illus.

Paperback
0 7148 3452 1

£ **22.95** UK
$ **35.00** US
€ **39.95** EUR
$ **49.95** CAN
$ **59.95** AUS

A History of Illuminated Manuscripts

2nd edition
Christopher de Hamel

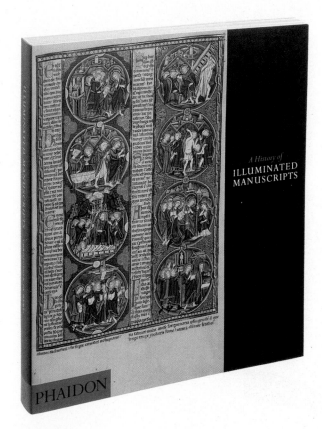

- **The standard work on the subject of the making of books, from the late Roman Empire to the Renaissance**
- **Includes some of Western civilization's most valued treasures, from the earliest monastic Gospel Books to the most lavish Books of Hours**
- **Revised and updated text and redesigned with a wealth of new colour illustrations**

Christopher de Hamel is Fellow Librarian of Corpus Christi College, Cambridge. For many years he was head of the Western Manuscripts department at Sotheby's in London. He is author of *The Book: A History of the Bible*, also published by Phaidon

'It is no mere history, but an original, lively and richly illustrated commentary.' *(Times Literary Supplement)*
'A wonderful introduction to handwritten books from the Dark Ages to the invention of printing in the 15th century.' *(Houston Chronicle)*
'Lavish, beautiful and sweeping look at the beginning of the printed word.' *(Graphic Arts Monthly)*

General
Non-Fiction

Art

Photography

Collector's
Editions

Film

Architecture

280 × 215 mm
11 × 8½ inches
80 pp
28 col, 42 b&w illus.

Paperback
0 7148 2468 2

£ **9.95** UK
$ **14.95** US
€ **16.95** EUR
$ **24.95** CAN
$ **29.95** AUS

The Illuminated Manuscript

Janet Backhouse

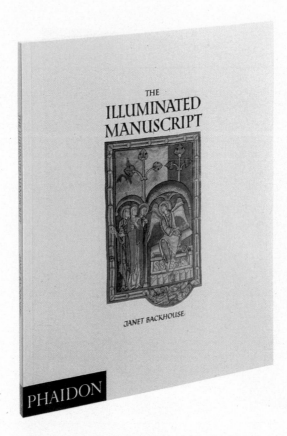

- A selection of outstanding examples from the British Library's world-renowned collection of illuminated manuscripts
- Covers more than 800 years of medieval book production
- Begins with the Lindisfarne Gospels and continues with a representative cross-section that reveals the remarkable variety of medieval manuscripts
- Full colour reproductions represent both superb examples of early book illustration and revealing commentary on medieval life and attitudes

Janet Backhouse was formerly Assistant Keeper in the Department of Manuscripts at the British Library. She is the author of *The Lindisfarne Gospels*, also published by Phaidon

Design

Fashion & Contemporary Culture

Decorative Arts The Art of the Book

Music & Performing Arts

Video

Index

280 × 215 mm
11 × 8½ inches
96 pp
31 col, 36 b&w illus.

Paperback
0 7148 2461 5

£ 9.95 UK
$ 14.95 US
€ 16.95 EUR
$ 24.95 CAN
$ 27.95 AUS

The Lindisfarne Gospels

Janet Backhouse

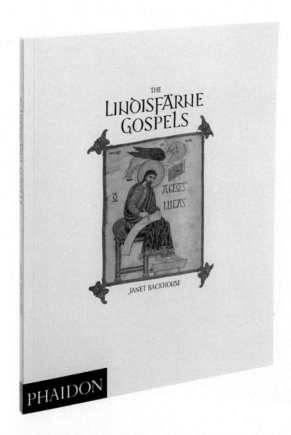

- The first book to make the Lindisfarne Gospels – one of the world's masterpieces of book painting – available to a wider public
- This precious relic of early Christianity in England was produced at the end of the 7th century in honour of Saint Cuthbert, and is one of Britain's greatest treasures
- Important illuminated pages are reproduced in colour from a new and accurate set of photographs
- Discusses the process by which the manuscript was made, and relates it to earlier and contemporary works of art

Janet Backhouse was formerly Assistant Keeper in the Department of Manuscripts at the British Library. She is the author of *The Illuminated Manuscript*, also published by Phaidon

General
Non-Fiction

Art

Photography

Collector's
Editions

Film

Architecture

240 × 181 mm
9³⁄₈ × 7¹⁄₈ inches
288 pp
8 col, 215 b&w illus.

Paperback
0 7148 2593 X

£ **16.95** UK
$ **24.95** US
€ **29.95** EUR
$ **35.00** CAN
$ **49.95** AUS

The Chinese Potter

A practical history of Chinese ceramics
Margaret Medley

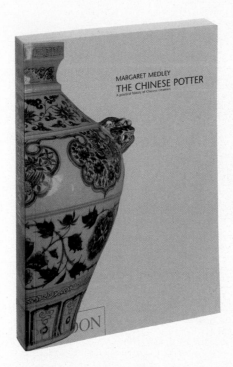

- A classic, groundbreaking study of the longest and most highly developed ceramic tradition in the world
- Encompasses early Neolithic earthenwares, the finely glazed stoneware pieces of the Song period, the years of Imperial patronage and export ware for the new markets of the West
- Makes full use of archaeological reports to show how differing geographical areas, materials and technology all shaped the evolution of Chinese ceramics

Margaret Medley was formerly Curator of the Percival David Foundation of Chinese Art, University of London, and a distinguished authority on Chinese ceramics

'A brilliant synthesis of a complex field of studies … it displays a wonderful mastery of the subject.' *(The Times)*
'*The Chinese Potter* remains the best introduction to Chinese ceramics for students and collectors alike. It is one of those rare scholarly publications which is not only well-ordered and concise, but also very readable.' (Rosemary Scott, Christie's)

Design

Fashion & Contemporary Culture

Decorative Arts
Pottery & Ceramics

Music & Performing Arts

Video

Index

290 × 250 mm
11³⁄₈ × 9⁷⁄₈ inches
240 pp
219 col, 100 b&w illus.

Hardback
0 7148 3202 2

£ 39.95 UK
$ 59.95 US
€ 65.00 EUR
$ 89.95 CAN
$ 99.95 AUS

The Potter's Art

A complete history of pottery in Britain
Garth Clark

- The first comprehensive overview of British pottery
- Traces its history from the rudimentary pots of the Middle Ages to the intellectually ambitious art of today's studio potters
- Examines the work of the artist-potters William De Morgan and the Martin brothers, and the studio potters Bernard Leach and Lucie Rie
- Focuses particularly on the human angle, describing the working conditions, lifestyles and characters of the potters

Garth Clark is the author of eight books and more than 800 essays, reviews and articles on modern ceramics. He founded the Institute for Ceramic History in 1979

'The strength of the book is its blend of technical information and stylistic developments.' (*Crafts*)
'Compulsively readable.' (*RSA Journal*)

General
Non-Fiction

Art

Photography

Collector's
Editions

Film

Architecture

280 × 240 mm
11 × 9¹₂ inches
288 pp
120 col, 480 b&w illus.

Paperback
0 7148 2948 X

£ **24.95** UK
$ **39.95** US
€ **39.95** EUR
$ **59.95** CAN
$ **69.95** AUS

Studio Pottery

Oliver Watson

- **Definitive reference work on one of the most significant movements in 20th-century British art – the catalogue of the national collection of British studio pottery held by the Victoria & Albert Museum in London**
- **Features more than 700 pieces dating from the beginnings of the movement to the 1980s**
- **Organized in the form of a biographical dictionary, with a substantial introduction**

Oliver Watson was formerly Curator of Ceramics at the Victoria & Albert Museum

'Page after page of beautiful photographs of pots. Quality you will find in abundance in this truly excellent book.' *(Artbook News)*

Design

Fashion & Contemporary Culture

Decorative Arts Pottery & Ceramics

Music & Performing Arts

Video

Index

290 × 250 mm
11³⁄₈ × 9⁷⁄₈ inches
240 pp
300 col, 60 b&w illus.

Paperback
0 7148 3979 5

£ **22.95** UK
$ **35.00** US
€ **39.95** EUR
$ **49.95** CAN
$ **59.95** AUS

The Decorative Tile in Architecture and Interiors

Tony Herbert and Kathryn Huggins

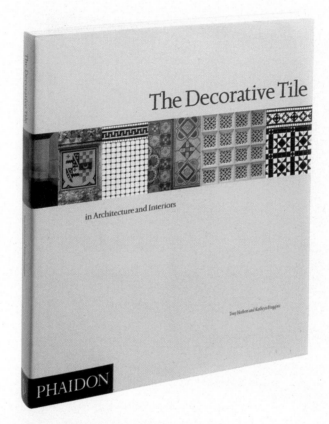

- An in-depth study of the use of ceramic tile – one of the oldest and most universally employed forms of architectural decoration
- Explores the innovative ways in which designers, architects and builders have put ceramic tile to use over the last 100 years
- Highlights the way in which the Industrial Revolution transformed the use of ceramic tile via new production methods and an expanded market for decorative building materials
- Illustrations depict examples from around the world, and include specially commissioned pictures of previously unpublished tile schemes

Tony Herbert is a writer and lecturer, and Chairman of the Tiles and Architectural Ceramics Society
Kathryn Huggins was responsible for the tile collections and displays at the Ironbridge Gorge Museum

'A beautifully presented book that expertly charts the variety of techniques used by designers across the world.' *(Homes and Gardens)*
'Sumptuously produced and crammed with impeccably researched information.' *(Country Living)*

General
Non-Fiction

Art

Photography

Collector's
Editions

Film

Architecture

280 × 240 mm
11 × 9½ inches
192 pp
90 col, 120 b&w illus.

Paperback
0 7148 3468 8

£ **19.95** UK
$ **29.95** US
€ **35.00** EUR
$ **45.00** CAN
$ **55.00** AUS

Hardback
0 7148 2611 1

£ **29.95** UK
$ **49.95** US
€ **49.95** EUR
$ **75.00** CAN
$ **75.00** AUS

The History of English Interiors

Text by Alan and Ann Gore, photographs by Peter Aprahamian

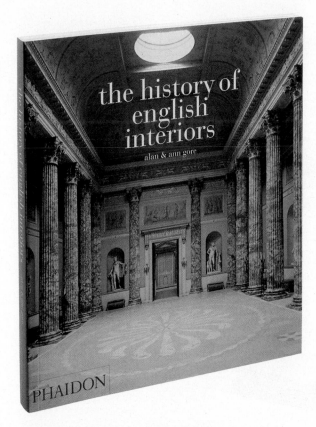

- The first complete history of English interior decoration
- Details and discusses all modes and periods, starting with the Normans and continuing through Gothic, Renaissance, Baroque, Rococo and Palladian styles
- Profiles English architects and designers from Inigo Jones in the 17th century to John Fowler in the 20th
- Featuring specially commissioned photographs of England's most remarkable interiors, many of which have never been published before, along with a list of houses open to the public

Alan Gore trained at the Architectural Association. From 1950 until 1977 he was a partner in the architectural practice of Gore, Gibbert and Saunders
Ann Gore also trained at the Architectural Association. Since 1980 she has lectured extensively in America on English social history and the decorative arts

'Few books on the subject of decoration in the home come with such authority.'
(House & Garden)

Design

Fashion &
Contemporary
Culture

Decorative Arts
Interiors

Music &
Performing Arts

Video

Index

280 × 240 mm
11 × 9¹₂ inches
160 pp
126 col illus.

Paperback
0 7148 2947 1

£ **17.95** UK
$ **24.95** US
€ **29.95** EUR
$ **39.95** CAN
$ **49.95** AUS

Grand Illusions

Contemporary interior murals
Caroline Cass, photographs by Tom Leighton

- A thorough study of mural and *trompe l'oeil* painting
- Examines murals from various periods and with various purposes, from the politically inspired public paintings of the 1930s to the corporate and commercial murals of today
- Includes work by more than 40 of the best contemporary artists in the field from England and America
- Most of the examples illustrated are situated in private houses or buildings, and thus are presented here for the first time to a wider audience

Caroline Cass is a painter and a muralist. She has worked in Washington DC and London

'Superb photos, with a lively, comprehensive text, illuminate what has hitherto been an almost secret subject.' *(Art Review)*

General
Non-Fiction

Art

Photography

Collector's
Editions

Film

Architecture

290 × 250 mm
11³⁄₈ × 9⁷⁄₈ inches
240 pp
170 col, 68 b&w illus.

Paperback
0 7148 4120 X

£ **22.95** UK
$ **35.00** US
€ **39.95** EUR
$ **49.95** CAN
$ **59.95** AUS

Elizabethan and Jacobean Style

Timothy Mowl

- A tour through the homes of the Elizabethan and Jacobean eras, and a detailed analysis of their architecture and interiors
- Places these buildings in the context of the rich social and cultural life of their period, between the accession of Elizabeth I in 1558 and James I's death in 1625
- Author argues controversially that the style represents the last flowering of a native genius that was eventually stifled by classicism
- Specially commissioned photography showcases the splendour of this particularly English form, with its exuberance and enduring romantic appeal

Timothy Mowl is an architectural historian and Lecturer in the History of Art at the University of Bristol

'A handsome introduction to the world of Jacobean chic.' *(Sunday Telegraph)*
'It is a marvellous book for two reasons. First, Mowl is that rare thing, an architectural historian who can write. Second, he is a man with a new thesis who challenges the orthodox view.' *(Financial Times)*

Design

Fashion &
Contemporary
Culture

Decorative Arts
Interiors

Music &
Performing Arts

Video

Index

290 × 250 mm
11³⁄₈ × 9⁷⁄₈ inches
240 pp
209 col, 13 b&w illus.

Paperback
0 7148 3453 X

£ **22.95** UK
$ **35.00** US
€ **39.95** EUR
$ **49.95** CAN
$ **59.95** AUS

Award

Winner History
category International
Architecture Book Awards
American Institute
of Architects, 1993

Adam Style

Steven Parissien

- A complete history of Adam style, a form of domestic Neo-Classicism named after the outstanding architect of the mid-Georgian era (1750–1785), Robert Adam
- Takes the reader through typical houses of the time in England and America, showing the way in which they were designed, decorated and furnished
- Winner in the History category, American Institute of Architects International Architecture Book Awards, 1993

Steven Parissien is the Director of Sotheby's Institute, London, and has previously worked for the Georgian Group and English Heritage. He is the author of *Regency Style*, *Palladian Style* and *Station to Station*, all published by Phaidon

'This volume, through a wonderful variety of graphic and photographic materials, examines the typical Adam-style house from its outer shell through the plasterwork and fittings, colours, furnishings and textiles.' *(AIA Jury)*
'A beautiful, highly original book from Phaidon Press – a groundbreaking book.' *(Apollo)*

General
Non-Fiction

Art

Photography

Collector's
Editions

Film

Architecture

290 × 250 mm
11³⁄₈ × 9⁷⁄₈ inches
240 pp
181 col, 77 b&w illus.

Paperback
0 7148 4026 2

£ **22.95** UK
$ **35.00** US
€ **39.95** EUR
$ **49.95** CAN
$ **59.95** AUS

Palladian Style

Steven Parissien

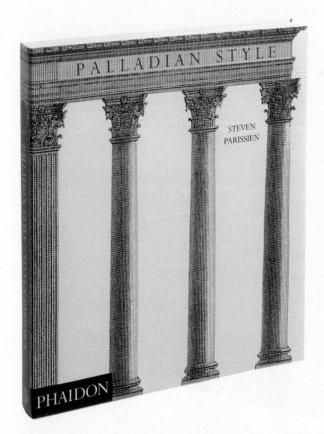

- A thorough examination of the Palladian style, inspired by the Classicism of the great Italian architect Palladio
- Shows how designers such as Burlington, Campbell and Kent adapted Palladio's ideas to the English climate and created a new style for town and country houses
- Discusses building materials, fixtures and fittings, as well as period colours and coverings
- Follows the style as it spread to the average home through pattern-books and became a major influence in the colonies of North America

Steven Parissien is the Director of Sotheby's Institute, London, and has previously worked for the Georgian Group and English Heritage. He is the author of *Regency Style*, *Adam Style* and *Station to Station*, all published by Phaidon

'Prettily illustrated, elegant and spacious in layout, *Palladian Style* is as much for reading as for reference.' (Brian Sewell, *Daily Telegraph*)

Design

Fashion &
Contemporary
Culture

Decorative Arts
Interiors

Music &
Performing Arts

Video

Index

290 × 250 mm
11⅜ × 9⅞ inches
240 pp
205 col, 74 b&w illus.

Paperback
0 7148 3454 8

£ **22.95** UK
$ **35.00** US
€ **39.95** EUR
$ **49.95** CAN
$ **59.95** AUS

Regency Style

Steven Parissien

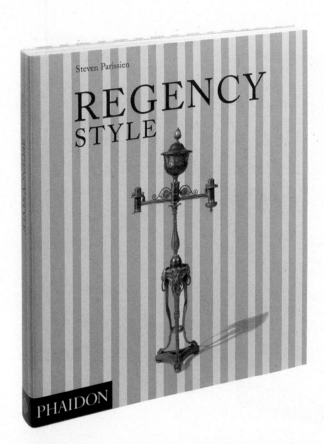

- A comprehensive survey of the Regency period (1780–1837), when the English fascination with interior decoration first emerged as a popular occupation for both the wealthy and the average house owner
- Traces the evolution of the eclectic, quintessentially British style, as it combined influences of the antique and the exotic with the technological innovations of the day
- Examines the Regency house of England and America from the outside in, from its architectural shell and its windows, doors and ironwork to the decoration, colour schemes and furniture for each room
- Brings to life the work of such key designers as John Soane and Thomas Hope

Steven Parissien is the Director of Sotheby's Institute, London, and has previously worked for the Georgian Group and English Heritage. He is the author of *Adam Style, Palladian Style* and *Station to Station,* all published by Phaidon

'An outstanding work of reference and beauty.' *(Interiors Magazine)*
'The two [along with *Adam Style*] most stunning art books of the year.' (Sir Roy Strong, *Sunday Express)*

General
Non-Fiction

Art

Photography

Collector's
Editions

Film

Architecture

290 × 250 mm
11³⁄₈ × 9⁷⁄₈ inches
240 pp
236 col, 44 b&w illus.

Paperback
0 7148 3631 1

£ **22.95** UK
$ **35.00** US
€ **39.95** EUR
$ **49.95** CAN
$ **59.95** AUS

Award

Winner of the Sir Banister
Fletcher award for
Excellence in Architectural
Book Publishing, 1996

Gothic Revival

Megan Aldrich

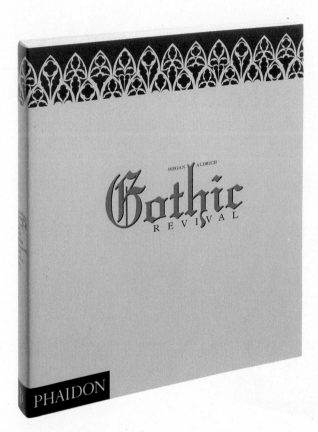

- Traces the story of the Gothic Revival from the 'Gothick' experiments of the 18th century to its ultimate embodiment in the Houses of Parliament
- Concentrates on the domestic forms of the style, from its use in country houses to its influence on the city streets of Europe and America
- Includes the work of great designers such as Pugin, Wyatt, Viollet-le-Duc and Burges
- With many illustrations of architecture, textiles, wallpapers and furnishings to demonstrate the style's worldwide influence

Megan Aldrich is a senior tutor at Sotheby's Educational Studies in London

'A luscious, in fact a totally gorgeous book, which all those who are interested in the Gothic style have a duty to possess. The pages drip with the most superb illustrations.' *(Udolpho)*

Design

Fashion & Contemporary Culture

Decorative Arts
Interiors

Music & Performing Arts

Video

Index

290 × 250 mm
11³⁄₈ × 9⁷⁄₈ inches
240 pp
175 col, 50 b&w illus.

Paperback
0 7148 3836 5

£ 22.95 UK
$ 35.00 US
€ 39.95 EUR
$ 49.95 CAN
$ 59.95 AUS

Chinoiserie

Dawn Jacobson

- A thorough examination of the Chinoiserie style – the timeless taste for decoration and architecture based on Chinese design
- Offers a window onto the exoticism of the East, and the way in which it has blended with Western sensibilities for hundreds of years
- Illustrates the influence of Chinoiserie on centuries' worth of applied arts, including gardens, interiors, furniture, tableware and tapestries

Dawn Jacobson is a South African-born writer and lecturer on the fine and decorative arts

'This is a very thorough, apt, entertaining and beautifully illustrated survey of the surprising ways in which East meets West.' *(Art Quarterly)*
'Dawn Jacobson's *Chinoiserie* [is] a lavishly illustrated but intellectually serious study of one of the most intriguing of all artistic colonizations.' *(The Times)*
'The author's style is in tune with her delightful subject.' *(World of Interiors)*

General
Non-Fiction

Art

Photography

Collector's
Editions

Film

Architecture

290 × 250 mm
11³⁄₈ × 9⁷⁄₈ inches
240 pp
289 col, 24 b&w illus.

Paperback
0 7148 3861 6

£ **22.95** UK
$ **35.00** US
€ **39.95** EUR
$ **49.95** CAN
$ **59.95** AUS

Moorish Style

Miles Danby

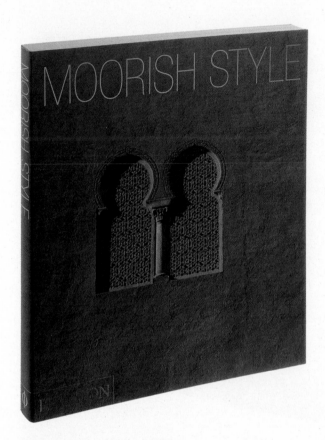

- The first book to examine Moorish style – from its origins in Islamic art and architecture to its influence on present-day buildings, interiors and gardens
- Discusses the architectural elements commonly found in mosques and palaces from Mogul India to Ottoman Turkey to Moorish Spain, and places them alongside contemporary examples from the Western world ranging from private homes to cinemas to synagogues
- Offers a complete study of the Alhambra in Granada, the finest surviving example of the style
- Illustrations show how the arts of the Islamic world provided inspiration for painters from Delacroix to Matisse

Miles Danby, Professor Emeritus of Architecture at Newcastle University, is an architect and lecturer with a special interest in the buildings of developing countries

'Every spread is a delight.' *(Los Angeles Times)*
'The presentation is outstanding … with much material that is little known and a great wealth of evocative colour photographs.' *(Archis)*

Design

Fashion & Contemporary Culture

Decorative Arts
Interiors

Music & Performing Arts

Video

Index

280 × 240 mm
11 × 9½ inches
232 pp
100 col, 80 b&w illus.

Paperback
0 7148 3469 6

£ **22.95** UK
$ **35.00** US
€ **39.95** EUR
$ **49.95** CAN
$ **59.95** AUS

Arts & Crafts Style

Isabelle Anscombe

- Surveys the Arts & Crafts movement of the 1870s and 1880s in Europe and North America
- Captures the essence of the movement in its search for a return to simplicity, quiet beauty and honesty of construction
- Includes Arts & Crafts textiles, furniture, ceramics and metalwork
- Features profiles of individual designers, including William Morris, Gustav Stickley, Frank Lloyd Wright, Christopher Dresser and their contemporaries

Isabelle Anscombe is an independent writer and journalist

'A handsomely illustrated survey including profiles of individual designers.' *(Homes and Gardens)*
'By the standards of today's books it is both useful and beautiful.' *(Crafts)*

General Non-Fiction

Art

Photography

Collector's Editions

Film

Architecture

290 × 250 mm
11³⁄₈ × 9⁷⁄₈ inches
240 pp
157 col, 55 b&w illus.

Paperback
0 7148 4328 8

£ **19.95** UK
$ **29.95** US
€ **35.00** EUR
$ **49.95** CAN
$ **59.95** AUS

Hardback
0 7148 2884 X

£ **39.95** UK
$ **69.95** US
€ **69.95** EUR
$ **98.00** CAN
$ **120.00** AUS

Art Deco Style

Bevis Hillier and Stephen Escritt

- The first book to explore Art Deco's pervasive influence in all areas of life
- Charts the worldwide manifestations of Art Deco, showing how it became the dominant style in architecture and design of the 1920s and 1930s
- Characterized by geometric shapes, stylized natural forms and the use of luxurious materials, Art Deco was inspired by sources as diverse as ancient Egypt and the Ballets Russes
- Illustrated with examples from around the world, from intricate jewellery to letterboxes and lampposts to landmark buildings

Bevis Hillier is the author of more than 20 books, including *Art Deco: A Design Handbook*, *The Style of the Century* and *The World of Art Deco*
Stephen Escritt is a specialist in 19th- and 20th-century decorative arts. A regular contributor to arts journals, he is author of *Art Nouveau* in Phaidon's Arts & Ideas series

'This richly illustrated book is the most comprehensive and wide-ranging study of the movement to date – a must for all deco-philes.' *(Homes & Gardens)*
'This splendid book, which combines wit with erudition, is destined to become the bible for Art Deco enthusiasts.' *(Birmingham Post)*

Design

Fashion &
Contemporary
Culture

Decorative Arts
Interiors

Music &
Performing Arts

Video

Index

290 × 250 mm
11³⁄₈ × 9⁷⁄₈ inches
240 pp
162 col, 120 duotone and
b&w illus.

Paperback
0 7148 3860 8

£ 22.95 UK
$ 35.00 US
€ 39.95 EUR
$ 49.95 CAN
$ 59.95 AUS

Hardback
0 7148 2985 4

£ 39.95 UK
$ 59.95 US
€ 65.00 EUR
$ 89.95 CAN
$ 99.95 AUS

Baroque Baroque

The Culture of Excess
Stephen Calloway

- Spotlights Baroque style in all its 20th-century manifestations: fashion, film, photography, design and interior decoration
- Traces the origins of the Baroque 'revival' that evolved as a rebellion against the sterilities of Modernism, and that thrives today as a colourful, opulent alternative to the minimalist aesthetic
- Charts the achievements of figures as diverse as the Sitwells, Cecil Beaton, Angus McBean, Coco Chanel and Fellini, and many other creative forces from the last 100 years
- Explores all facets of contemporary Baroque culture, from the extravagances of haute couture to the theatrical affectation of Hollywood to the fantastical whimsies of architecture and design

Stephen Calloway is a writer, journalist, lecturer, designer and consultant on historic interiors. He was formerly a Curator of Paintings at the Victoria & Albert Museum, London

General
Non-Fiction

Art

Photography

Collector's
Editions

Film

Architecture

290 × 250 mm
11³⁄₈ × 9⁷⁄₈ inches
240 pp
193 col, 99 b&w illus.
8 line drawings

Paperback
0 7148 4099 8

£ **22.95** UK
$ **35.00** US
€ **39.95** EUR
$ **49.95** CAN
$ **59.95** AUS

Hardback
0 7148 2879 3

£ **45.00** UK
$ **75.00** US
€ **75.00** EUR
$ **98.00** CAN
$ **125.00** AUS

Award

Winner History
category International
Architecture Book Awards
American Institute
of Architects, 1998

Modernism

Richard Weston

- A comprehensive survey that traces the course of Modernism from its 19th-century roots to its contemporary manifestations
- Explores the early Modernist movements – Cubism, Surrealism, Futurism and Purism – and concludes with the 'Postmodernist' experiments
- Shows for the first time how Modernist ideas were expressed in the visual arts, design, interiors, architecture and the decorative arts
- Winner in the Related Arts category, American Institute of Architects International Architecture Book awards

Richard Weston is a writer and lecturer. He is the author of a monograph on Alvar Aalto and *Town Hall, Säynätsalo* in the Architecture in Detail series, both published by Phaidon

'A fluent, stimulating overview of the movement ... Weston's is a lucid and highly readable history.' *(Daily Telegraph)*
'Its strength and virtue lie in the bringing together of a broad range of cultures: visual, literary and musical, in pursuit of the essence of Modernism.' *(Perspectives)*

Design

Fashion &
Contemporary
Culture

Decorative Arts
Interiors

Music &
Performing Arts

Video

Index

290 × 250 mm
11³⁄₈ × 9⁷⁄₈ inches
240 pp
160 col, 160 b&w illus.

Paperback
0 7148 3757 1

£ **22.95** UK
$ **35.00** US
€ **39.95** EUR
$ **49.95** CAN
$ **59.95** AUS

'Contemporary'

Architecture and interiors of the 1950s
Lesley Jackson

- The first book fully to explore the 'Contemporary' style that dominated architecture and design in the late 1940s and 1950s
- Surveys trends in taste and interior design at a time of economic regeneration and social renewal, when the positive spirit of the post-war era was reflected in the fresh, liberating expression of its buildings and home furnishings
- Illustrations depict key elements of 'Contemporary' style, from picture windows and open-plan interiors to vibrant fabric designs and patterned wallpapers, to streamlined kitchen appliances and Scandinavian and Italian furniture and light fixtures
- A lively appreciation of style both high and low

Lesley Jackson is a freelance writer and curator specializing in 20th-century design. She is the author of *The Sixties: Decade of Design Revolution*, also published by Phaidon

'Goes beyond the usual suspects ... to include Modernist expressions around the world ... a masterful job.' (*The New York Times*)
'An informative book whose presentation accurately reflects the era's colour and confidence.' (*Design Review*)
'Look at this book and admire the confidence of a bright new world.' (*World of Interiors*)

General
Non-Fiction

Art

Photography

Collector's
Editions

Film

Architecture

290 × 250 mm
11³⁄₈ × 9⁷⁄₈ inches
240 pp
268 col, 138 b&w illus.
7 line drawings

Paperback
0 7148 3963 9

£ **22.95** UK
$ **35.00** US
€ **39.95** EUR
$ **49.95** CAN
$ **59.95** AUS

The Sixties

Decade of design revolution
Lesley Jackson

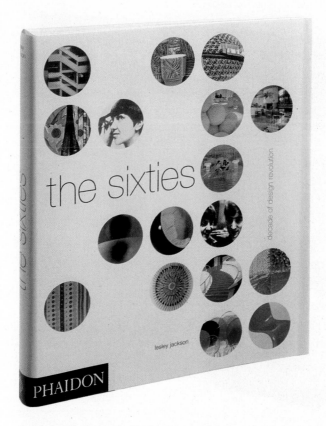

- An inspirational sourcebook charting one of the most radical decades in the history of design
- Shows the energy and dynamism of design in the Sixties that prompted a consumer 'youthquake' revolution
- Looks at design phenomena such as Op Art fabrics, plastic chairs, inflatable houses, mini skirts, paper furniture, pop glass and psychedelic posters
- A wide geographical look at the architecture of the United States, the applied arts of Scandinavia, fashion and popular culture in Britain and Italian furniture

Lesley Jackson is a freelance writer and curator specializing in 20th-century design. She is the author of *'Contemporary': Architecture and Interiors of the 1950s*, also published by Phaidon

'Packed with striking, rare reproductions and elegantly designed … A brilliant database on the 60s design landscape, by far the best published this decade.' *(I-D)*
'This book is scholarly, comprehensive, well researched and is destined to become an essential reference book of that decade.' *(Design Week)*

Design

Fashion &
Contemporary
Culture

Decorative Arts
Interiors

Music &
Performing Arts

Video

Index

Paperback large format	
290 × 250 mm	
11³⁄₈ × 9⁷⁄₈ inches	
240 pp	
109 col illus.	
0 7148 3646 X	
£ **19.95** UK	
$ **29.95** US	
€ **35.00** EUR	
$ **45.00** CAN	
$ **55.00** AUS	
Paperback mini format	
156 × 136 mm	
6¹⁄₄ × 5¹⁄₂ inches	
240 pp	
109 col illus.	
0 7148 3948 5	
£ **6.95** UK	
$ **9.95** US	
€ **9.95** EUR	
$ **14.95** CAN	
$ **16.95** AUS	
Point of Sale	
10-copy counterpack	
available	
0 7148 5176 0	

India Modern

Traditional forms and contemporary design
Herbert J M Ypma

- **A visually stunning compilation of modern Indian design and architecture**
- **Looks at roots and themes from village societies to Mogul palaces, showing how traditional forms and methods are reinvigorated in contemporary arts**
- **Images provide insight into the emergence of an exciting aesthetic that combines traditional forms and modern designs**
- **Also available in a handy mini format**

Herbert J M Ypma is founding editor and publisher of *Interior Architecture*

'*India Modern* explores everything from traditional building techniques to the importance of decoration within society. It's a mixture of stunning photographs and serious commentary.' *(World of Interiors)*
'Shows how the power and beauty of India's decorative heritage is being utilized in all aspects of the contemporary arts.' *(House and Leisure)*

General Non-Fiction

Art

Photography

Collector's Editions

Film

Architecture

Each volume
280 × 235 mm
11 × 9¹⁴ inches
128 pp
Over 100 col illus.

Paperback
Barcelona 0 7148 3759 8
London 0 7148 3761 X
New York 0 7148 3758 X
Paris 0 7148 3760 1
Rome 0 7148 3762 8

£ **12.95** UK
$ **19.95** US
€ **22.95** EUR
$ **29.95** CAN
$ **35.00** AUS

Inside series

Discovering the classic interiors of the world's favourite cities
Text by Joe Friedman

'Stunning photography is amply complemented by extensive practical gazetteer information.'

Design Council

- This series spotlights several of the world's most architecturally rich cities from a fresh angle, taking readers on a behind-the-scenes tour of interiors of various periods and styles
- Offers a rare glimpse behind the closed doors of some of the most significant buildings of our time, from museums and theatres to restaurants and residences
- Expert authors and photographers combine forces to highlight key architectural and decorative elements
- A directory of all featured buildings, complete with contact details and hours of operation, makes each book a valuable reference for those planning their travels

Design

Fashion &
Contemporary
Culture

Decorative Arts
Interiors

Music &
Performing Arts

Video

Index

Inside Barcelona
Photographs by Peter Aprahamian

- Explores the immensely varied
  atmospheres of a magical city
- Captures the variety from intimate shop
  interiors to the remarkable exuberant
  architectural fantasies of Antoni Gaudí

Inside London
Photographs by Peter Aprahamian

- Full of surprises, this book reveals one
  hundred of the capital's best-kept
  secrets
- Includes gentlemen's clubs, restaurants,
  hotels, shops, pubs, hospitals and
  historic town houses

Inside New York
Photographs by Richard Berenholtz

- A source of constant revelation
  displaying the work of architects,
  designers and craftsmen
- Includes a wide variety of buildings,
  from an extraordinary Art Deco church
  to the stately grandeur of the New York
  Public Library

Inside Paris
Photographs by Jérôme Darblay

- Brings to life the finest architectural
  treasures of this well-loved city
- Uncovers a variety of ages and styles,
  from the Roman baths at the Hôtel
  Cluny to a 1950s protopsychedelic
  brasserie in Pigalle

Inside Rome
Photographs by Francesco Venturi

- Offers fresh discoveries from one of the
  world's greatest cities
- Takes the reader on a privileged tour of
  the city's stunning private palaces and
  villas, as well as many less well-known
  public buildings and churches

20th Century Composers

Performing Arts

General
Non-Fiction

Art

Photography

Collector's
Editions

Film

Architecture

20th-Century Composers

'Phaidon's 20th-Century Composers series has become essential to music lovers of our time. All these books are profusely illustrated, always carefully chosen to illuminate the texts. What I would call a really good buy.' *Musical Opinion*

- A distinctive series on music, presenting comprehensive biographies of the great composers of our time
- Authoritative and engaging texts about the artists and their works to appeal to a general reader and musical enthusiast
- Explores a wide range of musical forms and personalities from Igor Stravinsky to the Beatles
- Clear narrative histories of the people, their art and their world combined with striking visual presentation and essential reference material
- Features either a single composer or a related group of composers per volume
- Each volume contains a classified list of works, as well as a selected bibliography and discography

Design

Fashion &
Contemporary
Culture

Decorative Arts

**Music &
Performing Arts**
20th Century
Composers

Video

Index

220 × 156 mm
8⁵⁄₈ × 6¹⁄₈ inches
240 pp
c.80 b&w illus.

Paperback
0 7148 3173 5

£ **14.95** UK
$ **24.95** US
€ **24.95** EUR
$ **39.95** CAN
$ **49.95** AUS

Award

Typographic Excellence
Type Directors' Club, 1995

American Pioneers

Ives to Cage and beyond
Alan Rich

- **The first survey of the American composers who invented new musical languages from the turn of the 20th century**
- **Includes the early pioneering flair of Charles Ives and, later, Henry Cowell and John Cage**
- **Examines the work of Carl Ruggles, Edgard Varèse, Harry Partch, Colin McPhee and Lou Harrison**

Alan Rich is an American critic with a passion for contemporary music. He writes for the *Los Angeles Weekly* and is author of a number of books and a series of interactive music programs for computers

'Smoothly executed. The chapter on Cage may well be the best introduction to his thought and work in English.' *(Gramophone)*

General Non-Fiction

Art

Photography

Collector's Editions

Film

Architecture

220 × 156 mm
8⁵⁸ × 6¹⁸ inches
240 pp
c.80 b&w illus.

Paperback
0 7148 3164 6

£ **14.95** UK
$ **24.95** US
€ **24.95** EUR
$ **39.95** CAN
$ **49.95** AUS

Béla Bartók

Kenneth Chalmers

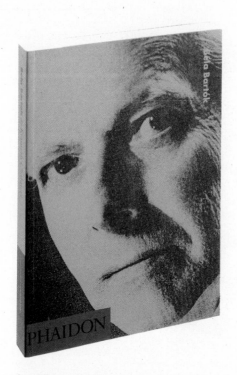

- Sets Béla Bartók (1881–1945) and his work in the context of his homeland Hungary and his native city Budapest, where he lived for most of his adult life
- Covers the full range of his work from his early explorations of the folklore of Hungary to his Third Piano Concerto composed on his deathbed in the United States
- Brings out the singular nature of his genius and the originality of his contribution to music

Kenneth Chalmers is an author, translator and composer who has written on Bartók, Berg, Stravinsky, Verdi and Weill, and collaborated on Decca's 20-volume Mozart Almanac

Design

Fashion &
Contemporary
Culture

Decorative Arts

**Music &
Performing Arts**
20th Century
Composers

Video

Index

220 × 156 mm
8⁵⁄₈ × 6¹⁄₈ inches
240 pp
c.80 b&w illus.

Paperback
0 7148 3203 0

£ **14.95** UK
$ **24.95** US
€ **24.95** EUR
$ **39.95** CAN
$ **49.95** AUS

The Beatles

Allan Kozinn

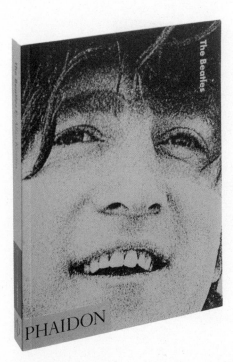

- Follows the extraordinary development of the four self-taught musicians from Liverpool from their beginnings until the break-up in 1970
- Examines why the innovative music of the Beatles – created, at least initially, as ephemera – has remained so durable
- Considers not only the commercially released disks but also studio outtakes, demos, unreleased recordings and broadcast performances
- Sets the group's evolution against the backdrop of the popular culture explosion of the 1960s

Allan Kozinn has written musical criticism for the *New York Times* since 1977 and won ASCAP awards for his work, including the book *Mischa Elman and the Romantic Style*

'A well-rounded, readable account. Makes a convincing case for putting the Beatles on the shelf between Bartók and Boulez.' *(The Sunday Times)*

General
Non-Fiction

Art

Photography

Collector's
Editions

Film

Architecture

220 × 156 mm
8⁵⁄₈ × 6¹⁄₈ inches
240 pp
c.80 b&w illus.

Paperback
0 7148 3701 6

£ **14.95** UK
$ **24.95** US
€ **24.95** EUR
$ **39.95** CAN
$ **49.95** AUS

Leonard Bernstein

Paul Myers

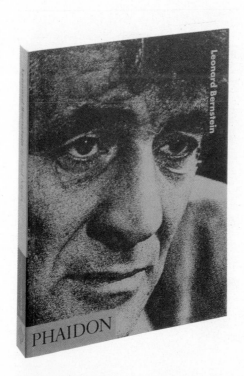

- Takes an inside look at Leonard Bernstein (1918–90), creator of the Broadway masterpiece, *West Side Story*, drawing on the author's personal knowledge of the American composer and conductor
- Covers all aspects of Bernstein's career, from his extraordinary early rise to fame as a conductor to his work as a world-famous composer, including his musicals and the score for *On the Waterfront*
- Examines fairly the paradoxes of a man who was brilliant, articulate, witty and charming but could also be vain, egocentric and demanding

Paul Myers is a freelance classical record producer whose work for Decca and Columbia (now Sony) and Naxos brought him into contact with Bernstein over many years

'Paul Myers writes concisely and entertainingly … will make readers long to hear the music.' (*Times Literary Supplement*)

Design

Fashion & Contemporary Culture

Decorative Arts

Music & Performing Arts
20th Century Composers

Video

Index

220 × 156 mm
8⅝ × 6⅛ inches
240 pp
c.80 b&w illus.

Paperback
0 7148 3277 4

£ **14.95** UK
$ **24.95** US
€ **24.95** EUR
$ **39.95** CAN
$ **49.95** AUS

Benjamin Britten

Michael Oliver

- A portrait of the life and work of Benjamin Britten (1913–76), the greatest English composer of his time, and the first of his generation to enjoy a wide international reputation
- Discusses how Britten's political and social convictions and sexuality directly or indirectly inspired much of his art
- Looks at Britten's reinvention of English opera and his work as a pioneer of music for film and radio

Michael Oliver is well known as a writer and broadcaster, having written and compiled numerous programmes for BBC Radio 3 and written regularly for *Gramophone* and other magazines for over 20 years. He is also the author of *Igor Stravinsky* in the 20th-Century Composers series

'Enthusiastically recommended.' *(Library Journal)*
'Finely balanced and beautifully written.' *(Opera)*
'Masterfully written. A highly recommended book.' *(Scenaria)*

General
Non-Fiction

Art

Photography

Collector's
Editions

Film

Architecture

220 × 156 mm
8⁵⁄₈ × 6¹⁄₈ inches
240 pp
c.80 b&w illus.

Paperback
0 7148 3932 9

£ **14.95** UK
$ **24.95** US
€ **24.95** EUR
$ **39.95** CAN
$ **49.95** AUS

Gabriel Fauré

Jessica Duchen

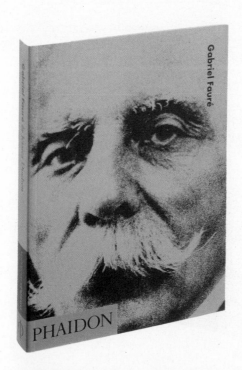

- Chronicles the life and career of French composer Gabriel Fauré (1845–1924), setting him in both his artistic and historical context
- Gives equal weight to Fauré's private and public lives, profiling the man behind the music
- Goes beyond the usual perception of Fauré as a dreamy, unworldly individual to reveal his ambition and decisiveness in his struggle to achieve recognition from France's musical establishment

Jessica Duchen is a freelance music journalist whose work appears frequently in the *Guardian* and *BBC Music Magazine*, among other publications. The founding editor of *Piano* magazine, she is the author of *Erich Wolfgang Korngold*, also in the 20th-Century Composers series

'A thorough and fascinating exploration of Fauré's life and work, and … the social, political and economic history of France during this period.' *(Classical Music)*
'Jessica Duchen is fully alive to [Fauré's] value and to the difficulties that have beset his reputation … Her claims for Fauré as a tough composer, grounding his music in a logic every bit as rigorous as Schoenberg's, are timely and just.' *(Gramophone)*

Design

Fashion &
Contemporary
Culture

Decorative Arts

**Music &
Performing Arts**
20th Century
Composers

Video

Index

220 × 156 mm
8⅝ × 6⅛ inches
240 pp
c.80 b&w illus.

Paperback
0 7148 3504 8

£ **14.95** UK
$ **24.95** US
€ **24.95** EUR
$ **39.95** CAN
$ **49.95** AUS

George Gershwin

Rodney Greenberg

- A colourful biography of George Gershwin (1898–1937), arguably the 20th century's greatest songwriter
- Places Gershwin's compositions within the context of the musical developments of his time
- Shows how a teenage song-plugger became internationally renowned in a career that spanned only two decades

Rodney Greenberg has produced and directed over 300 television music programmes, including the televised Promenade Concerts and three documentaries on George Gershwin

'An excellent critical account of Gershwin's musical development in the social and musical context of the first three decades of the century.' *(BBC Music Magazine)*

General Non-Fiction

Art

Photography

Collector's Editions

Film

Architecture

220 × 156 mm
8⁵⁄₈ × 6¹⁄₈ inches
240 pp
c.80 b&w illus.

Paperback
0 7148 3174 3

£ 14.95 UK
$ 24.95 US
€ 24.95 EUR
$ 39.95 CAN
$ 49.95 AUS

Hindemith, Hartmann and Henze

Guy Rickards

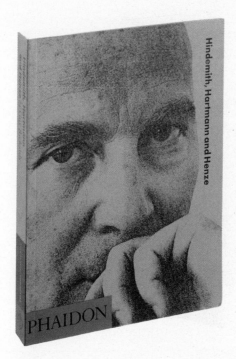

- Covers the work and lives of Paul Hindemith (1895–1963), Karl Amadeus Hartmann (1905–63) and Hans Werner Henze (b. 1926) who have dominated the mainstream development of German music
- Highlights the remarkable parallels between their careers, particularly their reactions to their native Germany
- Uses previously unpublished personal recollections of those who knew the composers as well as drawing on the author's interview with Henze

Guy Rickards is a freelance writer on music. He contributes to numerous publications including *Gramophone, Contemporary Music Review, BBC Music Magazine* and the *Guardian*. He is also author of Jean Sibelius in the 20th-Century Composers series

'It is a beautifully produced volume. Rickards' text does a magnificent job in interweaving the lives of these composers against the background of the calamitous history of their homeland, using a good deal of material not otherwise available in English.' *(London Magazine)*

Design

Fashion & Contemporary Culture

Decorative Arts

Music & Performing Arts 20th Century Composers

Video

Index

220 × 156 mm
8⁵⁄₈ × 6¹⁄₈ inches
240 pp
c.80 b&w illus.

Paperback
0 7148 3204 9

£ **14.95** UK
$ **24.95** US
€ **24.95** EUR
$ **39.95** CAN
$ **49.95** AUS

Jazz Greats

David Perry

- Recounts the history of jazz from its beginnings to the present day through the lives of 12 great jazz-men, including Louis Armstrong, Duke Ellington, Charles Mingus, Charlie Parker, John Coltrane and Miles Davis
- Draws on the author's interviews with jazz musicians and key witnesses, many recorded here for the first time
- Sets the lives against the social history, particularly slavery and the rise of the Civil Rights movement

David Perry is a writer, film-maker and radio producer with a special interest in jazz. He has written on jazz for the *Independent* and the *Observer*, and prepared a series of jazz portraits for BBC Radio 3

General
Non-Fiction

Art

Photography

Collector's
Editions

Film

Architecture

220 × 156 mm
8⅝ × 6⅛ inches
240 pp
c.80 b&w illus.

Paperback
0 7148 3155 7

£ **14.95** UK
$ **24.95** US
€ **24.95** EUR
$ **39.95** CAN
$ **49.95** AUS

Erich Wolfgang Korngold

Jessica Duchen

- Offers a reappraisal of the life and work of Erich Wolfgang Korngold (1897–1957), for so long dismissed as a 'film composer' in the classical music world
- Shows how he bridged the worlds of serious music, operetta and film music from his childhood in Vienna to his exile in Hollywood
- Argues that through his film music Korngold was one of the most influential composers of the 20th century

Jessica Duchen is a freelance music journalist whose work appears frequently in the *Guardian* and *BBC Music Magazine*, among other publications. The founding editor of *Piano* magazine, she is the author of *Gabriel Fauré*, also in the 20th-Century Composers series

'This is an inspired choice in this still early round of Phaidon's excellent, well-presented and illustrated 20th-Century Composers Series.' *(Classical Music)*
'Jessica Duchen's admirable biography will do much to advance the cause of Korngold.' *(Jewish Chronicle)*

Design

Fashion & Contemporary Culture

Decorative Arts

Music & Performing Arts
20th Century Composers

Video

Index

220 × 156 mm
8⅝ × 6⅛ inches
240 pp
c.80 b&w illus.

Paperback
0 7148 3795 4

£ **14.95** UK
$ **24.95** US
€ **24.95** EUR
$ **39.95** CAN
$ **49.95** AUS

György Ligeti

Richard Toop

- Appraises all the principal compositions of Hungarian composer György Ligeti (b. 1923), as well as his work as a teacher and mentor
- Situates his music within the context of the political and cultural history of post-war Europe
- Looks at Ligeti's diverse range of sources, from the folk music of his native Hungary to African and South American World music

Richard Toop is a musicologist, journalist and broadcaster and is Head of Musicology at the Sydney Conservatorium

General
Non-Fiction

Art

Photography

Collector's
Editions

Film

Architecture

220 × 156 mm
8⅝ × 6⅛ inches
240 pp
c.80 b&w illus.

Paperback
0 7148 3381 9

£ **14.95** UK
$ **24.95** US
€ **24.95** EUR
$ **39.95** CAN
$ **49.95** AUS

Minimalists

K Robert Schwartz

- First overview of Minimalism aimed at a general public
- Traces the lives of the Minimalist composers, of whom Philip Glass and Steve Reich are the best known, and discusses their most significant works
- Sets the Minimalists in the context of the artistic milieu from which they emerged, discussing the work of predecessors such as La Monte Young and Terry Riley
- By looking at the work of their successors, such as John Adams, Michael Nyman, Louis Andriessen and Arvo Pärt, new light is thrown on the Minimalists themselves

K Robert Schwarz taught at Brooklyn College, City University of New York, and wrote for the *New York Times*, *Opera News* and *Rolling Stone*

'Attractively produced, easily readable.' *(Musical Times)*

Design

Fashion & Contemporary Culture

Decorative Arts

Music & Performing Arts
20th Century Composers

Video

Index

220 × 156 mm
8⁵⁄₈ × 6¹⁄₈ inches
240 pp
c.80 b&w illus.

Paperback
0 7148 3507 2

£ 14.95 UK
$ 24.95 US
€ 24.95 EUR
$ 39.95 CAN
$ 49.95 AUS

Carl Nielsen

Jack Lawson

- The first biography in English on the Danish composer Carl Nielsen (1865–1931)
- Reveals much that is new and previously unpublished about Nielsen's life and times
- Emphasizes the composer's versatility, from the dramatic heights of his two operas to the simplicity of his popular songs and the complexity of his six symphonies

Jack Lawson is founder and secretary of the Carl Nielsen Society of Great Britain. He has written on Nielsen's music for CD and programme notes, and for magazines including *Classic CD* and *Opera Now*

'The photographs are among the book's greatest assets, since they are both well chosen and excellently reproduced. The accompanying descriptions are tastefully written, factual and informative.' *(Classical Music)*
'The ideal introduction to a still under-appreciated composer.' *(Hi-Fi News)*

General
Non-Fiction

Art

Photography

Collector's
Editions

Film

Architecture

220 × 156 mm
8⅝ × 6⅛ inches
240 pp
c.80 b&w illus.

Paperback
0 7148 3251 0

£ 14.95 UK
$ 24.95 US
€ 24.95 EUR
$ 39.95 CAN
$ 49.95 AUS

A Polish Renaissance

Bernard Jacobson

- Looks at four Polish composers, Andrzej Panufnik (1914–91), Witold Lutoslawski (1913–94), Krzystof Penderecki (b. 1933) and Henryk Górecki (b. 1933), who have changed the shape of music in the second half of the 20th century
- Traces the development of their radically differing creative approaches in spite of their common national origins
- Examines the changing political regimes by which they were affected and their relationship with the various musical movements of their time

Bernard Jacobson was Artistic Director of the Residentie Orkest (Hague Philharmonic), 1992–4, and is widely published as an author and translator

Design

Fashion & Contemporary Culture

Decorative Arts

Music & Performing Arts 20th Century Composers

Video

Index

220 × 156 mm
8⅝ × 6⅛ inches
240 pp
c.80 b&w illus.

Paperback
0 7148 3503 X

£ 14.95 UK
$ 24.95 US
€ 24.95 EUR
$ 39.95 CAN
$ 49.95 AUS

Francis Poulenc

Benjamin Ivry

- Discusses the work of Francis Poulenc (1899–1963) in the context of his colourful personal life and turbulent times
- The author uses recently published documents to shed new light on the composer and the man
- Reveals the composer as more complex and contradictory than we might suppose from the wit and charm of his music
- Evaluates his fine songs and religious works as well as his humorous, insouciant pieces

Benjamin Ivry is an arts correspondent based in Paris. He has been music critic for *Seven Days* and a regular contributor to *Opera News*

'Ivry's much-needed and informative *Poulenc* captures the French between-wars scene vividly.' *(Sunday Telegraph)*
'His narrative is fluent, full of interesting stories and very thorough.' *(Classical Music)*
'Such a fascinating man; such fascinating music; such good reading.' *(American Record Guide)*

220 × 156 mm
8⁵⁄₈ × 6¹⁄₈ inches
240 pp
c.80 b&w illus.

Paperback
0 7148 3513 7

£ 14.95 UK
$ 24.95 US
€ 24.95 EUR
$ 39.95 CAN
$ 49.95 AUS

Sergey Prokofiev

Daniel Jaffé

- A revealing and comprehensive biography of Sergey Prokofiev (1891–1953), versatile Russian composer and pianist, who is best known for the ballet *Romeo and Juliet* and his work for children, *Peter and the Wolf*
- Examines the works of Prokofiev, who primarily wrote for the stage, also contributed notably to the genres of symphony and concerto with works inseparable from the political context in which they were composed
- Shows how pressure from Soviet authority, following his return to Russia after years abroad, stimulated as much as it limited his creativity – ultimately leading to the denunciation of his music in 1948 as 'formalistic'

Daniel Jaffé is a freelance music journalist, specializing in 20th-century music, and is currently the Reviews Editor at *Classic CD* magazine

'A thoroughly researched and well-balanced appraisal of Prokofiev's life and works, beautifully presented in tandem with some fascinating and previously unavailable photographic illustrations.' *(Classic CD)*
'An excellent introduction.' *(BBC Music Magazine)*

Design

Fashion &
Contemporary
Culture

Decorative Arts

**Music &
Performing Arts**
20th Century
Composers

Video

Index

220 × 156 mm
8⁵⁸ × 6¹⁸ inches
240 pp
c.80 b&w illus.

Paperback
0 7148 3291 X

£ **14.95** UK
$ **24.95** US
€ **24.95** EUR
$ **39.95** CAN
$ **49.95** AUS

Giacomo Puccini

Conrad Wilson

- A polemical, passionate and rational attempt to set the composer of *La Bohème* and *Madame Butterfly* among the immortal greats
- Fully explores the contradictions in Puccini's personality, a man who revelled in the worldly success his operas brought him yet remained insecure about his creative powers
- Draws attention to the felicity, daring and extraordinary colouring of Puccini's music

Conrad Wilson was music critic of the *Scotsman* from 1963 to 1991 and now writes for the *Herald*. Author of several publications, including a history of Scottish opera, he was for many years Programme Editor of the Edinburgh Festival

'Fascinating and fastidiously researched. A fine book, both emotionally profound and waspishly witty.' *(The Scotsman)*
'Thoroughly readable and quietly perceptive.' *(Guardian)*

General
Non-Fiction

Art

Photography

Collector's
Editions

Film

Architecture

220 × 156 mm
8⁵⁸ × 6¹⁸ inches
240 pp
c.80 b&w illus.

Paperback
0 7148 3270 7

£ **14.95** UK
$ **24.95** US
€ **24.95** EUR
$ **39.95** CAN
$ **49.95** AUS

Maurice Ravel

Gerald Larner

- Examines Maurice Ravel (1875–1937), composer of works such as *Boléro* and *Pavane pour une Infante défunte*, as both a composer and a man
- Traces Ravel's emotional preoccupations and their effect on his work through events in his life and in the society around him
- Adds to our understanding of an enigmatic and intensely private composer

Gerald Larner was music critic of the *Guardian* for many years and currently writes for *The Times*. He has broadcast and written extensively on French culture

'Excellent, conversational, full of vivid colour and dry wit.' *(The Scotsman)*
'A fluent and lucid introduction. His text is expertly paced.' *(Classical Music)*
'Full of insights and contriving to tell us much about the music.' *(Sunday Telegraph)*

Design

Fashion & Contemporary Culture

Decorative Arts

Music & Performing Arts
20th Century Composers

Video

Index

220 × 156 mm
8⅝ × 6⅛ inches
240 pp
c.80 b&w illus.

Paperback
0 7148 3169 7

£ **14.95** UK
$ **24.95** US
€ **24.95** EUR
$ **39.95** CAN
$ **49.95** AUS

Alfred Schnittke

Alexander Ivashkin

- Presents a fascinating portrait of Russian composer Alfred Schnittke (1934–98), whose music was inextricably linked to the strictures of life in the Soviet Union
- Gives a detailed and admiring discussion of Schnittke's music and his theories
- Argues that the various stylistic elements in his works – his polystylism – may be perceived as part of a new, more universal musical language
- The first book on Schnittke published in English

Alexander Ivashkin currently teaches cello and music history at the University of Canterbury, New Zealand. An accomplished cellist and writer on music, he is also a close friend of the Schnittke family

'So much of the material is new that this book is a must for anyone remotely interested in the subject.' *(Gramophone)*
'Ivashkin has written what is undoubtedly the fullest account to date in any language of Schnittke's life and work, and one which is unlikely to be surpassed.' *(London Magazine)*

General
Non-Fiction

Art

Photography

Collector's
Editions

Film

Architecture

220 × 156 mm
8⁵⁄₈ × 6¹⁄₈ inches
240 pp
c.80 b&w illus.

Paperback
0 7148 3581 1

£ **14.95** UK
$ **24.95** US
€ **24.95** EUR
$ **39.95** CAN
$ **49.95** AUS

Jean Sibelius

Guy Rickards

- The first single-volume biography of Sibelius (1865–1957) in English to be published in nearly a decade
- Includes much new material not previously available
- Examines the paradox of a composer who saw himself as a cosmopolitan figure in European music but was also a nationalist tone-poet closely tied to Finland's move towards independence

Guy Rickards is a freelance writer on music. He contributes to numerous publications, including *Gramophone*, *Contemporary Music Review*, *BBC Music Magazine* and the *Guardian*. He is also author of *Hindemith, Hartmann and Henze* in the 20th-Century Composers series

Design

Fashion &
Contemporary
Culture

Decorative Arts

**Music &
Performing Arts**
20th Century
Composers

Video

Index

220 × 156 mm
8⁵⁸ × 6¹⁸ inches
240 pp
c.80 b&w illus.

Paperback
0 7148 3794 6

£ **14.95** UK
$ **24.95** US
€ **24.95** EUR
$ **39.95** CAN
$ **49.95** AUS

Richard Strauss

Tim Ashley

- A novel exploration of popular German composer Richard Strauss (1864–1949), who remains one of the most controversial figures in the history of music
- Places Strauss's life in the broader context of German history, also evaluating the charges of careerist opportunism and Nazi collaboration
- Reveals the paradoxes that lay beneath Strauss's flamboyant public persona
- Discusses his work in the light of the personal, artistic, literary and political influences that shaped it

Tim Ashley is a freelance writer and journalist. His work appears regularly in the *Guardian*, *Literary Review* and *Opera*. He lectures widely on 19th- and 20th-century German music and literature, and is the author of several opera librettos

'Tim Ashley's beautifully written, analytical but accessible introduction to Strauss in Phaidon's excellent series.' *(Sunday Times)*
'A clear-eared, clear-minded tribute to greatness, fluently written.' *(Guardian)*

General Non-Fiction

Art

Photography

Collector's Editions

Film

Architecture

220 × 156 mm
8⁵⁸ × 6¹⁸ inches
240 pp
c.80 b&w illus.

Paperback
0 7148 3158 1

£ **14.95** UK
$ **24.95** US
€ **24.95** EUR
$ **39.95** CAN
$ **49.95** AUS

Igor Stravinsky

Michael Oliver

- The first comprehensive biography for the general listener to appear in English since the composer's death
- Devotes particular attention to the composer's childhood in pre-revolutionary Russia, which was a formative influence
- Charts his discovery by Diaghilev, his collaborations with choreographers, dancers, painters and designers as well as with writers
- Concentrates on Stravinsky's creativity, describing how his musical mind worked and relating this to his complex and fascinating personality

Michael Oliver is well known as a writer and broadcaster, having written and compiled numerous programmes for BBC Radio 3 and written regularly for *Gramophone* and other magazines for over 20 years. He is also the author of *Benjamin Britten* in the 20th-Century Composers series

'A near-ideal introduction to the composer.' *(Gramophone)*

Design

Fashion & Contemporary Culture

Decorative Arts

Music & Performing Arts
20th Century Composers

Video

Index

220 × 156 mm
8⁵⁄₈ × 6¹⁄₈ inches
240 pp
c.80 b&w illus.

Paperback
0 7148 3157 3

£ **14.95** UK
$ **24.95** US
€ **24.95** EUR
$ **39.95** CAN
$ **49.95** AUS

Anton von Webern

Malcolm Hayes

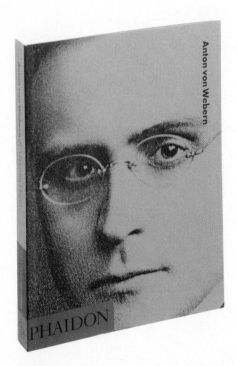

- A compelling look at the life and work of composer Anton von Webern (1883–1945), who was born into the aristocratic, musical heritage of Vienna
- Shows how an early passion for Renaissance vocal music continually haunted von Webern's compositions
- Discusses his studies with Schoenberg and conversion to the 12-note technique, which he used to create a sound characteristically his own
- Explores von Webern's influence on musicians of subsequent generations

Malcolm Hayes is a music journalist and specialist on the music of Webern and Schoenberg. He has written extensively for *The Times* and *Daily Telegraph*

'Provides a vital point of access to those seeking a deeper understanding or enjoyment of his music.' *(Gramophone)*

General
Non-Fiction

Art

Photography

Collector's
Editions

Film

Architecture

Richard Wagner: Der Ring des Nibelungen

A companion, translation and commentary
Rudolph Sabor

Each volume
220 × 156 mm
8⁵⁄₈ × 6¹⁄₈ inches
c.200 pp
c.20 b&w illus.
c.70 in companion volume

Paperback

£ 9.95 UK
$ 14.95 US
€ 16.95 EUR
$ 24.95 CAN
$ 29.95 AUS

5-copy boxed set
0 7148 3702 4

£ 45.00 UK
$ 69.95 US
€ 75.00 EUR
$ 98.00 CAN
$ 125.00 AUS

'Best of the music books was Rudolph Sabor's idiosyncratic, cheeky and incisive Translation and Commentaries on Wagner's Ring.' *Observer*

'This is Sabor at his best. An indispensable part of the Wagner lover's library. And for those new to the Ring cycle – what better place to start!' *Opera Now*

'The clarity, detail, comprehensiveness and sheer usefulness of the volumes cannot be praised too highly. I sincerely hope this will be a model for further companions to other opera composers and their work.' *Financial Times*

- Companion volumes to the librettos of Wagner's *Der Ring des Nibelungen*, including a new translation
- Topics range from the genesis and literary sources of the *Ring* to its performance history
- Introduces and examines both the story and the characters of the *Ring* and clarifies the use of leitmotif and literary and musical idiom
- Offers scene-by-scene synopses, introductions to all the new leitmotifs of that scene, a bibliography and selective discography

Rudolph Sabor is a writer and lecturer whose books include *The Real Wagner*. He frequently gives lectures on Wagner and reviews the Wagner Festival in Bayreuth for the major broadsheets and music periodicals

Design

Fashion &
Contemporary
Culture

Decorative Arts

**Music &
Performing Arts**

Video

Index

Der Ring des Nibelungen
a companion
0 7148 3650 8

Das Rheingold
translation
and commentary
0 7148 3651 6

Die Walküre
translation
and commentary
0 7148 3652 4

Siegfried
translation
and commentary
0 7148 3653 2

Götterdämmerung
translation
and commentary
0 7148 3654 0

- The four volumes *Das Rheingold, Die Walküre, Siegfried* and *Götterdämmerung* present Rudolph Sabor's ingenious translation of Wagner's libretto to each part of his famous Tetralogy
- The translation runs side-by-side with the German text, preserves the original metre and elucidates the complexities of Wagner's intricate libretto
- The Phaidon Ring volumes are unprecedented in presenting next to the translation not only a running commentary on the drama but also the names of the leitmotifs as they occur
- Sabor's translations are supplemented by scene-by-scene synopses, short discussions of each leitmotif new to each scene, a discography, videography and full bibliography
- A list of the motifs in the opera featured in the respective volume as well as all motifs in the *Ring* cycle conclude each volume

General
Non-Fiction

Art

Photography

Collector's
Editions

Film

Architecture

240 × 210 mm
9¹⁄₂ × 8¹⁄₄ inches
288 pp
16 col, 230 b&w illus.

Paperback
0 7148 2736 3

£ **16.95** UK
$ **24.95** US
€ **29.95** EUR
$ **39.95** CAN
$ **49.95** AUS

A History of the Theatre

2nd edition
Glynne Wickham

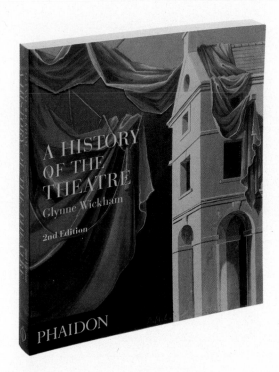

- Outlines the development of the art of drama throughout the world over the last 3,000 years, ranging from theatre's origins in primitive dance rituals up to the present day
- Highly readable, incisive and deeply imbued with a personal viewpoint that stresses the primacy of live performance
- Based on the author's lifelong practical experience as a teacher, researcher and professional director

Glynne Wickham was, until his retirement, Professor of Drama at the University of Bristol, a post he held with distinction for more than 20 years

Design

Fashion &
Contemporary
Culture

Decorative Arts

**Music &
Performing Arts**
Performing Arts

Video

Index

246 × 192 mm
9¹₂ × 8¹₄ inches
192 pp
123 col, 100 two-col,
over 350 b&w illus.

Paperback
0 7148 2644 8

£ **15.95** UK
€ **24.95** EUR
$ **45.00** AUS

Not available in the
US and Canada

Stagecraft

The complete guide to theatrical practice
Trevor R Griffiths

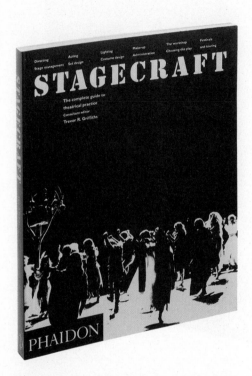

- **The complete, practical manual of modern theatrical practice**
- **Covers every aspect of the subject, from choosing a play to backstage and front-of-house management**
- **A book that can guide even the inexperienced amateur to attain professional standards**

Trevor R Griffiths is Professor and Programme Director in the Department of Performing Arts and Theatre Studies at London Metropolitan University. He has worked in many areas of theatre since the age of 12. He is chairman of London's Foco Novo Theatre Group, a leading British fringe company

'One of the best manuals of good theatre practice yet produced.' *(Times Educational Supplement)*

General
Non-Fiction

Art

Photography

Collector's
Editions

Film

Architecture

290 × 250 mm
11³⁄₈ × 9⁷⁄₈ inches
208 pp
over 160 tritone illus.

Hardback
0 7148 2966 8

£ **29.95** UK
$ **45.00** US
€ **49.95** EUR
$ **69.95** CAN
$ **89.95** AUS

Nureyev

Edited by Howard Brown

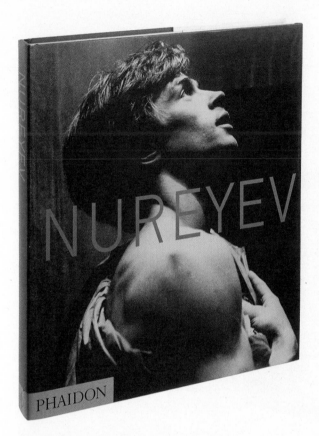

- Presents the greatest images of Nureyev's legendary dancing career
- Includes photographs of the dancer by Snowdon, Henri Cartier-Bresson, Anthony Crickmay, David Bailey, Houston Rogers and Cecil Beaton
- Augmented by a complete list of Nureyev's performances

Howard Brown, editor and designer, has worked for both photographic and ballet clients as a graphic designer. He has worked with several photographers and is a consultant to the Zelda Cheatle Photographers Gallery, London. He has also created programmes and booklets for both the Royal Ballet School and the English National Ballet School

Design

Fashion &
Contemporary
Culture

Decorative Arts

**Music &
Performing Arts**
Performing Arts

Video

Index

'The book offers
a stunning visual
record. It is a fine
celebration of Nureyev's
extraordinary talent.

Mail on Sunday

Each volume
210 × 145 mm
8¼ × 5¾ inches
c.128 pp
80 two-col,160 b&w illus.

Paperback

£ 9.95 UK
$ 14.95   US
€ 16.95 EUR
$ 24.95 CAN
$ 27.95 AUS

Phaidon Theatre Manuals

Not only are the manuals attractive, they are practical, concise and free from theories.'

Times Educational Supplement

- Guides the reader on how to research and construct costumes of many different kinds
- Explains how to identify elements of a play that will make for a success and how to choose and guide collaborators towards putting this into practice
- Useful to both the novice and the experienced technician and supplemented with a glossary and index

David Mayer, the Series Editor, is Head of the Department of Drama at Manchester University
Michael Holt is Senior Lecturer on scene design at Manchester University and undertakes professional productions throughout the world
Michael McCaffery is a freelance professional director with productions in Great Britain, Ireland and throughout Europe
Neil Fraser is Lecturer in lighting design at the Royal Academy of Dramatic Art, London. He has worked extensively as lighting designer for London shows
Terry Hawkins has worked extensively in theatre administration, most recently at the Oxford Stage Company and London's Young Vic Theatre
Pauline Menear teaches stage management at the Royal Academy of Dramatic Art, London

Design

Fashion &
Contemporary
Culture

Decorative Arts

**Music &
Performing Arts**
Performing Arts

Video

Index

Costume and Make-up
Michael Holt
0 7148 2512 3

Directing a Play
Michael McCaffery
0 7148 2513 1

Lighting and Sound
Neil Fraser
0 7148 2514 X

**Stage Design
and Properties**
Michael Holt
0 7148 2515 8

**Stage Management
and Theatre
Administration**
Pauline Menear
and Terry Hawkins
0 7148 2516 6

- *Costume and Make-up* defines the costume designer's role and explains the techniques used by professionals
- *Directing a Play* is an invaluable guide for theatre directors, covering all stages of theatrical production, from initial preparation to final performance
- *Lighting and Sound* offers the reader a comprehensive introduction to the art of theatre lighting and sound
- *Stage Design and Properties* is a guide and resource for imaginative stage design solutions for both amateurs and professionals with glossary, bibliography and list of suppliers and stockists
- *Stage Management and Theatre Administration* sheds light on a crucial aspect of staging theatre productions

Video

General Non-Fiction

Art

Photography

Collector's Editions

Film

Architecture

Box dimensions
194 × 155 mm
7⁵⁄₈ × 6¹⁄₈ inches

Available
in English-language
PAL VHS

incl VAT £ **14.95** UK
€ **24.95** EUR

Marketing Information
A free 15-minute
sample video is available.
Contact your local
representative or the
Phaidon sales office
for further details.

Point of Sale
118-unit Spiner
supplied on loan
with order to fill
0 7148 6055 7
12 copy Counter Pack
0 7148 3516 1

Phaidon Video: An exploration of art on film

'Invaluable insights into the artists' public and private faces.' *The Artist*

'Over 50 first-class videos at only £14.95/€ 24.95 each … excellent value.' *Times Educational Supplement*

- A collection of powerful and arresting videos on art, fashion and photography
- Diverse and definitive, programmes cover artists from Chagall to Chanel, Lichtenstein to Leibovitz and Delacroix to Dufy
- A fascinating spectrum of art, both past and present
- Invaluable insights into the artists' public and private faces
- Intelligent and thought-provoking commentaries
- Rare opportunities to watch major modern artists at work
- Engaging dialogues between the artists and respected critics
- Remarkable value

Design

Fashion & Contemporary Culture

Decorative Arts

Music & Performing Arts

Video

Index

Alvar Aalto
Technology and nature
*Written and directed
by Ywe Jalander*
59 mins, phv 6050
0 7148 6050 6

· Documents Finnish architect Alvar Aalto's work in Finland, Italy, Germany and the US
· Analyses his successful harmonization of new technologies and materials with a sympathetic interest in the user and the natural environment

Francis Bacon
*Edited and presented
by Melvyn Bragg
Produced and directed
by David Hinton*
55 mins, phv 6003
0 7148 6003 4

· Made on the occasion of Bacon's major retrospective at the Tate Gallery in 1985
· Includes some of the last footage of the artist in his studio
· Features commentaries by Bacon on other artists including Rubens, Cézanne, Picasso, Balthus, Giacometti, Shakespeare and Baudelaire
· With candid revelations about Bacon's childhood, his friends and influences

Balthus the Painter
*Edited by Jo Ann Kaplan,
Stephen Parry
Produced by Emma Crichton-Miller
Directed by Mark Kidel*
58 mins, phv 6059
0 7148 6059 X

· Based around a series of conversations in which Balthus talks about his inspirations, subject matter and the modern world
· With contributions from family and friends including Thadee Klossowski, Jean Clair, Director of the Musée Picasso in Paris, and a former child model

Bauhaus
The face of the 20th century
*Written and narrated
by Frank Whitford
Produced by Julia Cave*
50 mins, phv 6002
0 7148 6002 6

· Covers the full range of the work of the Bauhaus in architecture, design and other fields
· Includes contributions from architects, teachers, ex-students and current experts on the Bauhaus
· With vintage footage of the work of its founding members

Christian Boltanski
*Edited and presented
by Melvyn Bragg
Produced and directed
by Gerald Fox*
52 mins, phv 6045
0 7148 6045 X

· An intriguing and highly personal interview ranging over Boltanski's career
· Conveys the complex relationship between individual experience and the momentum of history
· Shows the artist at work on recent projects

Pierre Bonnard
In search of pure colour
Directed by Didier Baussy
50 mins, phv 6004
0 7148 6004 2

· Shot largely on location in the South of France in the houses and landscape of Bonnard's paintings
· Traces Bonnard's lifelong search for 'pure colour'
· Examines the friendship and influence of fellow artists including Gauguin, Cézanne, Seurat, Renoir and Matisse

Arthur Boyd
*Edited and presented
by Melvyn Bragg
Produced and directed
by Don Featherstone*
51 mins, phv 6005
0 7148 6005 0

· Filmed at Boyd's wilderness homestead amid the spectacular scenery of the Shoalhaven River in New South Wales
· Shows the artist at work on two new major paintings commissioned especially for the film

Anthony Caro
*Edited and presented
by Melvyn Bragg
Produced and directed
by Nigel Wattis*
50 mins, phv 6032
0 7148 6032 8

· Records Caro's 60th birthday retrospective at the Serpentine Gallery, London
· Shows the artist's working process
· Includes thought-provoking discussions with Caro

General
Non-Fiction

Art

Photography

Collector's
Editions

Film

Architecture

Cézanne
Three colours Cézanne
*Written and presented
by Matthew Collings
Directed by Janice Sutherland*
59 mins, phv 6056
0 7148 6056 5

- Filmed in Paris and the
South of France
- Analyses the radical nature
of Cézanne's art
- Includes commentary from
scholars and artists

Chagall
*Edited and presented
by Melvyn Bragg
Produced and directed
by Kim Evans*
53 mins, phv 6006
0 7148 6006 9

- Made shortly before
Chagall's death in 1985
- The artist talks about his
work and is shown creating
a stained-glass window

Chanel, Chanel
*Written and edited
by Richard Howorth
Directed by Eila Hershon
and Roberto Guerra*
62 mins, phv 6041
0 7148 6041 7

- Chanel director Karl
Lagerfeld explores the
Chanel fashion phenomenon
- Draws on a rich collage of
fashion images and archive
footage, including a late
interview with Chanel

Chillida
*Directed by Laurence Boulting
Produced by William Leeson*
60 mins, phv 6033
0 7148 6033 6

- Charts the career of Basque
sculptor Eduardo Chillida
- Shows the artist preparing
monumental works in iron
and a series of pieces cut
from clay blocks
- Includes the artist's own
commentaries

The Life and Work
of Edgar Degas
The unquiet spirit
*Written and narrated
by David Thompson
Produced and directed
by Ann Turner*
60 mins, phv 6007
0 7148 6007 7

- Covers Degas' paintings,
drawings, sculptures, prints
and photographs
- Explores Degas'
preoccupation
with unguarded moments
- Spans the artist's full career

Delacroix
The restless eye
*Written and narrated
by Colin Nears
Directed by Colin Nears*
60 mins, phv 6046
0 7148 6046 8

- Dramatizes the development
of Delacroix's work through
readings from the artist's
own journal
- Shows his Paris studio and
country retreat
- Presents an invaluable
insight into the public
and private faces of a key
artistic figure of 19th-
century France

Paul Delvaux
The sleepwalker of
Saint-Idesbald
*Written by Frank Maubert
and Adrian Maben
Directed by Adrian Maben*
54 mins, phv 6008
0 7148 6008 5

- Filmed when Delvaux was in
his nineties, the first
documentary of its kind
shows the artist reflecting
on his art, family and
experiences
- Covers the full scope of an
artistic career that defies
categorization in any school
or movement

Otto Dix
The painter is the eyes
of the world
*Written and directed
by Reiner E Moritz*
59 mins, phv 6009
0 7148 6009 3

- Traces the development of
Dix's career as a whole,
including the great series
of etchings 'The War' and his
strikingly direct portraits
- Vividly evokes the
continuing relevance of Dix's
work and its power to shock

Design

Fashion & Contemporary Culture

Decorative Arts

Music & Performing Arts

Video

Index

Donatello
The first modern sculptor
Written by Charles Avery
Script Associate and
narration David Thompson
Produced by Ann Turner
86 mins, phv 6034
0 7148 6034 4

- Shot on location in Italy
- Explores the technical prowess and expressive range of one of the greatest sculptors of the Italian Renaissance
- Contributors include art historian Charles Avery and sculptors Peter Rockwell, Elizabeth Frink and Henry Moore

Marcel Duchamp
A game of chess
Directed by Jean-Marie Drot
56 mins, phv 6010
0 7148 6010 7

- An in-depth interview with Marcel Duchamp at the time of his first ever one-man show (at the Pasadena Art Museum) five years before his death
- Records an engaging dialogue between Duchamp and film-maker Jean-Marie Drot

Raoul Dufy
Painter and decorator
Directed by Andrew Snell
Produced by Elizabeth Queenan
53 mins, phv 6011
0 7148 6011 5

- Covers every aspect of Dufy's work from ceramics and textiles to book illustration and paintings
- Contains archive footage
- Contributors include Dufy's own associates and dealers

Max Ernst
Double-length
Directed by Peter Schamoni
Produced by Mechthild Offermanns
and Matthew Reinders
102 mins, phv 6012
0 7148 6012 3

- Explores Ernst's ceaseless technical experimentation
- Contains extensive interview sequences with Ernst himself

Lucio Fontana
Reaching out into space
A film by Pierre Néel
and Wieland Schmied
Written and directed by
Pierre Néel
50 mins, phv 6013
0 7148 6013 1

- Explores Italian artist Lucio Fontana's theories and groundbreaking concept of Spatialism
- Contributions from critics, friends and artists provide a wide-ranging assessment of Fontana's experimental work

Norman Foster
Directed by Mark Kidel
53 mins, phv 6060
0 7148 6060 3

- Follows the work of architect Norman Foster in his office and on the site of major projects
- Shows how his designs combine concern for minimal environmental damage with maximum technological efficiency

González
Directed by Barrie Gavin
Produced by Laurence Boulting and William Leeson
61 mins, phv 6035
0 7148 6035 2

- Documents the career of the innovative Catalan sculptor Julio González
- Contains interviews with younger contemporaries including the painter Hans Hartung
- Offers a compelling reassessment of González's achievement

Frans Hals of Antwerp
Written and directed by Jonne Severijn
55 mins, phv 6014
0 7148 6014 X

- Focuses on Hals's accomplished and intriguing portraits and his artistic technique
- Reassesses this most popular but least well understood of Dutch masters
- Illuminates his influence on later artists

General
Non-Fiction

Art

Photography

Collector's
Editions

Film

Architecture

Gilbert and George
Double-length
Edited by Trevor Batt,
Vincent Narduzzo and
Marc Eskenazi
Directed and produced
by Gerald Fox
104 mins, phv 6064 6

Available in 3 TV systems
PAL 0 7148 6064 6
NTSC 0 7148 6065 4
SECAM 0 7148 6066 2

£ **19.95** UK incl VAT
€ **35.00** EUR
$ **29.95** US
$ **39.95** CAN
$ **45.00** AUS

- One of the most engaging and insightful films about artistic practice ever made
- Filmed to mark the unveiling of a new body of work based on bodily fluids and called 'The Fundamental Pictures'
- Traces the history of Gilbert and George back to their first meeting at St Martin's School of Art in 1969
- Watches the duo in their studio creating new work and follows them through their everyday lives
- Comments on shows of their photoworks in London, Shanghai and Bologna

Winner of the Royal Television Society Arts Film of the Year, 1998

Winner of the Grand Prix, 16th International Festival of Films on Art, Montreal, 1998

Winner of the British Academy of Film and Television Arts for Best Art Film, 1998

Patrick Heron
Edited and presented
by Melvyn Bragg
Produced and directed
by John Read
53 mins, phv 6015
0 7148 6015 8

- Includes an extended interview with the artist on the occasion of his 1985 retrospective
- Shot on location in Heron's home and studio in Cornwall

David Hockney:
Joiner Photographs
Edited and presented
by Melvyn Bragg
Directed by Don
Featherstone
Produced by Nick Evans
51 mins, phv 6038
0 7148 6038 7

- Shows Hockney in his Los Angeles studio exploring his technique for creating photographic collages or 'joiners'
- The artist talks about his experiments and the nature of visual representation

Hockney at the Tate
Edited and presented
by Melvyn Bragg
Produced and directed
by Alan Benson
51 mins, phv 6016
0 7148 6016 6

- An extended interview with Hockney, filmed at his 1988 Tate Gallery retrospective
- The artist comments on his own work and on the artistic process generally

David Hockney:
Pleasures of the Eye
Edited by Sylvia Kamm
Directed by Gero von Boehm
56 mins, phv 6061
0 7148 6061 1

- Hockney discusses his philosophy, life and work, commenting in detail on major pieces of the 1980s
- The artist is shown organizing shows in Rotterdam and London in 1995

Design

Fashion & Contemporary Culture

Decorative Arts

Music & Performing Arts

Video

Index

Howard Hodgkin
Edited and presented
by Melvyn Bragg
Directed by Melissa Raimes
52 mins, phv 6062
0 7148 6062 X

- British artist Howard Hodgkin explains how his art attempts to transform transient emotion into something concrete and lasting
- The artist discusses his use of colour and his choice of themes

Jasper Johns
Ideas in paint
Produced and directed
by Rick Tejada-Flores
56 mins, phv 6017
0 7148 6017 4

- Filmed at the time of Johns's retrospective exhibition at the 1988 Venice Biennale
- Includes conversations with the painter and footage showing him at work in his studio

Frida Kahlo
Directed by Eila Hershon and Roberto Guerra
62 mins, phv 6018
0 7148 6018 2

- Traces the life and work of Mexican painter Frida Kahlo, linking images to the life-events they record
- Draws extensively on Kahlo's extraordinary diary, providing a vivid analysis of key works
- Explores Kahlo's use of indigenous Mexican art traditions

Annie Leibovitz
Edited and presented
by Melvyn Bragg
Directed by Rebecca Frayn
Produced by Belinda Allen
51 mins, phv 6039
0 7148 6039 5

- Combines an in-depth interview with American photographer Annie Leibovitz with a survey of her career
- Includes commentary from Mick Jagger, *Rolling Stone* editor Jann Wenner and others
- Shows Leibovitz on a photo assignment with actress Demi Moore

Roy Lichtenstein
Edited and presented by
Melvyn Bragg
Produced and directed by
Chris Hunt
49 mins, phv 6019
0 7148 6019 0

- Based on a rare interview with the intensely private Lichtenstein
- Traces Lichtenstein's career, from his early affiliation with Abstract Expressionism to his later work
- The artist describes how he transfers 'found' images to large canvases and discusses the rationale behind his choices of comic-strip frames

Jacques Lipchitz
Produced and directed
by Bruce Bassett
59 mins, phv 6036
0 7148 6036 0

- Shows the Lithuanian-born sculptor Jacques Lipchitz working on three massive public commissions in Italy in the 1970s
- Lipchitz's commentary takes the development of modern art out of the purely academic arena to imbue it with a profound sense of a search for freedom of expression

Magritte
Monsieur René Magritte
Written and narrated
by Edwin Mullins
Directed by Adrian Maben
51 mins, phv 6020
0 7148 6020 4

- Analyses the work of Surrealist master René Magritte by tracing his imagery back to bizarre and tragic childhood experiences
- Surveys Magritte's entire career
- Includes archive footage of the artist talking about his life and work
- With amusing excerpts from Magritte's home movies

Masaccio
A view of mankind
Written and narrated
by Sir Lawrence Gowing
Produced by Christopher
Burstall
40 mins, phv 6000
0 7148 6000 X

- Sir Lawrence Gowing demonstrates how Masaccio made one of the great breakthroughs in the history of visual representation – the depiction of the human subject in three-dimensional space
- Analyses Masaccio's masterpieces

General
Non-Fiction

Art

Photography

Collector's
Editions

Film

Architecture

Miró
Theatre of dreams
Written and narrated
by Roland Penrose
Directed by Robin Lough
Produced by Christopher
Martin
57 mins, phv 6021
0 7148 6021 2

- Made shortly before Miró's
  death
- Shows Miró discussing his
  creative process with painter
  and critic Roland Penrose
- Includes footage of Miró
  working in his studio

Mondrian
Mr boogie-woogie man
Written and presented
by Matthew Collings
Directed by Janice Sutherland
51 mins, phv 6058
0 7148 6058 1

- Examines in detail key
  paintings by Mondrian
- Demonstrates the social
  theories of art that
  dominated his lifestyle
  and work

Malcolm Morley
The outsider
Directed by Mike Mortimer
51 mins, phv 6022
0 7148 6022 0

- Covers the entire range of
  Morley's art
- Morley talks to Patrick
  Malahide and critic David
  Sylvester about the
  experiences that informed
  his wry outlook
- Films the artist at work

**Robert Motherwell
and the New York School**
Storming the citadel
Written by Kenneth Cavander
Produced and directed
by Catherine Tatge
56 mins, phv 6023
0 7148 6023 9

- Made shortly before
  Motherwell's death
- Charts the battle led by
  Abstract Expressionists to
  make American painting
  equal to that of Europe
- Fascinating archive footage

Helmut Newton
Frames from the edge
Directed by Adrian Maben
Produced by Adrian Maben
and Martine Vigouroux
96 mins, phv 6048
0 7148 6048 4

- Explores the subtly varied
  moods of Newton's eroticism
  through different
  commercial and private
  commissions
- Highlights Newton's
  meticulous approach

Ben Nicholson
Written, narrated and
directed by John Read
Produced by Anne Balfour
Fraser
53 mins, phv 6024
0 7148 6024 7

- An eloquent survey of the
  career of one of the 20th
  century's most original
  artists
- Explores Nicholson's artistic
  formation and the places
  where he worked

Isamu Noguchi
Written, narrated, produced
and directed by Bruce W
Bassett
56 mins, phv 6037
0 7148 6037 9

- Encompasses the whole
  range of American artist
  Isamu Noguchi's output,
  from sculpture to
  calligraphic brush drawing,
  landscape gardening,
  furniture design, clay
  abstractions and theatrical
  settings
- Shows Noguchi working in
  Detroit, Japan, Mexico City
  and Paris
- The artist talks freely about
  his life and ideas

Claes Oldenburg
Edited and presented
by Melvyn Bragg
Produced and directed
by Gerald Fox
54 mins, phv 6057
0 7148 6057 3

- Surveys the career of one
  of Pop Art's foremost
  exponents
- Contributors include Roy
  Lichtenstein, Jim Dine and
  James Rosenquist
- Includes coverage of the
  installation of Giant Soft
  Shuttlecock at the
  Guggenheim Museum,
  New York, in 1995

Design

Fashion & Contemporary Culture

Decorative Arts

Music & Performing Arts

Video

Index

Jackson Pollock
Edited and presented
by Melvyn Bragg
Produced and directed
by Kim Evans
52 mins, phv 6025
0 7148 6025 5

- Makes extensive use of contemporary footage of Pollock at work, including his notorious 'drip-and-splash' manner of Action painting
- Places this legendary artist in a clear art-historical context
- Includes commentary from many of Pollock's friends and associates

Raphael. Volume 1:
The Apprentice Years
Written and narrated
by David Thompson
Produced and directed
by Ann Turner
58 mins, phv 6026
0 7148 6026 3

- The first part of a two-part reappraisal of Raphael's work examines his career up to the age of 25
- Shot on location in Urbino, Perugia, Florence and Rome
- Provides in-depth coverage of all Raphael's early work, focusing in particular on his innovative treatment of the Madonna and Child

Raphael. Volume 2:
The Prince of Painters
Written and narrated
by David Thompson
Produced and directed
by Ann Turner
59 mins, phv 6027
0 7148 6027 1

- The second part of a two-part reappraisal of Raphael, following his later career as papal protégé
- Explores the influence of contemporary artists and thinkers, including Michelangelo, and the Classical art of ancient Rome
- Examines the evolution of some of Raphael's best-known images

Robert Rauschenberg:
Man at Work
Edited by Colin Minchin
Produced by Andrea Miller
Directed by Chris Granlund
50 mins, phv 6067
0 7148 6067 0

- Made on the occasion of Rauschenberg's major 1997 retrospective at the Guggenheim Museum, New York
- Interviewed at home and in his studio on Captiva Island, Florida, Rauschenberg talks about his life and explains the evolution of some of his best-known works
- Includes archive footage and interviews with friends and associates

Paula Rego
Edited and presented
by Melvyn Bragg
Produced and directed
by Melissa Raimes
50 mins, phv 6028
0 7148 6028 X

- Rego reveals her work's roots in childhood memories, nursery rhymes and the imagery of her native Portugal
- With commentary by critic Germaine Greer and art historian Ruth Rosengarten

The Real Rembrandt
The search for a genius
Written by George Hulshof
and Kees van Langeraad
Directed by Kees van
Langeraad
Produced by Jet Willers
54 mins, phv 6029
0 7148 6029 8

- A fascinating study of modern scientific techniques applied to art
- A full overview of Rembrandt's work

Sir Joshua Reynolds
Artist of the portrait
Written and directed
by Christopher Martin
61 mins, phv 6030
0 7148 6030 1

- Presents a wide-ranging assessment of Reynolds's artistic and intellectual achievements
- Explores Reynolds's subtle and intelligent interpretations of the human face

The Life and Work
of Georges Seurat
Point counterpoint
Written and narrated
by David Thompson
Produced and directed
by Ann Turner
71 mins, phv 6047
0 7148 6047 6

- Explores the optical theory behind Seurat's 'rational' technique for reproducing the effects of light
- Discusses his focus on the working class and lower bourgeois social arena

W Eugene Smith
Photography made difficult
*Written by Jan Hartman
from the letters and
journals of W Eugene Smith
Directed by Gene Lasko
Produced by Kirk Morris*
89 mins, phv 6040
0 7148 6040 9

- Profiles American
photographer W Eugene
Smith
- Analyses Smith's 'heroic'
achievements in relation to
his complex personality

**The Story of Fashion.
Volume 1: Remembrance
of Things Past**
Artistic Adviser
Karl Lagerfeld
*Directed by Eila Hershon
and Roberto Guerra*
61 mins, phv 6042
0 7148 6042 5

- The first of three films on
the story of fashion from the
18th century to the 20th
- Interviews with key figures
'Even if you have read the
book, flicked through the
mags, been to the movies
and think you've seen it all,
there is a freshness about
this material and its
presentation.' *(The Herald)*

**The Story of Fashion.
Volume 2: The Art and
Sport of Fashion**
Artistic Adviser
Karl Lagerfeld
*Directed by Eila Hershon
and Roberto Guerra*
63 mins, phv 6043
0 7148 6043 3

- The second film in this series
examines the relationship
between style and history,
fashion and its social context
- Highlights the influence
of individual designers
- Looks at the role of fashion
spinoffs, such as perfume,
and the unchanging
tradition of high-class men's
tailoring

**The Story of Fashion.
Volume 3: The Age
of Dissent**
Artistic Adviser
Karl Lagerfeld
*Directed by Eila Hershon
and Roberto Guerra*
60 mins, phv 6044
0 7148 6044 1

- The third film in this series
analyses styles of the 1960s
to 1980s
- Leading designers discuss
contemporary approaches to
fashion in the UK, France,
Italy and the US, and assess
the impact of Japanese
design concepts

**Vermeer – Light, Love
and Silence**
*Edited and presented
by Melvyn Bragg
Written, produced and
directed by Michael Gill*
53 mins, phv 6063
0 7148 6063 8

- Looks at the social, political
and scientific context in
which Vermeer worked
- Explains his techniques and
process of composition
- Jonathan Miller and Svetlana
Alpers explore the meaning
of his settings and subjects,
and the intensity that makes
his paintings so moving

Vermeer
The spell of a woman
*Written and narrated
by Sir Lawrence Gowing
Produced by Christopher
Burstall*
53 mins, phv 6001
0 7148 6001 8

- Sir Lawrence Gowing offers a
highly personal tribute to
Vermeer
- Vermeer's images are
explored for fresh clues to
his artistic personality, and
his technical mastery is
examined

**The World of the Painter
Paolo Veronese**
Between art and inquisition
*Directed by Renate and
Wolfgang Liebenwein*
60 mins, phv 6031
0 7148 6031 X

- Surveys Veronese's career
- Examines his technical
achievements in perspective
and group compositions and
his sumptuous colouring
- Documents his conflict with
the Inquisition over his
interpretation of the Last
Supper
- Provides a vivid evocation
of Venice at the height of
its splendour

Andy Warhol
*Edited and presented
by Melvyn Bragg
Produced and directed
by Kim Evans*
79 mins, phv 6049
0 7148 6049 2

- Surveys Warhol's
development, from his early
commercial art to his
emergence as a leading
figure of American Pop Art
in the 1960s
- Highlights Warhol's activities
as a film-maker
- Shows how his images
acquired iconic status

Index

General Non-Fiction

Art

Photography

Collector's Editions

Film

Architecture

Design

Fashion & Contemporary Culture

Decorative Arts

Music & Performing Arts

Video

Index

Design

Fashion & Contemporary Culture

Decorative Arts

Music & Performing Arts

Video

Index